ALGEBRA
and
TRIGONOMETRY

Algebra
and Trigonometry

PRENTICE-HALL MATHEMATICS SERIES

ALBERT A. BENNET, EDITOR

Algebra
and Trigonometry

Irwin Miller

Simon Green

Arizona State University

Prentice-Hall, Inc.
Englewood Cliffs, N. J.

Library of Congress Catalog Card Number: 62-11732

Seventh Printing·····················September, 1966

Printed in the United States of America

02171-C

Preface

In this book we have attempted to present a rigorous and orderly development of algebra and trigonometry stressing fundamental mathematical ideas. We believe that not only is it desirable to emphasize the logical development of mathematics but also that the reader finds the material easier when this is done.

The real fun in doing mathematics comes from discovering relations that unify ideas and make them simpler. To this end, we have included the three main ideas of algebra and trigonometry — numbers, functions, and equations — in three distinct parts. We have grouped some important extensions of these ideas in a fourth part. Thus, we do not "integrate" algebra and trigonometry by sprinkling topics in trigonometry liberally throughout the book, nor do we collect trigonometry arbitrarily in one section of the book. In fact, we have introduced the subject of trigonometry from the point of view of functions, using the trigonometric functions to strengthen the reader's understanding of the function concept.

In Part I, we give an axiomatic development of the real and complex number systems. Most of the algebraic manipulations are, presumably, familiar to the reader, but experience has indicated time and again that review of these topics is essential. We have chosen to accomplish this purpose at the same time that we demonstrate the axiomatic approach that underlies all mathematics. Thus, we insist that the reader *justify* the use of the "familiar" algebraic operations.

In Part II, we introduce the concept of a function. We define functions in terms of correspondences between elements of two sets, and we take care that the reader understands just what kinds of correspondences are meant. We introduce logarithms and the trigonometric functions as examples of non-algebraic functions to broaden the understanding of the function concept and to demonstrate the scope of this concept. Thus, we introduce trigonometry from the analytic point of view — through the definition of trigonometric functions on domains of real numbers — rather than introducing this topic from the traditional "triangle-measurement" point of view.

In Part III, we introduce the important mathematical concept of relations, illustrating this concept with a thorough discussion of conditional equations, identities, and inequalities, and including trigonometric equations and identities. The ideas of conditional equations lead into a discussion of systems of equations, and prepare the ground for the introduction of a new algebraic system, matrix algebra. A unification of the theory of systems of linear equations is more satisfactorily achieved through a discussion of elementary matrix algebra than through the usual tedious discussion of determinants.

In Part IV, we present topics which, although important in themselves, would have cluttered up the orderly presentation of the main ideas. Thus, the applied problem of the solution of triangles is presented briefly, as an offshoot of trigonometry rather than as a main idea. No textbook is complete if it leaves the reader with the feeling that there is nothing more to learn. Thus, we introduce the extensive topics of series (including an introduction to the concept of a limit) and probability in Part IV. We hope to leave the reader with the impression that there is much more to learn, but we try not to present oversimplified ideas that will later have to be unlearned.

The problems have been placed at the end of each section, and they are divided into two sets. Problems A are a graded set of the more manipulative problems, intended to give practice in applying what has been discussed in the text. Problems B serve a twofold purpose. First, they are intended to stimulate the more mature reader to think more deeply about what he is studying. Second, occasionally they introduce allied topics that cannot be discussed in the text. Problems B may be used to supplement the text material. and we have intended that their use will help make the text more flexible.

We would like to acknowledge the helpful suggestions of many of our colleagues in the Department of Mathematics at Arizona State University. In particular, we owe a great debt of gratitude to Dr. John E. Freund, whose encouragement and careful review of the manuscript have contributed much to this book. We wish to thank our several typists, especially Miss Dawn Lander who bore the main burden.

Irwin Miller
Simon Green

Contents

PART 1

Numbers

The purpose of Part I is to develop the logical structure of the number system. Although it may be assumed that the student is familiar with numbers and operations with numbers, he needs a deeper insight into the foundations upon which the number system is based.

A collection of numbers, or any other collection of objects, form what we shall call a **set.** Thus, we speak of "the set of integers," or "the set of books in the school library," etc. A set may be described by listing its individual members, which are also called **elements.** For example, the set of vowels in the English alphabet may be indicated as {A, E, I, O, U}. It is also possible to describe a set by specifying a rule that determines whether or not a given element belongs to the set. For example, we may speak of the set of all voters in a certain precinct without having to list each one of them. In Part I, we shall describe certain sets of numbers already familiar to the student and introduce a set of numbers that may be new to the student by stating the rules that admit an element, or number, to each such set.

1

The Real
Number System

1.1 Axioms for the Real Number System

The student is well aware that symbols such as 2, -3, $\sqrt{5}$, etc., stand for
familiar numbers and that the symbols $+$, $-$, $\cdot$, and $\div$ are used to denote
the four fundamental operations "add," "subtract," "multiply," and
"divide," respectively.   He also knows that letters such as a, b, x, y, etc.,
may be used in place of such familiar numbers to achieve generality.
For example, if we wish to say that every pair of such numbers has a sum,
we may write $a + b$ with the understanding that a and b can be any such
numbers.   Otherwise, we would have to list every possible pair of such
numbers and display each sum, an impossible task.   The letter a, for
example, may represent any specific member of a given collection of
numbers.

The numbers we have been discussing are elements of a set which we
call the system of **real numbers.**   Since it is not possible to describe this
set by listing each of its elements, it will be necessary to do so by specifying certain rules, or axioms, that determine when an element belongs to
the set.   In this section, we shall present the axioms for a **field** because
the set of real numbers forms a special kind of field.   The property that
makes the field of real numbers a special one involves the ordering of its

elements. We shall postpone the discussion of ordering until Section 1.8. The field axioms for the system of real numbers are as follows.

Axiom 1. *To each pair of real numbers* a *and* b *there is a unique* **sum** a + b, *and a unique* **product** a · b. *The sum and product are also real numbers.*

Axiom 2a. *There is a real number, denoted by the symbol* 0, *obeying the law* a + 0 = a *for every real number* a. *This element* 0 *is called the* **additive identity.**

Axiom 2b. *There is a real number, denoted by the symbol* 1, *obeying the law* a · 1 = a *for every real number* a. *This element is called the* **multiplicative identity.**

Axiom 3. *The real numbers obey the following* **commutative laws of addition and multiplication**:

$$a + b = b + a \qquad (Addition)$$
$$a \cdot b = b \cdot a \qquad (Multiplication)$$

Axiom 4. *The real numbers obey the following* **associative laws of addition and multiplication**:

$$(a + b) + c = a + (b + c) \qquad (Addition)$$
$$(a \cdot b) \cdot c = a \cdot (b \cdot c) \qquad (Multiplication)$$

Axiom 5. *The real numbers obey the following* **distributive law**:

$$a \cdot (b + c) = a \cdot b + a \cdot c$$

Axiom 6a. *Corresponding to each real number* a, *there is a unique real number* (−a), *obeying the law* a + (−a) = 0. *The number* (−a) *is called the* **negative** *of* a.

Axiom 6b. *Corresponding to each real number* a, *except* 0, *there is a unique real number* a^{-1}, *obeying the law* a · a^{-1} = 1. *The number* a^{-1} *is called the* **reciprocal** *of* a.

Axiom 1 tells us that there corresponds *one and only one* sum and product to each pair of real numbers. Moreover, this sum and product are also real numbers. This property is called the property of **closure,** and we say that the set of real numbers is *closed* under the operations of addition and multiplication.

Axiom 2 tells us that the elements 0 and 1 play a special role. According to this axiom, we may add 0 to any real number, and the sum is the number itself. Furthermore, we may multiply any real number by 1, and the product is the number itself. Thus, we call 0 and 1 the additive and multiplicative identities, respectively, because addition of 0 or multiplication by 1 leaves any real number unchanged.

From experience we know that it does not matter whether we add 2 to 3 or 3 to 2; in both cases, the sum is 5. Similarly, $3 \cdot 2 = 2 \cdot 3 = 6$. These rules are stated formally in the commutative laws (Axiom 3). Referring to addition, we shall use the following terminology: The numbers a and b forming the sum $a + b$ will be called **terms**. Referring to multiplication, we shall use the following terminology: The numbers a and b, forming the product $a \cdot b$, will be called **factors**. (If a sum or product is composed of more than two real numbers, the same words, "term" or "factor," respectively, are used to denote each of these numbers.) Wherever there can be no ambiguity, we shall drop the symbol "$\cdot$" for multiplication. Thus, we may write $ab = a \cdot b$, but we may not write $23 = 2 \cdot 3$.

Experience also tells us that if we add three numbers, we may add the third to the sum of the first two, or we may add the sum of the last two to the first. Thus, Axiom 4 states that the order of addition of three real numbers is immaterial, and we may omit the parentheses, writing

$$a + b + c = (a + b) + c = a + (b + c).$$

Similarly, we may write $abc = (ab)c = a(bc)$. The associative laws (Axiom 4) may be extended to more than three numbers; for example,

$$2 + 3 + 4 + 5 = (2 + 3) + (4 + 5) = 5 + 9 = 14$$

and

$$2 \cdot 3 \cdot 4 \cdot 5 = (2 \cdot 3) \cdot (4 \cdot 5) = 6 \cdot 20 = 120$$

The distributive law (Axiom 5) shows how to distribute a factor over the sum of two numbers. This law can be extended to sums of more than two numbers, for example, $a(b + c + d) = ab + ac + ad$. Also note that this law applies to products of sums, such as $(a + b)(c + d)$. Repeated application of the distributive law shows that

$$(a + b)(c + d) = a(c + d) + b(c + d) = ac + ad + bc + bd$$

By Axiom 6, each real number has a companion real number with respect to addition (its negative), and each real number, *except* 0, has a companion real number with respect to multiplication (its reciprocal). The word "inverse" also is used to denote such companion numbers. Thus, $(-a)$ also is called the **additive inverse** of a, and a^{-1} also is called the **multiplicative inverse** of a provided that a is different from 0.

These axioms for the real number field are of basic importance because, as we shall see, the entire structure of algebra rests on them. Although one may prove many important theorems by means of these axioms, we shall confine ourselves in the remainder of this chapter to proofs of those theorems needed for the development of the elements of algebra and trigonometry.

1.2   Subtraction

Axiom 6a states that we can associate with each real number a its negative $(-a)$. Since $(-a)$ also is a real number, the negative of $(-a)$, denoted by $[-(-a)]$, is a real number by virtue of the same axiom.   However, more can be said about the real number $[-(-a)]$, as we shall show in the following theorem.

Theorem 1.1. $[-(-a)] = a$

Proof: Since $[-(-a)]$ is the negative of $(-a)$, then

$$(-a) + [-(-a)] = 0 \qquad\qquad \text{(Axiom 6a)}$$

However, application of the commutative law of addition to Axiom 6a also shows that

$$(-a) + a = 0$$

These two equations show that the negative of $(-a)$ can be written in the form $[-(-a)]$ or in the form a.   By Axiom 6a, the negative of a real number is unique, and we must have

$$[-(-a)] = a$$

which completes the proof.

This theorem can be used to simplify such expressions as, for example, $\{-[-(-4)]\}$.   By Theorem 1.1, $[-(-4)] = 4$, therefore,

$$\{-[-(-4)]\} = (-4)$$

Whenever there can be no ambiguity, we shall agree to write $-a$ for $(-a)$.   Thus, we may write $(-4) = -4$, but we cannot drop the parentheses in the expression $-(-4)$, for example and write $--4$ because $--4$ is meaningless.   As a consequence of Theorem 1.1, if a number a is preceded by an even number of negative signs, it equals a, but if it is preceded by an odd number of negative signs, it equals $-a$.

We are now ready to give meaning to the operation of subtraction.   It was not necessary to mention this operation in the axioms because it may be implied by the operation of addition, as follows.

Definition 1.1. *To* **subtract** b *from* a *means to add* −b *to* a. *In symbols,*

$$a - b = a + (-b)$$

The number $c = a - b$ is called the **difference** of a and b. This definition shows that the negative sign $(-)$ plays a dual role in mathematics. First, it denotes the negative of a number, and second, it is the symbol for the operation of subtraction. Furthermore, if $c = a - b$, we have

$$c + b = a - b + b = a \qquad \text{(Axiom 6a)}$$

Thus

$$c = a - b \quad \text{implies} \quad c + b = a$$

Similarly, we can show that

$$c + b = a \quad \text{implies} \quad c = a - b$$

Thus, the statement

$$c = a - b \quad means \quad c + b = a$$

We shall now show that $-(a + b) = -a - b$. This result does not follow directly from the distributive law because this law shows how to multiply a *real number* by a sum, and we have the symbol " $-$ " which is not a real number. We can, however, prove this assertion as follows.

$$
\begin{aligned}
(a + b) + (-a - b) &= a + b + (-a) + (-b) && \text{(Axiom 4)} \\
&= a + (-a) + b + (-b) && \text{(Axiom 3)} \\
&= 0 + 0 && \text{(Axiom 6a)} \\
&= 0 && \text{(Axiom 2a)}
\end{aligned}
$$

Since we have shown that $a + b + (-a - b) = 0$, then $-a - b$ is the negative of $a + b$ (Axiom 6a). However, the negative of $a + b$ also can be written in the form $-(a + b)$. Therefore,

$$-(a + b) = -a - b$$

which completes the proof.

We may use Definition 1.1 and the foregoing conclusions to reduce the operation of subtraction to that of addition as shown in the following examples.

Example 1.1. Subtract 9 from 5.

Solution: Let $c = 5 - 9$. Then

$$-c = -(5 - 9) = -5 - (-9) = -5 + 9 \quad \text{or} \quad -c = 9 - 5$$

This is equivalent to $5 + (-c) = 9$. Since 4 is the number that must be added to 5 to give 9, then $-c = 4$, and $c = -4$.

Example 1.2. Subtract -4 from -3.

Solution: Let $c = -3 - (-4)$. Then $c = -3 + 4$, which is equivalent to $c + 3 = 4$. Since 1 is the number that must be added to 3 to give 4, $c = 1$.

Although each step was shown in the examples above, the student need not display as much detail when solving similar problems. Thus, to solve the problem: "Subtract $4 - (-6)$ from -5," it is sufficient to write

$$-5 - [4 - (-6)] = -5 - (4 + 6) = -5 - 10 = -15$$

However, it is instructive to observe how many of the axioms for the real numbers are required to solve even such simple problems as illustrated in Examples 1.1 and 1.2.

1.3 Multiplication

The number 0 behaves in a special way under the operation of multiplication. Although it may seem self-evident that $a \cdot 0 = 0$ for any real number a, this fact must be proved.

Theorem 1.2. $a \cdot 0 = 0$

Proof:

$$
\begin{aligned}
0 &= ab - ab & \text{(Axiom 6a)} \\
&= a(b + 0) - ab & \text{(Axiom 2a)} \\
&= ab + a \cdot 0 - ab & \text{(Axiom 5)} \\
&= ab - ab + a \cdot 0 & \text{(Axiom 3)} \\
&= 0 + a \cdot 0 & \text{(Axiom 6a)} \\
&= a \cdot 0 & \text{(Axiom 2a)}
\end{aligned}
$$

The following theorems are needed to multiply the negative of a number by another number. Theorem 1.3 states that the product of the negative of a number and a number equals the negative of the product of the numbers.

Theorem 1.3. $(-a)b = a(-b) = -ab$

Proof:
$$0 = a \cdot 0 = a[b + (-b)] = ab + a(-b)$$
Therefore,
$$-ab = a(-b)$$

Also,
$$0 = b[a + (-a)] = ba + b(-a) = ab + (-a)b$$

Therefore,
$$-ab = (-a)b$$

Theorem 1.4 states that the product of the negatives of two numbers equals the product of the numbers themselves.

Theorem 1.4. $(-a)(-b) = ab$

Proof:
$$\begin{aligned} 0 = (-a) \cdot 0 &= (-a)[b + (-b)] \\ &= (-a)b + (-a)(-b) \\ &= -ab + (-a)(-b) \end{aligned}$$

Also $\qquad\qquad\qquad 0 = -ab + ab$

Therefore, $\qquad\qquad (-a)(-b) = ab$

The student should justify each step in the proofs of Theorems 1.3 and 1.4 as we have done in the proof of Theorem 1.2.

Example 1.3. Apply the theorems above to multiply $(3 - 2)(4 - 5)$.

Solution:
$$\begin{aligned} (3 - 2)(4 - 5) &= 3(4 - 5) + (-2)(4 - 5) \\ &= 3 \cdot 4 + 3(-5) + (-2)4 + (-2)(-5) \\ &= 12 - 15 - 8 + 10 \\ &= -1 \end{aligned}$$

Example 1.4. Multiply $(a - b)(c - d)$.

Solution:
$$\begin{aligned} (a - b)(c - d) &= a(c - d) + (-b)(c - d) \\ &= ac - ad - bc + bd \end{aligned}$$

Finally, we shall prove that the reciprocal of the product of two numbers equals the product of the reciprocals of these numbers.

Theorem 1.5. $(ab)^{-1} = a^{-1}b^{-1}$ $\quad (a \neq 0 \text{ and } b \neq 0)$

Proof:
$$\begin{aligned} (ab)(a^{-1}b^{-1}) &= aa^{-1}bb^{-1} && \text{(Axioms 3 and 4)} \\ &= 1 \cdot 1 && \text{(Axiom 6b)} \\ &= 1 && \text{(Axiom 2b)} \end{aligned}$$

Therefore, $a^{-1}b^{-1}$ is the reciprocal of ab. However, $(ab)^{-1}$ also is the reciprocal of ab, and every number has a unique reciprocal (Axiom 6b). Thus we must have

$$(ab)^{-1} = a^{-1}b^{-1}$$

which completes the proof.

1.4   Division

Like subtraction, the operation of division was not mentioned in the axioms because it may be implied by the operation of multiplication. Accordingly, we state the following definition.

> **Definition 1.2.** *To* **divide** a *by* b (b $\neq$ 0) *means to multiply* a *by* b^{-1}. *In symbols*,
>
> $$\frac{a}{b} = ab^{-1}$$

The number $c = a/b$ is called the **quotient** of a and b. Since $(a/b)b = (ab^{-1})b = abb^{-1} = a$, we conclude that $c = a/b$ means $cb = a$. Also, if we let $a = 1$ in Definition 1.2, we note that $b^{-1} = 1/b$.

Again, we emphasize that b must be different from 0 for division to be defined. For, if b were equal to 0, then bc would equal 0 for every number c. Thus, there would not be a *unique* quotient $c = a/b$; that is, c would not be defined. For this reason, *division by 0 is excluded*.

When we compare the operations of subtraction and division, we observe that there is a parallel between the additive inverse $-a$ and the multiplicative inverse a^{-1}. On page 6 we proved that the negative of the negative of a number is the number itself; we shall now prove that the reciprocal of the reciprocal of a nonzero number is the number itself, or $(a^{-1})^{-1} = a$, with $a \neq 0$.

> **Theorem 1.6.** $(a^{-1})^{-1} = a$ $(a \neq 0)$

Proof: Since $(a^{-1})^{-1}$ is the reciprocal of a^{-1}, then

$$a^{-1}(a^{-1})^{-1} = 1$$

by Axiom 6b. However, application of the commutative law of multiplication to Axiom 6b also shows that

$$a^{-1}a = 1$$

These two equations show that the reciprocal of a^{-1} can be written in the form $(a^{-1})^{-1}$ or in the form a. By Axiom 6b, the reciprocal of a nonzero real number is unique, and we must have

$$(a^{-1})^{-1} = a$$

which completes the proof.

We have proved that the inverse of the inverse of a number is the number itself, regardless of whether we speak of the additive or the multiplicative inverse. We shall now prove that the negative of the reciprocal of a number equals the reciprocal of the negative of that number.

Theorem 1.7. $-a^{-1} = (-a)^{-1}$

Proof:

$$(-a)(-a^{-1}) = aa^{-1} \qquad \text{(Theorem 1.4)}$$
$$= 1 \qquad \text{(Axiom 6b)}$$

Thus, $-a^{-1}$ is the reciprocal of $-a$, or

$$-a^{-1} = (-a)^{-1},$$

which completes the proof.

Axiom 6b and Definition 1.2 guarantee that $c = a/b$ is a real number if $b \neq 0$. Therefore, there corresponds to a/b its negative $-a/b$ and its reciprocal $(a/b)^{-1}$ (if $a \neq 0$) satisfying

$$\frac{a}{b} + \left(-\frac{a}{b}\right) = 0 \quad \text{and} \quad \left(\frac{a}{b}\right)\left(\frac{a}{b}\right)^{-1} = 1$$

respectively. We shall now prove the useful theorem that

$$-\frac{a}{b} = \frac{-a}{b} = \frac{a}{-b}$$

that is, the negative of a/b equals the negative of a divided by b and also equals a divided by the negative of b. A companion theorem about the reciprocal of a/b is stated in Problem B-8.

Theorem 1.8. $-\dfrac{a}{b} = \dfrac{-a}{b} = \dfrac{a}{-b}$ $\quad (b \neq 0)$

Proof:

$$\frac{a}{b} + \frac{(-a)}{b} = ab^{-1} + (-a)b^{-1} \qquad \text{(Definition 1.2)}$$
$$= b^{-1}[a + (-a)] \qquad \text{(Axioms 3 and 5)}$$
$$= b^{-1} \cdot 0 \qquad \text{(Axiom 6a)}$$
$$= 0 \qquad \text{(Theorem 1.2)}$$

Also,

$$\frac{a}{b} + \frac{a}{(-b)} = a[b^{-1} + (-b)^{-1}] \qquad \text{(Definition 1.2 and Axiom 5)}$$

$$= a[b^{-1} - b^{-1}] \qquad \text{(Theorem 1.7)}$$

$$= a \cdot 0 \qquad \text{(Axiom 6a)}$$

$$= 0 \qquad \text{(Theorem 1.2)}$$

Thus, $(-a)/b$ and $a/(-b)$ are both negatives of a/b. However, the negative of a/b is $-(a/b)$. Since there is one and only one negative of a/b, we must conclude that

$$-\frac{a}{b} = \frac{-a}{b} = \frac{a}{-b}$$

which completes the proof.

We may use Definition 1.2 and the foregoing conclusions to reduce the operation of division to that of multiplication, as shown in the following examples.

Example 1.5. Divide 6 by 3.

Solution: Let

$$c = \frac{6}{3}$$

Then

$$3c = 6$$

However, the number by which 3 must be multiplied to obtain 6 is 2. Therefore, $c = 2$.

Example 1.6. Divide 3 by -6.

Solution: Let

$$c = \frac{3}{-6}$$

Then

$$(-6)c = -6c = 3$$

Therefore

$$-6cc^{-1} = 3c^{-1}$$

or

$$-6 = 3c^{-1}$$

However, $-6 = 3(-2)$, and by comparison, we conclude that

$$c^{-1} = -2$$

and

$$c = (-2)^{-1} = \frac{1}{-2} = -\frac{1}{2}$$

PROBLEMS A

1. Perform the indicated operations and state after each step which of the axioms or theorems were used.

(a) $5 + (-3)$

(b) $5 - (-3)$

(c) $4 + (-6) + 9$

(d) $-4 + 9 - 6$

(e) $4 - [(-6) + 9]$

(f) $5(-3)$

(g) $5[- (-3)]$

(h) $5(3 - 2)$

(i) $(-5)(-4 + 6)$

(j) $-3[3 + (-11)(2 - 7)]$

2. Perform the indicated operations and state after each step which of the axioms or theorems were used.

(a) $a - (b - c)$

(b) $a - (b - c) + (b + c)$

(c) $a - [b - c + b + c]$

(d) $(-a)(-b)c$

(e) $ab(-c)(d)$

(f) $(a - b)c$

(g) $(-c)(a - b)$

(h) $(x - y)(u + v)$

(i) $(x - y)(-u + v)$

(j) $(x - y)[(-u) + (-v)]$

(k) $(-x)(-y) - xy$

(l) $(-x)(-y)(-z) - x(-y)z$

3. The following expressions were obtained by the distributive law. Rewrite them in their original form as the product of two factors. For example, $ac + bc = (a + b)c$.

(a) $xa + ya$

(b) $x(-a) + ya$

(c) $x(-a) - ya$

(d) $(x - a)y + (-x - b)y$

(e) $(y - 2)z + (x - 3)z$

(f) $ac + ad + bc + bd$

(g) $xy + ay + bx + ab$

(h) $ax - bx + ay - by$

4. *Divide.* (State what axioms or theorems are used in each step and what, if any, restrictions must be placed on any letters.)

(a) -6 by 3

(b) 4 by -2

(c) $(4 - 3)$ by 2^{-1}

(d) $(8 - 2)$ by 3

(e) abc by ac

(f) $-ab$ by ac

(g) 3^{-1} by 2^{-1}

(h) a^{-1} by b^{-1}

(i) 1 by a^{-1}/b^{-1}

(j) a/b^{-1} by c

(k) $ab + ac$ by $b + c$

(l) $ab - ac$ by $b - c$

PROBLEMS B

1. Write down the commutative law for subtraction. Is this law true for the real numbers? (Give a counter-example.)

2. Write down the associative law for division. Is this law true for the real numbers?

3. Is the commutative law for division true for the real numbers?

4. The distributive law for multiplication over addition is given in Axiom 5. Write down the distributive law for division over addition. Is this law true for the real numbers?

5. If we interchange the symbols of addition and multiplication in the distributive law (Axiom 5), we obtain the distributive law of addition over multiplication. Is this law true for the real numbers? (A very similar law *is* true for the algebra of sets.)

6. If division by zero were allowed, we could write, for example,

$$\frac{5}{0} = x \quad \text{and} \quad \frac{1}{0} = y$$

Prove that this would imply that $5 = 1$. Can you generalize this result?

7. Prove that $-0 = 0$.

8. Prove that the reciprocal of a/b is b/a, provided a and b do not equal zero. (That is, prove $(ab^{-1})^{-1} = a^{-1}b$, when $a \neq 0$, $b \neq 0$.)

9. Prove that $1^{-1} = 1$.

1.5 Classification of the Real Numbers

When we take a closer look at the set of real numbers, we soon discover that it contains certain classes or subsets of numbers that satisfy some of the axioms listed on page 4 but not others. For example, the ordinary "counting numbers" 1, 2, 3, . . . constitute such a subset. In this section, we shall define certain of these subsets; namely, the sets of *natural numbers, integers, rational numbers,* and *irrational numbers.*

When man began to keep track of his possessions, he developed an elementary concept of number by associating with certain physical sets (his children, his sheep, etc.) the idea of "how many?" In this way he created symbols, where each symbol stands for a certain set and represents the number of objects in that set. Thus, the property of "one-ness," or "two-ness," etc., shared by many of his possessions, was abstracted by symbols such as 1, 2, ... These numbers have become known as the **natural numbers.**

When we examine the set of natural numbers, we discover that this set does not obey all the laws stated in the axioms for the real numbers. First, there is no element 0 because the sum of two natural numbers is always greater than either one. Second, the negative of any natural number cannot be a natural number because one cannot find a natural number which, when added to another natural number, produces a sum of 0. Third, the multiplicative inverse of any natural number *except* 1 cannot be a natural number because one cannot find a natural number which, when multiplied by another natural number, produces a product of 1. (The sole exception is $1 \cdot 1 = 1$.)

In spite of these deficiencies, the set of natural numbers is closed under the operations of addition and multiplication; it has a multiplicative identity; and it obeys the commutative, associate, and distributive laws stated in the axioms for the set of real numbers.　There is, in addition, one important property possessed by the set of natural numbers that is not shared by the set of non-natural numbers; namely, the set of natural numbers has a *least element*, 1.

Now, we shall attempt to eliminate some of the previously mentioned deficiencies by adding to the set of natural numbers certain other numbers.　If we introduce the **negative integers** $-1, -2, \ldots$ with the understanding that $(-1) = -1, (-2) = -2$, and so on (that is, the negative of the natural number a is denoted by the negative integer $-a$), then this augmented set of numbers satisfies Axiom 6a.　If we also include the element 0, satisfying Axiom 2a, we have the set of numbers

$$\ldots, \quad -2, \quad -1, \quad 0, \quad 1, \quad 2, \quad \ldots$$

called the set of **integers**.　This new set of numbers is closed under the operation of subtraction, as well as addition and multiplication.　Thus, if a and b are any integers, then $a - b$ also is an integer.　Note that there is no least element in the set of integers.

The set of integers still lacks one property; namely, when we multiply two integers we cannot obtain the multiplicative identity 1, except when we multiply 1 or -1 by itself.　Therefore, we shall extend the set of integers, as follows.

Definition 1.3. *Any number that can be written in the form* a/b, *where* a *and* b *are integers and* b $\neq$ 0, *is called a* **rational number.**

Thus, the familiar fractions $\frac{1}{2}, \frac{2}{3}, -\frac{3}{4}$, etc., are examples of rational numbers.　Setting $b = 1$ in Definition 1.3, we note that every integer is also a rational number; that is, the set of integers is contained in the set of rational numbers.

Now we shall show that the reciprocal of any rational number except 0 is a rational number.　It may be proved (Problem B-8, Section 1.4) that $(a/b)^{-1} = b/a$, if $a \neq 0$ and $b \neq 0$.　However, b/a is in the form given in Definition 1.3, since a and b are integers.　Thus, $(a/b)^{-1}$ is a rational number.　By the definition of division (Definition 1.2) and the fact that the set of rational numbers is closed under the operation of multiplication, it follows that this set is closed under the operation of division.

It may be proved that the set of rational numbers satisfies *all* the axioms for a field, given on page 4.　This need not imply, however, that any real number also is a rational number.　For example, if we wish to measure the length of the diagonal of a square having a side of length 1, it can be shown that the resulting number, $\sqrt{2}$, is not a rational number; that is, it cannot be expressed in the form a/b where a and b are integers.   Any real number, such as $\sqrt{2}$, that is not a rational number is called an **irrational number.**

The classification of the real numbers can be visualized as shown in Figure 1.1.

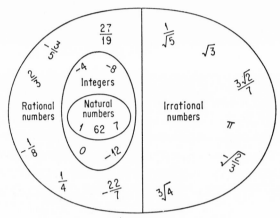

FIGURE 1.1

1.6   The Irrational Numbers

In the early history of mathematics, it was believed that all numbers were rational.   The early Pythagoreans labored under this illusion and produced many "proofs" of theorems in geometry which were based upon this assumption.   It was when they considered the problem of measuring the diagonal of a unit square (a square having side 1) that they quite reluctantly recognized the existence of irrational numbers, that is, numbers that could not be expressed in the form a/b, where a and b are integers and $b \neq 0$.

Let us consider the Pythagorean problem of measuring the diagonal of a unit square. Let x represent the length of the diagonal, and consider the shaded right triangle of Figure 1.2.   By the theorem of Pythagoras, we have

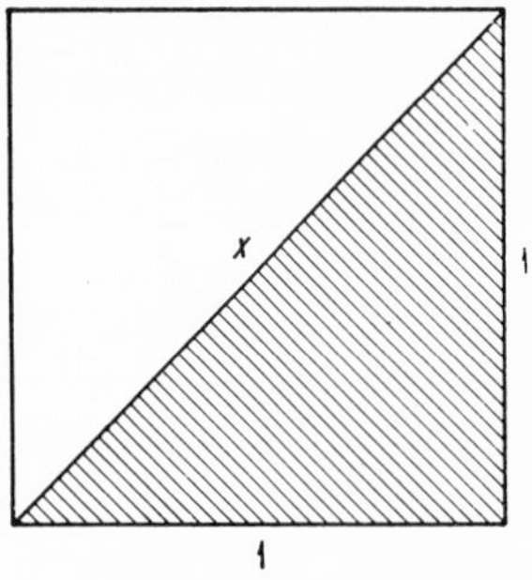

$$x \cdot x = 1 + 1 = 2$$

FIGURE 1.2

It is not possible to find a rational number x such that $x \cdot x$ equals 2.   This was actually proven by the Pythagoreans who, according to legend, kept the discovery a secret because the existence of irrational numbers was not in keeping with the Pythagorean philosophy.

There is an essential distinction between rational and irrational numbers which becomes evident when we attempt to write such numbers as decimals. We assume that the student is familiar with the process whereby a rational number may be written as a decimal. For example,

$$\frac{3}{4} = .75, \frac{2}{7} = .285714285714\ldots, \quad \text{etc.}$$

Every rational number can be expressed as a decimal by the usual process of division. For example, to express the rational number $\frac{2}{7}$ as a decimal we could use the following scheme.

$$
\begin{array}{r}
.2857142\ldots \\
7\,\overline{\smash)2.000000\ldots} \\
\underline{1\ 4} \\
60 \\
\underline{56} \\
40 \\
\underline{35} \\
50 \\
\underline{49} \\
10 \\
\underline{7} \\
30 \\
\underline{28} \\
20
\end{array}
$$

Thus, first we divide 7 into 20 and note that the quotient is 2 and the remainder is 6. Then we divide 7 into 60 and note that the quotient is 8 and the remainder is 4, and so on. Since the only possible remainders when dividing by 7 are 0, 1, 2, 3, 4, 5, and 6, sooner or later a remainder will repeat. (In fact, this repetition must occur on or before the seventh division.) As soon as a remainder repeats, a new cycle starts which gives rise to the same integers in the quotient and in the same order that they appeared before. Now, if one of the remainders were zero, then all subsequent remainders would be zero, and we would have a **terminating decimal.** (A terminating decimal is indicated as .25, .375, and so on.) If, in contrast, the remainders should repeat, we would have a **repeating decimal.** (A repeating decimal is shown by indicating the repeating part with a bar; for example,

$$.1313\ldots = .\overline{13}, \quad \text{and} \quad 1.38576576\ldots = 1.38\overline{576}.)$$

It requires very little generalization of the argument for $\frac{2}{7}$ to show that *every rational number may be expressed as a terminating decimal or as a repeating decimal.*

Conversely, every terminating or repeating decimal may be written as a ratio of two integers and therefore, represents a rational number. For example, the terminating decimal .125 is equal to 125/1,000, which also equals $\frac{1}{8}$. Methods may be devised to express any repeating decimal as a ratio of two integers (see Problem B-2 and Chapter 15).

We may conclude from this discussion that *every decimal that is neither terminating nor repeating represents an irrational number.*

PROBLEMS A

1. Express each of the following rational numbers as a decimal and indicate which is repeating and which is terminating.

(a) $\frac{1}{3}$ (b) $\frac{3}{8}$
(c) $\frac{22}{7}$ (d) $\frac{6}{1}$
(e) $\frac{71}{9}$ (f) $\frac{123}{37}$

2. Express the following terminating decimals as a ratio of two integers.

(a) .25   (b) .3175
(c) .0437   (d) .0075

3. Which of the following numbers is rational, and which is irrational?

(a) $\frac{138}{312}$ (b) $.\overline{3}$
(c) .715   (d) $.\overline{13}$
(e) .141421 ... (not repeating)   (f) $(.\overline{3}) \cdot (.141421 ...)$

PROBLEMS B

1. Prove that every rational number can be expressed as a repeating or terminating decimal. *Hint:* Let the rational number be a/b and consider the possible remainders when dividing a by b.

2. Express $x = .\overline{12}$ as a fraction. *Hint:* Write $100x - x = 99x = 12$.

3. Express $x = .135\overline{125}$ as a fraction.

1.7 The Real Line

As we have seen, every real number can be represented by a decimal. Also, it is possible to associate the points on a line with the real numbers. Consider the line shown in Figure 1.3 and locate a point 0 on the line, called the **origin.** Now, select another point on the line at a convenient distance to the right of 0. We associate the right-hand end-point of the

resulting interval with the number 1 and call this interval the **unit interval.**
With reference to the origin and the unit interval, we can put the real
numbers in one-to-one correspondence with the points on this line.
("One-to-one correspondence" means that every point corresponds to

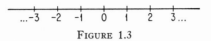

FIGURE 1.3

exactly one real number, and every real number corresponds to exactly
one point.)   We agree to associate every point to the *right* of 0 with a
positive number and every point to the *left* of 0 with a **negative number.**
This convention implies that every real number is associated with a
directed distance from the origin.   More generally, if we move from any
point on the line to the right, it is said that we move in the positive direction, and if we move to the left, we move in the negative direction.

The three concepts of origin, unit distance, and direction make it
possible to place the integers in one-to-one correspondence with specific
points on a line.   Thus, the point corresponding to the positive integer a
is located by moving through a distance of a units to the *right* of 0, and
the point corresponding to the negative integer $-a$ is located by moving
a units to the *left* of 0, as shown in Figure 1.3.   Thus, for example, if we
start at the point 2 and move 3 units to the left, we reach the point -1.

The rational numbers may be located on the line in one of two ways.
For example, $\frac{2}{7}$ can be found *exactly* by dividing the unit interval into
seven equal parts or subintervals and locating the right-hand end-point of
the second subinterval.   As another example, the rational number $-\frac{10}{3}$
lies between -3 and -4, and may be located as follows: Divide the interval from -3 to -4 into three equal subintervals, then locate the left-
hand end-point of the first subinterval to the left of -3, as shown in
Figure 1.4.

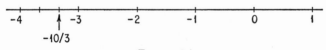

FIGURE 1.4

The decimal representation of any rational number can be used to find
the *approximate* location of the corresponding point.   For example, $\frac{1}{3}$
may be represented by the repeating decimal $.\overline{3}$ which also may be
written as

$$\frac{3}{10} + \frac{3}{100} + \cdots$$

To find the corresponding point, divide the unit interval into ten equal
subintervals and locate the fourth subinterval, as shown in Figure 1.5.

Then, subdivide this interval into ten equal parts and locate the fourth sub subinterval and keep repeating this process. Eventually, an interval will be reached which contains the point corresponding to ⅓ and which is small enough to meet any desired degree of accuracy.

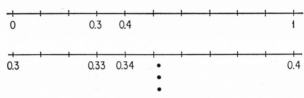

FIGURE 1.5

We have seen that each integer and each rational number can be located *exactly* on a line with the use of a *limited number of subdivisions.* It is not possible, however, to locate an irrational number with the use of a limited number of subdivisions. However, let us try to locate the irrational number $\sqrt{2}$, for example, employing the same method that was used to locate the rational number ⅓. The student may remember that $\sqrt{2}$ is represented by the decimal 1.41421 . . . which is neither terminating nor repeating. It may be located approximately, as follows: Divide the interval from 1 to 2 into ten equal subintervals and locate the fifth sub-interval. Then, subdivide this subinterval into ten equal parts and locate the second sub subinterval. Continue this process locating the fifth sub sub subinterval, then the third sub sub sub subinterval, etc., as shown in Figure 1.6. Eventually, an interval will be reached which

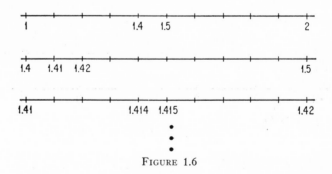

FIGURE 1.6

contains the point corresponding to $\sqrt{2}$ and which is small enough to meet any desired degree of accuracy.

We have illustrated the processes whereby the real numbers may be placed in one-to-one correspondence with the points on a line. We may refer to this line as the line of real numbers, or the **real line.** In fact, it is not necessary to maintain any verbal distinction between the points on the real line and the real numbers, and it is perfectly permissible to refer to the *point* $\frac{1}{3}$ as if it were the *number* $\frac{1}{3}$, and vice versa.

With reference to their decimal representation, we have pointed out that the essential distinction between the rational numbers and the irrational numbers is that the irrational numbers are represented by non-repeating and nonterminating decimals.   With reference to the real line, we may say that the irrational points cannot be located exactly with a limited number of equal subdivisions.   For this reason, the irrational points on the real line are said to be incommensurable, or "unmeasurable." In contrast, every rational point may be located exactly, using the same general method that we employed to find the point $\frac{2}{7}$.

PROBLEMS A

1. Locate the following rational numbers *exactly* on the real line.

(a) $\frac{3}{2}$ (b) $\frac{24}{5}$

(c) $-\frac{2}{3}$ (d) $-\frac{16}{9}$

(e) $.\overline{13}$ (f) $-2.\overline{66}$

2. Make a sketch similar to Figure 1.6 to locate each of the following irrational numbers correct to two decimal places.

(a) $.315\ldots$ (b) $1.742\ldots$

(c) $2.863\ldots$ (d) $-.091\ldots$

PROBLEMS B

1. How many operations of subdivision into tenths are required to locate $1.41421\ldots$ (the square root of 2) on the real line to within a maximum error of .0001?

2. When will the second process for finding a rational point result in its exact location?

3. Given two different rational numbers, no matter how close together on the real line, show that there is an irrational number located between them. *Hint:* Use a process similar to that illustrated in Figure 1.6.

4. Given two different irrational numbers, show that there is a rational number located between them.

1.8   Order

The results of the preceding section can be used to illustrate the principle for ordering the real numbers given in the following definition.

Definition 1.4. *If* a *and* b *are real numbers*

(1) a < b (a *is less than* b) *if and only if* a − b *is a negative number.*

(2) a > b (a *is greater than* b) *if and only if* b < a.

It is easily seen that Definition 1.4 is equivalent to the following: $a < b$ means that a lies to the *left* of b on the real line, and $a > b$ means that a lies to the *right* of b on the real line.

In Section 1.1 the set of real numbers was characterized as a field. It was also stated that this set is a special kind of field, namely, a field with a special property of ordering. Accordingly, we now add the following axioms to those given in Section 1.1.

Axiom 7. *Given real numbers* a *and* b, *one and only one of the following relations holds:*

(1) $a < b$

(2) $a > b$

(3) $a = b$

Axiom 8. *If* a > 0 *and* b > 0, *then*

(1) $a + b > 0$

(2) $ab > 0$

It follows, from Axiom 7, that every real number is positive, negative, or zero. Using Axiom 8, it can be shown that the sum of two negative numbers is a negative number; the product of two negative numbers is a positive number; and the product of a positive number and a negative number is a negative number.

There is one more important concept connected with the ordering of the real numbers that is implicit in our discussion of the real line. This concept holds that the real numbers form a *complete* ordered field. It is not possible to go into a rigorous discussion of complete ordering in this book. Intuitively, complete ordering means that every point on the real line corresponds to a real number, and vice versa. In other words, there are no "gaps" on the real line.

The following theorems can be proved from Definition 1.4 and Axioms 7 and 8.

Theorem 1.9. *If* a < b *and* b < c, *then* a < c.

Proof: If $a < b$, then $a - b < 0$, and $a - b$ is a negative number.

Similarly, $b - c$ is a negative number.   Thus,

$$(a - b) + (b - c) = a - c$$

is the sum of two negative numbers and, by an extension of Axiom 8, it is also a negative number.   Consequently, $a - c$ is a negative number, or $a - c < 0$ which establishes that $a < c$ and completes the proof.

It follows from this theorem that if $a < b$ and $b < c$, we may write $a < b < c$ and say that b is **contained between** a and c.

Theorem 1.10. *If* a $<$ b *then* a $+$ c $<$ b $+$ c *for any real number* c.

Proof: Proceeding as in the proof of Theorem 1.9, we write

$$(a + c) - (b + c) = a - b$$

However, $a - b < 0$ by hypothesis; thus

$$(a + c) - (b + c) < 0$$

or

$$a + c < b + c$$

which completes the proof.

Theorem 1.11. *If* a $>$ b *and* c $>$ 0, *then* ac $>$ bc.   *If* a $>$ b *and* c $<$ 0, *then* ac $<$ bc.

Proof: We have

$$ac - bc = (a - b)c$$

If $c > 0$, $(a - b)c$ is the product of two positive numbers, and it is positive; in other words, $ac - bc > 0$.   However, if $c < 0$, $(a - b)c$ is the product of a positive number and a negative number, and it is negative; in other words, $ac - bc < 0$.   Thus, $ac > bc$ if $c > 0$, and $ac < bc$ if $c < 0$, which completes the proof.

The following examples make use of Definition 1.4 and Theorems 1.9, 1.10, and 1.11.

Example 1.7. If $a > 1$, show that $1/a < 1$.

Solution: By Theorem 1.11, with $c = 1/a$, we have

$$a\frac{1}{a} > 1\frac{1}{a}$$

or

$$1 > \frac{1}{a}$$

Example 1.8. If $2a - 12 > 0$, show that $a > 6$.

Solution: By Theorem 1.10, with $c = 12$, we have

$$2a > 12$$

By Theorem 1.11 with $c = \frac{1}{2}$, we have

$$a > 6$$

PROBLEMS A

1. Arrange the following in increasing order: -3, $\frac{3}{4}$, 1.1, $-\frac{1}{8}$, 2.

2. Prove that $\frac{1}{4} < \frac{2}{5}$
(a) by locating these numbers on the real line.
(b) by using Theorem 1.11.

3. If $2x + 3 > 4$, prove that $x > \frac{1}{2}$.

4. If $b - a > 0$, is it true that $ab - a > b - a$?

5. If $b - a > 0$, is $b + 5 > a + 2$?

6. If $a < b$, show that $a < \dfrac{a + b}{2} < b$.

7. If $-a > 2$ and $2 > -b$, is $a > b$?

PROBLEMS B

1. Is there a greatest number in each of the following sets? If so, what is it?
(a) The set of natural numbers.
(b) The set of integers.
(c) The set of negative numbers.
(d) The set of rational numbers less than zero.
(e) The set of non-negative real numbers.

2. Is there a least number in each set described in Problem 1? If so, what is it?

3. Prove the following:
(a) The sum of two negative numbers is a negative number.
(b) The product of two negative numbers is a positive number.
(c) The product of a positive and a negative number is a negative number.

1.9 Absolute Value

If a is any point on the real line, its *directed distance* from the origin is a positive number when a lies to the right of 0, and it is a negative number when a lies to the left of 0. The **absolute value** or **magnitude** of any point on the real line is defined to be a positive number, or zero, which equals the distance of that point from the origin without regard to direction. Formally, we state the following definition.

Definition 1.5. *If* a *is any real number, its* **absolute value** *is denoted by* $|a|$ *and*

(1) $|a| = a$ if $a > 0$

(2) $|a| = -a$ if $a < 0$

(3) $|a| = 0$ if $a = 0$

It follows from Definition 1.5, for example, that $|2| = |-2| = 2$. This definition can be used to express the distance d between any two points a and b on the real line. Since convention dictates that d be positive,

$$d = a - b \quad \text{if} \quad a > b \quad \text{and} \quad d = b - a \quad \text{if} \quad a < b$$

In other words, *the distance between* a *and* b *equals* $|a - b|$. (Could we also have said that $d = |b - a|$?)

The rules for multiplication and division with absolute values may be derived from Definition 1.5 by considering all possible combinations of signs. For example, let us prove the following theorem.

Theorem 1.12. $|ab| = |a| \cdot |b|$

Proof: If neither a nor b equals 0, then there are four possible combinations of signs as follows:

(1) $a > 0$ and $b > 0$, thus $|a| = a$, and $|b| = b$

(2) $a > 0$ and $b < 0$, thus $|a| = a$, and $|b| = -b$

(3) $a < 0$ and $b > 0$, thus $|a| = -a$, and $|b| = b$

(4) $a < 0$ and $b < 0$, thus $|a| = -a$, and $|b| = -b$

In case (1)

$$|a| \cdot |b| = ab = |ab|$$

In case (2),

$$|a| \cdot |b| = a(-b) = -ab = |ab| \quad \text{since} \quad -ab > 0$$

In case (3),

$$|a| \cdot |b| = (-a)b = -ab = |ab|$$

In case (4),

$$|a| \cdot |b| = (-a)(-b) = ab = |ab| \quad \text{since} \quad ab > 0$$

Finally, if $a = 0$, or $b = 0$, or both, then both products ab and $|a| \cdot |b|$ equal 0. By Axiom 7, there can be no further possibilities, and the proof is complete.

The following theorem is stated without proof.

Theorem 1.13. $\dfrac{|a|}{|b|} = \dfrac{|a|}{|b|}, \quad b \neq 0$

The proof of Theorem 1.13 is similar to the proof of Theorem 1.12.
It may be tempting to conclude from these theorems that

$$|a + b| = |a| + |b|$$

A simple example shows that this conclusion is not valid. If we let $a = 6$ and $b = -4$, we have

$$|6 + (-4)| = |2| = 2$$

but

$$|6| + |-4| = 6 + 4 = 10$$

In this case

$$|a + b| < |a| + |b|$$

If you work a few more examples of this kind, you will soon discover that

$$|a + b| = |a| + |b|$$

only when a and b have the same sign or either equals zero, and

$$|a + b| < |a| + |b|$$

when a and b have opposite signs. We may summarize the statement that $|a + b|$ is at most equal to $|a| + |b|$ by writing

$$|a + b| \leq |a| + |b|$$

read "$|a + b|$ is **less than or equal to** $|a| + |b|$." It is also possible to establish that

$$|a - b| \geq |a| - |b|$$

that is, $|a - b|$ is **greater than or equal to** $|a| - |b|$.

PROBLEMS A

1. Find the absolute values of the following numbers.
(a) 2   (b) -3
(c) $6 + 2$ (d) $4 - 7$
(e) $-3 + 8$ (f) $-1 - 9$
(g) $(-5)(12)$ (h) $(-2)(-4)$
(i) $\dfrac{3}{2}$ (j) $\dfrac{12}{-4}$

2. What numbers have the following absolute values?

(a) 2

(b) $\dfrac{7}{2}$

(c) -3

(d) -8.6

(e) $|-3|$

(f) $|-8.6|$

3. Find the set of values of x for which

(a) $\left|\dfrac{x}{2}\right| = 1$

(b) $|3x| = 6$

(c) $|x - 1| = 2$

(d) $|3 - x| = 4$

PROBLEMS B

1. Prove that
$$|a + b| \leq |a| + |b|$$
Hint: Use distances on the real line to establish that
$$|a - b| \leq |a| + |b|$$
and substitute $-b$ for b.

2. Prove that
$$|a - b| \geq |a| - |b|$$
Hint: Let $a = (a - b) + b$ and use the result of Problem **1.**

3. Prove that
$$|a + b| \geq |a| - |b|$$

4. When do the equal signs apply in Problems **1, 2,** and **3?**

2

Fractions, Exponents and Polynomials

2.1 Factoring

From Axiom 2b for the set of real numbers, every real number can be represented as the product of 1 by the number itself. There are certain integers that also can be written as products of other integers. For example, $6 = 1 \cdot 6 = 2 \cdot 3$, but 5 only can be written as the product of 5 and 1. (Of course, we could have written $5 = 1 \cdot 1 \cdot 5$, but this is redundant because repeated application of Axiom 2a shows that $1 = 1 \cdot 1 = 1 \cdot 1 \cdot 1 = \ldots$, etc.) Accordingly, we subdivide the positive integers into two sets as follows.

Definition 2.1 *A positive integer greater than 1 is a* **prime number** *if it cannot be expressed as the product of two positive integers except itself and 1. If a positive integer other than 1 is not a prime number, it is called a* **composite number.**

It is often desirable to express a composite number as a product of two or more integer factors. For example, $12 = 3 \cdot 4$. This procedure is called **factoring.** Any composite number is said to be **completely factored** if it is written as the product of prime factors only. For example, 12 is completely factored if it is written as the product $12 = 2 \cdot 2 \cdot 3$.

28

If a and b are positive integers and a equals 1 or is a factor of b, then b is called a **multiple** of a. For example, 12 is a multiple of 1, 2, 3, 4, 6, and 12. Furthermore, if a and b are both factors of c, then c is called a common multiple of a and b. Thus, 12 is a **common multiple** of 2 and 3, 2 and 4, 3 and 6, etc.

Now consider, for example, all common multiples of the integers 2 and 3, such as 6, 12, 18, 24, etc. Of these multiples, 6 is the smallest. Such a number is called the **least common multiple** (abbreviated LCM) of 2 and 3. This concept is generalized in the following definition.

Definition 2.2. *The LCM of two or more positive integers is the smallest positive integer that is a common multiple of all these integers.*

To illustrate this definition, let us find the LCM of 6, 8, and 12. First, we shall factor each of these numbers completely, to obtain

$$6 = 2 \cdot 3$$
$$8 = 2 \cdot 2 \cdot 2$$
$$12 = 2 \cdot 2 \cdot 3$$

Now any common multiple of these three integers must contain the factors 6, 8, and 12. Therefore, it must contain the factor 2 *at least* three times and the factor 3 *at least* once. (For example, if it did not contain 2 at least three times, it could not contain the factor 8.) Thus, the least common multiple, or LCM, of 6, 8, and 12 is $2 \cdot 2 \cdot 2 \cdot 3 = 24$.

As another example, let us find the LCM of 9, 14, and 28. We have

$$9 = 3 \cdot 3$$
$$14 = 2 \cdot 7$$
$$28 = 2 \cdot 2 \cdot 7$$

The required LCM is

$$2 \cdot 2 \cdot 3 \cdot 3 \cdot 7 = 252$$

If two or more positive integers have no prime factors in common, they are called **relatively prime numbers.** For example, $6 = 2 \cdot 3$ and $25 = 5 \cdot 5$ have no prime factors in common and are relatively prime. It follows from the foregoing discussion that the LCM of two relatively prime positive integers is their product.

PROBLEMS A

1. List the first ten positive prime numbers. (The tenth is 29.)

2. Which of the following numbers is prime and which is composite?
(a) 74   (b) 67
(c) 233   (d) 2475

3. Each of the following is a multiple of what numbers?

(a) 8   (b) 16
(c) 11   (d) 32
(e) 24   (f) 100

4. Find the LCM of the following numbers.

(a) 12 and 18   (b) 21 and 69
(c) 9, 15, and 27   (d) 18, 28, and 10
(e) 4, 6, 8, and 16   (f) 6, 10, 14, and 18

5. Which of the following pairs of numbers is relatively prime?

(a) 7 and 14   (b) 6 and 18
(c) 41 and 4   (d) 365 and 7
(e) 120 and 720   (f) 233 and 111

PROBLEMS B

1. Prove that if b is a multiple of a and c is a multiple of a, then $b + c$ is a multiple of a.   *Hint:* Write $b = ad_1$, and $c = ad_2$, where d_1 and d_2 are positive integers.

2. Which of the following sets is closed under addition?

(a) All positive integers n such that n is a multiple of 6.
(b) All positive integers that are common multiples of 3 and 7.

2.2   Fractions

The operation of division was defined by Definition 1.2.   The symbol a/b, standing for the quotient of the real numbers a and b is called a **fraction.** The number a is called the **numerator,** and b is called the **denominator.** If the numerator or the denominator of a fraction is itself a fraction, or if both are fractions, then a/b is called a **complex fraction.**   Otherwise, a/b is called a **simple fraction.**   In the following discussion of operations with fractions, we shall make use of the concepts discussed in the preceding section.   It shall be understood throughout that the denominator of every fraction is different from zero.

The same fraction can be written in many different ways; for example,

$$\frac{1}{2} = \frac{2}{4} = \frac{3}{6} = \frac{1/4}{2/4}$$

and so on.   The following theorem enables us to identify two equal fractions.

Theorem 2.1. $\dfrac{a}{b} = \dfrac{c}{d}$ *if and only if* $ad = bc$, *where* $bd \neq 0$.

Proof: The phrase "if and only if" means that the implication goes both ways. Thus, we shall have to prove (1) if $a/b = c/d$, then $ad = bc$, and (2) if $ad = bc$, then $a/b = c/d$.

(1)
$$\frac{a}{b} = \frac{c}{d}$$
$$ab^{-1} = cd^{-1}$$
$$ab^{-1}bd = cd^{-1}bd$$
$$ad = bcd^{-1}d = bc$$

(2)
$$ad = bc$$
$$ad(bd)^{-1} = bc(bd)^{-1}$$
$$adb^{-1}d^{-1} = bcb^{-1}d^{-1}$$
$$ab^{-1}dd^{-1} = bb^{-1}cd^{-1}$$
$$ab^{-1} = cd^{-1}$$
$$\frac{a}{b} = \frac{c}{d}$$

The reader should fill in the justification for each step. As a corollary to this theorem, it will be left to the reader to prove that $a/b = ac/bc$ (see Problem B-1); that is, factors common to the numerator and the denominator of a fraction may be cancelled.

Since the same rational number can be written as a fraction in different ways, it is useful to define what is meant by a fraction in **lowest terms.** We say that a fraction whose numerator and denominator are positive integers is in lowest terms when the numerator and the denominator are relatively prime numbers. Thus, for example, the fraction $\frac{14}{21}$ has the factor 7 common to the numerator and denominator and equals $\frac{2}{3}$, which is in lowest terms. In general, such a fraction is reduced to lowest terms by dividing the numerator and denominator by all common factors different from 1.

The following theorems establish the rules for multiplication and division of fractions.

Theorem 2.2. $\dfrac{a}{b} \cdot \dfrac{c}{d} = \dfrac{ac}{bd}$

Proof:

$$\frac{a}{b} \cdot \frac{c}{d} = ab^{-1}cd^{-1}$$

$$= acb^{-1}d^{-1}$$

$$= ac(bd)^{-1}$$

$$= \frac{ac}{bd}$$

Theorem 2.3. $\dfrac{a/b}{c/d} = \dfrac{ad}{bc}$

Proof:

$$\frac{a/b}{c/d} = \frac{ab^{-1}}{cd^{-1}}$$

$$= ab^{-1}c^{-1}d$$

$$= adb^{-1}c^{-1}$$

$$= ad(bc)^{-1}$$

$$= \frac{ad}{bc}$$

Theorem 2.2 states that the product of two fractions equals the fraction whose numerator is the product of the numerators of the original fractions and whose denominator equals the product of the original denominators. According to Theorem 2.3 we divide one fraction by another when we multiply the first fraction by the reciprocal of the second. For example,

$$\frac{2/3}{5/7} = \frac{2}{3} \cdot \frac{7}{5} = \frac{14}{15}$$

The following theorem establishes the rule for adding two fractions having the *same denominator*.

Theorem 2.4. $\dfrac{a}{c} + \dfrac{b}{c} = \dfrac{a+b}{c}$

Proof:

$$\frac{a}{c} + \frac{b}{c} = ac^{-1} + bc^{-1}$$

$$= (a+b)c^{-1}$$

$$= \frac{a+b}{c}$$

To add two fractions having different denominators first we convert them to fractions having the same denominator. Then we add them with the use of Theorem 2.4. For example,

$$\frac{1}{8} + \frac{1}{12} = \frac{12}{96} + \frac{8}{96} = \frac{20}{96} = \frac{5}{24}$$

The labor may be reduced if the denominator common to the two fractions to be added is the **least common denominator** (abbreviated LCD). The LCD of a set of fractions is the LCM of their denominators. Thus, in adding $\frac{1}{8} + \frac{1}{12}$, the LCD is the LCM of 8 and 12, or 24, and we have

$$\frac{1}{8} + \frac{1}{12} = \frac{3}{24} + \frac{2}{24} = \frac{5}{24}$$

To perform the subtraction $a/b - c/d$, first apply Theorem 1.8 to write

$$-\frac{c}{d} = \frac{-c}{d},$$

then find the LCD; finally, use Theorem 2.4 to add, For example,

$$\frac{1}{8} - \frac{1}{12} = \frac{3}{24} + \frac{-2}{24} = \frac{3 - 2}{24} = \frac{1}{24}$$

A complex fraction may be reduced to a simple fraction by combining all fractions in the numerator and all fractions in the denominator, reducing each to lowest terms, and dividing. An equivalent method is to find the LCD of *all* fractions in both the numerator and the denominator and to multiply both the numerator and the denominator by this LCD. These methods are illustrated in the following example.

Example 2.1. Reduce to a simple fraction in lowest terms.

$$\frac{\dfrac{3}{5} - \dfrac{4}{9}}{\dfrac{1}{6} + \dfrac{3}{4}}$$

Solution: We may do this problem in two ways.

(a)

$$\frac{3}{5} - \frac{4}{9} = \frac{27 - 20}{45} = \frac{7}{45}$$

$$\frac{1}{6} + \frac{3}{4} = \frac{2 + 9}{12} = \frac{11}{12}$$

$$\frac{\dfrac{3}{5} - \dfrac{4}{9}}{\dfrac{1}{6} + \dfrac{3}{4}} = \frac{\dfrac{7}{45}}{\dfrac{11}{12}} = \frac{7}{45} \cdot \frac{12}{11} = \frac{84}{495} = \frac{28}{165}$$

(b) The LCD of the four simple fractions $\frac{3}{5}$, $\frac{4}{9}$, $\frac{1}{6}$, and $\frac{3}{4}$ is 180. Multiplying the numerator and denominator of the complex fraction by 180, we obtain

$$\frac{\dfrac{3}{5} \cdot 180 - \dfrac{4}{9} \cdot 180}{\dfrac{1}{6} \cdot 180 + \dfrac{3}{4} \cdot 180} = \frac{108 - 80}{30 + 135} = \frac{28}{165}$$

PROBLEMS A

1. Which of the following sets consists entirely of equal fractions?

(a) $\frac{1}{3}$, $\frac{4}{12}$

(b) $\frac{5}{7}$, $\frac{9}{11}$

(c) $\frac{1}{3}$, $\frac{2}{3}$, $\frac{4}{3}$

(d) $\frac{4}{5}$, $\frac{8}{10}$, $\frac{12}{15}$

(e) $\dfrac{a}{b+c}$, $\dfrac{ad}{bd+cd}$

(f) $\dfrac{a}{b}$, $\dfrac{ac}{bc}$, $\dfrac{a+c}{b+c}$

2. Perform the indicated operations and reduce the answer to lowest terms.

(a) $\frac{1}{2} + \frac{1}{3}$

(b) $\frac{1}{2} - \frac{1}{3}$

(c) $\frac{1}{4} - \frac{1}{3}$

(d) $\frac{2}{3} \cdot \frac{9}{5}$

(e) $\frac{2}{3} + \frac{9}{5}$

(f) $\dfrac{1}{a} + \dfrac{1}{b}$

(g) $\dfrac{a}{b} - \dfrac{b}{a}$

(h) $\dfrac{a}{b} \cdot \dfrac{b}{a}$

(i) $\dfrac{1/a}{1/b}$

(j) $\dfrac{a/b}{b/c}$

(k) $\dfrac{\frac{1}{2} + \frac{1}{3}}{\frac{4}{5}}$

(l) $\dfrac{\frac{3}{7} - \frac{2}{5}}{\frac{3}{5} + \frac{2}{7}}$

(m) $4 + \dfrac{\frac{1}{8} - \frac{3}{8}}{\frac{5}{24}}$

(n) $\dfrac{\frac{1}{2} + \frac{1}{4}}{\frac{1}{8} + \frac{1}{16}} \cdot \dfrac{\frac{1}{3} + \frac{1}{4}}{\frac{1}{5} - \frac{1}{6}}$

(o) $\dfrac{\frac{1}{2}}{\frac{1}{4} + \frac{1}{8}} \Big/ \dfrac{\frac{1}{4}}{\frac{1}{2} - \frac{1}{8}}$

(p) $\dfrac{\frac{5}{6} + \frac{7}{12}}{\frac{4}{5} - \frac{8}{25}} \Big/ \dfrac{\frac{7}{18} - \frac{2}{9}}{\frac{3}{10} + \frac{4}{25}}$

3. Find the reciprocal of each number.

(a) $\frac{2}{3}$

(b) 12

(c) $\dfrac{a}{a+b}$

(d) $\dfrac{a}{b} \cdot \dfrac{c}{d}$

(e) $\dfrac{1}{a} + \dfrac{1}{b}$

(f) $1 - \dfrac{1}{a-1}$

PROBLEMS B

1. If $b \neq 0$ and $c \neq 0$, prove that $a/b = ac/bc$.

2. Evaluate the following fraction.

$$\cfrac{1 + 1}{1 + \cfrac{1}{1 + \cfrac{1}{1 + 1}}}$$

3. Consider the set of all fractions having the denominator d and any integer for the numerator.
(a) Prove that this set is closed under the operations of addition and subtraction.
(b) Is this set closed under multiplication?   Under division?
(c) Does this set have an additive identity?   If so, what is it?
(d) Does this set have a multiplicative identity?   If so, what is it?
(e) Does every element of this set have an additive inverse?   If so, how is it obtained?
(f) Does every nonzero element of this set have a multiplicative inverse?
(g) Is this set a field?   Why?

2.3 Integer Exponents

When any real number a is to be multiplied by itself n times, the product $a \cdot a \cdot \ldots \cdot a$ is represented by the abbreviated notation a^n.   (If $n = 1$, we simply write a instead of a^1.)   The number n indicates how many times the factor a appears in the product and is called the **exponent of a.** The number a^n is called the **nth power of a.**   Since n counts the number of times a appears in a product, *this interpretation of* a^n *makes sense only when* n *is a natural number.*

The following laws of exponents follow directly from this definition when m and n are natural numbers and a and b are any real numbers.

Theorem 2.5.

(1) $a^m a^n = a^{m+n}$

(2) $(ab)^n = a^n b^n$

(3) $(a^m)^n = a^{mn}$

Proof: Part (1) can be proved by writing

$$a^m = \underbrace{a \cdot a \cdot \ldots \cdot a}_{m}$$

(there are m factors a) and

$$a^n = \underbrace{a \cdot a \cdot \ldots \cdot a}_{n}$$

Thus,

$$a^m a^n = \underbrace{a \cdot a \cdot \ldots \cdot a}_{m} \cdot \underbrace{a \cdot a \cdot \ldots \cdot a}_{n}$$

$$= \underbrace{a \cdot a \cdot \ldots \cdot a}_{m+n}$$

That is, $a^m a^n$ consists of m factors a multiplied by n factors a; therefore, it contains $m + n$ factors a and can be written as a^{m+n}. Can you prove Parts (2) and (3) in a similar way?

We now consider the nth power of the reciprocal of a or $(a^{-1})^n$. If we define the symbol a^{-n} so that $a^{-n} = (a^{-1})^n = (a^n)^{-1}$ for all natural numbers n and all real numbers a except $a = 0$, then Theorem 2.5 holds. Theorem 2.5-3 follows directly from the definition of a^{-n}. Theorems 2.5-1 and 2.5-2 also may be extended to include the negative integers.

It is now possible to extend the laws of exponents to include subtraction of exponents. Since $a^m/a^n = a^m(a^n)^{-1} = a^m a^{-n}$, the following theorem is analogous to Theorem 2.5-1.

Theorem 2.6. *If* m *and* n *are nonzero integers,* m $\neq$ n, *and* a $\neq$ 0, *then*

$$\frac{a^m}{a^n} = a^{m-n}$$

Proof:

  (a) If $m > n$,

$$\frac{a^m}{a^n} = \underbrace{a \cdot a \cdot \ldots \cdot a}_{m-n}$$

$$= a^{m-n}$$

  (b) If $m < n$,

$$\frac{a^m}{a^n} = \frac{1}{\underbrace{a \cdot a \cdot \ldots \cdot a}_{n-m}}$$

$$= \frac{1}{a^{n-m}}$$

$$= (a^{n-m})^{-1}$$

$$= a^{m-n}$$

If $m = n$, the expression a^{m-n} becomes formally a^0. If we want Theorem 2.6 also to hold when $m = n$, we must *define* a^0 to equal 1 because $a^m/a^n = 1$ when $m = n$. The restriction that $a \neq 0$ should be emphasized because a^m/a^n is meaningless when $a = 0$. In particular, the symbol 0^0 is undefined.

In the following examples, "simplify" means "remove all negative and zero exponents and reduce all complex fractions to simple fractions."

Example 2.2. Simplify $\dfrac{3a^4b^{-2}}{6a^{-1}b^3}$.

Solution:

$$\frac{3a^4b^{-2}}{6a^{-1}b^3} = \frac{3a^{4-(-1)}}{6b^{3-(-2)}} = \frac{a^5}{2b^5}$$

Example 2.3. Simplify $\dfrac{(x^{-n}y)^2}{x^0 - y^{-1}}$.

Solution:

$$\frac{(x^{-n}y)^2}{x^0 - y^{-1}} = \frac{(x^{-n})^2 y^2}{1 - \dfrac{1}{y}} = \frac{x^{-2n}y^3}{y - 1} = \frac{y^3}{x^{2n}(y - 1)}$$

PROBLEMS A

1. Simplify the following expressions.

(a) $2a^{-3}$

(b) $(4x)^{-1}$

(c) $3u^2v^{-3}$

(d) $\left(\dfrac{b}{2}\right)^0$

(e) $\dfrac{x^{-2}}{x^{-1} - 2x^{-2}}$

(f) $\dfrac{3a 4^b}{2^{ab}}$

(g) $(a^2b^z)^m$

(h) $(x^{-1} + y^{-1})^2$

(i) $(u^{-1} + v^{-1})^{-1}$

(j) $(a^z + b^{-z})(a^{-z} + b^z)$

(k) $\dfrac{y^{-a}}{y^{-b}} + \dfrac{y^{-b}}{y^{-a}}$

(l) $\dfrac{a^3/b^{-2}}{a^{-2}/b^3}$

PROBLEMS B

1. Prove Part 2 of Theorem 2.5.

2. Prove Part 3 of Theorem 2.5.

2.4 Rational Exponents

The symbol a^n sometimes can be given a meaning consistent with Theorems 2.5 and 2.6 even when the exponent n is a rational number. First, let us set $n = 1/q$, where q is an integer not equal to zero. If Theorem 2.5-3 is to hold, we must have $(a^{1/q})^q = (a^q)^{1/q} = a^1 = a$. If a and q are such that $a^{1/q}$ is defined, we call $a^{1/q}$ the **principal qth root of a** and note that raising the principal qth root of a to the power q gives us back the number a. A more general property is described formally in the following definition.

> **Definition 2.3.** *Any real number* r *is called a* **qth root of a** *if and only if* q *is a positive integer and* r *is such that* a $=$ r^q.

This definition does not imply that every real number a has a real root for every integer q. Let us see what restrictions we must place on a and q. Suppose, for example, that $a = -1$ and $q = 2$; then $-1 = r^2$; but there is no real number r whose square is equal to -1. The proof of this statement is immediate. Setting $b = 0$ in Axiom 7 for the real numbers (page 22) we see that $a < 0$, or $a > 0$, or $a = 0$ for every real number a. Thus, every real number is positive, negative, or zero. Now, if r is positive, r^2 is positive and cannot equal -1. If r is negative, r^2 is the product of two negative numbers, and again, it is positive and cannot equal -1. Finally, if $r = 0$, $r^2 = 0 \neq -1$. Since Axiom 7 allows no other alternatives, we can only conclude that there is no real 2nd root of -1. A similar argument will establish that *there is no real* q*th root of* a *when* a *is negative, and* q *is an even integer.* Can you give an example to show that there is at least one real odd qth root of a negative number?

More can be said about the number of real qth roots possessed by the real number a. If a is positive, it will have exactly one real and positive qth root, the principal qth root of a, denoted by $a^{1/q}$ or $\sqrt[q]{a}$. In contrast, if a is negative and q is an *odd integer*, the only real qth root of a is a negative number. It is the principal qth root, again denoted by $a^{1/q}$ or $\sqrt[q]{a}$. If q is a positive integer greater than 2, the symbol $\sqrt[q]{a}$ is called a **radical**; q is called its **index** and a is called its **radicand**. If $q = 2$, the symbol $\sqrt{a}$ is used instead of $\sqrt[2]{a}$, and it represents the *square root* of a. For example, the principal square root of 4 is $\sqrt{4} = 2$, and the principal cube root of -27 is denoted by $\sqrt[3]{-27}$ and equals -3.

By Definition 2.3, the statement $\sqrt{4} = 2$ means $2^2 = 4$. Note also that $(-2)^2$ equals 4 and, therefore, that -2 is also a square root of 4. Since the principal square root of 4 equals 2, and the square root -2 is the negative of 2, it is properly denoted by $-\sqrt{4}$.

We are now ready to extend the meaning of a^n to include rational exponents. Letting $n = p/q$, where p and q are integers, the fraction p/q is in lowest terms, and $q > 0$, we *define* $a^{p/q}$ to equal $(a^{1/q})^p$. Thus, $a^{p/q}$ is the pth power of the principal qth root of a, and it also may be written in the radical form $\sqrt[q]{a^p}$. To determine whether $a^{p/q}$ is a real number, we must first be sure that the fraction p/q is in lowest terms and such that the denominator is a positive integer. For example, $(-8)^{4/12}$ is not defined because no 12th root of -8 is real, but $(-8)^{1/3} = -2$.

We have defined $a^{p/q}$ for p/q in lowest terms and $q > 0$ in such a way that Theorem 2.5-3 holds for $a > 0$. However, if $a < 0$ this theorem is not necessarily true; for example,

$$[(-1)^2]^{1/2} \neq -1$$

It can be shown that Theorems 2.5-1, 2.5-2, and 2.6 are also true when m and n are put in the form p/q in lowest terms, $q > 0$, and $a > 0$. The following examples apply Theorems 2.5 and 2.6 to the simplification of expressions involving rational exponents.

Example 2.4. Find the value of $\left(\dfrac{8}{27}\right)^{2/3}$.

Solution:

$$\left(\frac{8}{27}\right)^{2/3} = \left(\frac{8^{1/3}}{27^{1/3}}\right)^2 = \left(\frac{2}{3}\right)^2 = \frac{4}{9}$$

Example 2.5. Perform all operations and eliminate as many exponents and radicals as possible.

$$\sqrt[4]{\frac{256x^8y^{-3}}{z^4}} \qquad (x > 0, y > 0, z > 0)$$

Solution:

$$\sqrt[4]{\frac{256x^8y^{-3}}{z^4}} = \frac{4x^2y^{-3/4}}{z} = \frac{4x^2}{zy^{3/4}}$$

Example 2.6. Find the value of $\sqrt[3]{2\sqrt{16}}$.

Solution:

$$\sqrt[3]{2\sqrt{16}} = \sqrt[3]{2 \cdot 4} = \sqrt[3]{8} = 2$$

If an expression contains several terms involving radicals, those terms having the same index and radicand may be combined with the use of the distributive law, as illustrated in the following examples.

Example 2.7. Combine like terms. $3\sqrt{2} - 4\sqrt{8} + \sqrt{18}$.

Solution:

$$
\begin{aligned}
3\sqrt{2} - 4\sqrt{8} + \sqrt{18} &= 3\sqrt{2} - 4\sqrt{4 \cdot 2} + \sqrt{9 \cdot 2} \\
&= 3\sqrt{2} - 4 \cdot 2\sqrt{2} + 3\sqrt{2} \\
&= (3 - 8 + 3)\sqrt{2} \\
&= -2\sqrt{2}
\end{aligned}
$$

Example 2.8. Combine like terms. $\sqrt[3]{ax^2} + 2\sqrt[6]{a^2x^4} \quad (x > 0)$.

Solution:

$$
\begin{aligned}
\sqrt[3]{ax^2} + 2\sqrt[6]{a^2x^4} &= (ax^2)^{1/3} + 2(a^2x^4)^{1/6} \\
&= a^{1/3}x^{2/3} + 2a^{1/3}x^{2/3} \\
&= 3a^{1/3}x^{2/3}
\end{aligned}
$$

The solution to Example 2.8 might just as well have been written in the form $3\sqrt[3]{ax^2}$ or in the form $\sqrt[3]{27ax^2}$, depending upon which is most useful in a given problem. As shown in this example, many problems involving the combination and simplification of radicals are more easily solved if the exponential notation is used rather than the radical notation.

In dealing with fractions involving radicals, it is often useful to find an equal fraction having no radicals in the denominator, a process called **rationalizing the denominator.** For example, if the denominator consists of a single square root, multiplication of the numerator and denominator by this radical will rationalize the denominator, as illustrated in the following example.

Example 2.9. Rationalize the denominator. $\dfrac{x + y}{2\sqrt{z}} \quad (z > 0)$.

Solution:

$$
\frac{x + y}{2\sqrt{z}} \cdot \frac{\sqrt{z}}{\sqrt{z}} = \frac{(x + y)\sqrt{z}}{2z}
$$

If the denominator consists of the sum or difference of two numbers, at least one of which is a square root, it may be rationalized by multiplying the numerator and denominator of the fraction by the difference or the sum of these numbers, respectively, as shown in the following example.

Example 2.10. Rationalize the denominator.

$$
\frac{a + b}{\sqrt{b} - 2\sqrt{a}} \quad (b \geq 0, a \geq 0, \quad \text{and} \quad \sqrt{b} \neq 2\sqrt{a})
$$

Solution:

$$\frac{a+b}{\sqrt{b}-2\sqrt{a}} \cdot \frac{\sqrt{b}+2\sqrt{a}}{\sqrt{b}+2\sqrt{a}} = \frac{(a+b)(\sqrt{b}+2\sqrt{a})}{b-2\sqrt{ab}+2\sqrt{ab}-4a}$$

$$= \frac{(a+b)(\sqrt{b}+2\sqrt{a})}{b-4a}$$

In this section the meaning of a^n has been extended to include all rational values of n for $a > 0$, and it has been pointed out that a^n is not real if a is negative and n is a rational fraction in lowest terms with an even denominator. The kind of numbers that arise in this exceptional case will be discussed in Chapter 3. It is possible also to define a^n when n is an irrational number and $a > 0$, but it is necessary to find its value by means of successive approximations. This problem is discussed in Chapter 5.

PROBLEMS A

1. Find the value of the following:

(a) $\sqrt[4]{16}$

(b) $\sqrt[3]{-8}$

(c) $\left(\frac{16}{49}\right)^{3/2}$

(d) $\left(-\frac{27}{64}\right)^{-1/3}$

(e) $(.008)^{1/3}$

(f) $(.04)^{-.5}$

2. Perform all operations and eliminate as many exponents and radicals as possible.

(a) $\sqrt{x^4}$

(b) $(\sqrt[3]{x})^6$

(c) $\sqrt{\frac{x^2 y^0}{9}}$ $(x > 0)$

(d) $\sqrt[4]{\frac{a^2 x^{-8}}{y^6}}$ $(a > 0, x > 0\ y > 0)$

(e) $\sqrt{\sqrt[4]{a^4}}$ $(a > 0)$

(f) $\sqrt{x}\sqrt[3]{x}\sqrt[4]{x}$ $(x > 0)$

(g) $\frac{2\sqrt{ab}}{\sqrt[4]{a^{3/2}b^{1/2}}}$ $(a > 0, b > 0)$

(h) $\frac{\sqrt[6]{(a+b)^2}}{\sqrt[3]{a+b}}$ $(a+b > 0)$

(i) $\sqrt[3]{27\sqrt[4]{x^{-8}}}$ $(x \neq 0)$

(j) $\sqrt{2\sqrt[3]{4\sqrt[4]{16x^{-12}}}}$ $(x > 0)$

3. Combine like terms and rationalize any denominator.

(a) $\sqrt{8} - \sqrt{32}$

(b) $\sqrt[3]{40} + \sqrt[3]{5}$

(c) $\frac{2a^{1/2}b^3 - 6ab^4}{a^{1/3}b^2}$ $(a > 0, b \neq 0)$

(d) $\sqrt[4]{h^2} - \sqrt{4h} + \sqrt[3]{h^{3/2}}$ $(h > 0)$

(e) $\frac{3}{\sqrt{3}+\sqrt{2}}$

(f) $\frac{1}{\sqrt{2}-\sqrt{3}}$

(g) $\dfrac{\sqrt{x}}{\sqrt{x} + \sqrt{y}}$ $(x > 0,\ y > 0)$

(h) $\dfrac{a^{1/2}b^2}{(ab)^{1/2} - (ab)^{-1/2}}$ $(a > 0,\ b > 0,\ ab \neq 1)$

(i) $\sqrt{x^{-1} + y^{-1}}$ $(x^{-1} + y^{-1} > 0)$

(j) $\dfrac{(a - b\sqrt{c})(a + b\sqrt{c})}{a^2 - b^2 c}$ $(|a| \neq |b|,\ c > 0)$

PROBLEMS B

1. Under what conditions is Theorem 2.5-1 true when m and n are rational numbers?   Give a proof.

2. Under what conditions is Theorem 2.5-2 true when n is a rational number? Give a proof.

3. Under what conditions is Theorem 2.6 true when m and n are rational numbers?   Give a proof.

2.5 Polynomials

In our discussion of the real number system, we examined four funda-mental rational operations and the operation of taking roots.   We shall now discuss the application of these operations to variables.

A **variable** can stand for any element of a given set.   Thus, a variable behaves somewhat like a pronoun in language.   For example, the pro-noun "he" may refer to some specific person, but it does not denote which person.   Similarly, the variable x may refer to some specific element of a given set (such as the set of real numbers), but it does not denote which element.   In particular, a letter is called a **constant** if it can represent *only one* specific number during a given discussion.   It is customary to use the first several letters of the alphabet, $a, b, c, \ldots$, as constants, and to use the last several letters of the alphabet, $z, y, x, \ldots$, as variables.

The four fundamental rational operations — addition, subtraction, multiplication, and division — together with the operations of taking roots, described in Section 2.4, are the **elementary algebraic operations.** Any expression generated by applying a limited number of elementary algebraic operations to constants and variables is called an **algebraic expression.**   For example,

$$4x^{-3} - \sqrt{x^2 + 2}$$

is an algebraic expression *in the variable* x and

$$x^2 - xy + \sqrt[3]{y}$$

is an algebraic expression *in the two variables* x *and* y. An algebraic expression is said to be a **rational algebraic expression** in a given variable if that variable is involved only in rational operations. Thus, the expression

$$\frac{x^2 + \sqrt{y}}{\sqrt{3}}$$

is rational in x, but not in y.

A rational algebraic expression in the variable x is called an integral expression or a **polynomial in x** if it can be written in the form

$$a_0 + a_1 x + a_2 x^2 + \ldots + a_n x^n$$

where n is a positive integer or zero and $a_0, \ldots, a_n$ are constants. The constants $a_0, a_1, a_2, \ldots, a_n$ are called the **coefficients** of $x^0, x^1, x^2, \ldots, x^n$, respectively. The number n, representing the largest exponent of x, is called the **degree** of the polynomial. In a polynomial of degree n, any of the coefficients may equal zero except a_n. Thus, $3x^5 - 1$ is a polynomial of degree 5 with

$$a_0 = -1, \quad a_1 = a_2 = a_3 = a_4 = 0, \quad \text{and} \quad a_5 = 3$$

It is customary and convenient to write a polynomial so that the exponents of x are either in ascending or in descending order.

The expression

$$\frac{4x^3 + 2x^2 - 3x}{2x} \qquad (x \neq 0)$$

for example, is not in the form given above. However, it is equivalent to

$$2x^2 + x - \frac{3}{2}$$

which is recognized as a polynomial in x of degree 2. Furthermore, the expression

$$3x^{3/2} - 2x^{1/2} + 7 \qquad (x \geq 0)$$

is not a polynomial in x. However, if we write this expression in the form

$$3(\sqrt{x})^3 - 2(\sqrt{x}) + 7 \qquad (x \geq 0)$$

it is recognized as a polynomial in $\sqrt{x}$ of degree 3.

Any non-zero constant c may be written in the form $c = c \cdot x^0$, and it is, therefore, a polynomial of degree 0. Thus, the set of non-zero real numbers can be regarded as a subset of the set of polynomials; namely, the set of polynomials of degree 0 with real coefficients. The number 0 also is regarded as a polynomial, but it is not assigned a degree.

2.6   Addition and Multiplication of Polynomials

All the rational operations defined at this point can be applied to polynomials. Let us consider a polynomial of degree n in the variable x having real coefficients. If x represents an element chosen from the set of real numbers, the polynomial represents a real number. This follows from the fact that the polynomial is formed by adding and subtracting products of real numbers, and the set of real numbers is closed under the operations of addition, subtraction, and multiplication. Thus, the operations performed on polynomials must be so defined that they are consistent with the structure of these operations as performed on real numbers.

Accordingly, if we want to *add* the polynomials $3x^2 - 2x + 1$ and $x - 4$, for example, we may think of x as a real number and use the associative, commutative, and distributive laws to write

$$(3x^2 - 2x + 1) + (x - 4) = 3x^2 + (-2x + x) + (1 - 4)$$
$$= 3x^2 + x(-2 + 1) + (1 - 4)$$
$$= 3x^2 - x - 3$$

Thus, we see that the sum of these two polynomials is also a polynomial, and its degree does not exceed that of the higher degree polynomial in the sum. This example may be generalized to produce the following definition.

Definition 2.4. *Given the polynomials*

$$a_0 + a_1x + a_2x^2 + \ldots + a_mx^m$$

and

$$b_0 + b_1x + b_2x^2 + \ldots + b_nx^n$$

with m $<$ n, *their* **sum** *is*

$$(a_0 + b_0) + (a_1 + b_1)x + (a_2 + b_2)x^2 + \ldots + (a_m + b_m)x^m$$
$$+ b_{m+1}x^{m+1} + \ldots + b_nx^n$$

Thus, the sum of a polynomial of degree m *and a polynomial of degree* n *is a polynomial whose degree is the greater of the two numbers* m *and* n *if* m $\neq$ n *and does not exceed* m *if* m $=$ n.

Of course, we may subtract a polynomial from another polynomial with the use of the same definition. The following examples illustrate Definition 2.4.

Example 2.11. Add $4x^5 - 3x^4 + x$ and $x^7 + 7x^4 - 3x - 2$.

Solution:

$$(4x^5 - 3x^4 + x) + (x^7 + 7x^4 - 3x - 2) = x^7 + 4x^5 + (-3 + 7)x^4 + (1 - 3)x - 2$$
$$= x^7 + 4x^5 + 4x^4 - 2x - 2$$

Example 2.12. Subtract $3x^3 - 4x^2 + 5$ from $3x^3 + x^2 - 2x + 1$.

Solution:

$$(3x^3 + x^2 - 2x + 1) - (3x^3 - 4x^2 + 5) = (3 - 3)x^3 + [1 - (-4)]x^2 - 2x + (1 - 5)$$
$$= 5x^2 - 2x - 4$$

We note from Example 2.12 that the sum or difference of two poly-nomials of the same degree can have a degree lower than that of the two polynomials.

We now make use of the distributive law to define the product of two polynomials.

Definition 2.5. *Given the polynomials*

$$a_0 + a_1x + a_2x^2 + \ldots + a_mx^m$$

and

$$b_0 + b_1x + b_2x^2 + \ldots + b_nx^n$$

their **product** *is*

$$a_0(b_0 + b_1x + b_2x^2 + \ldots + b_nx^n) + a_1x(b_0 + b_1x + b_2x^2 + \ldots + b_nx^n)$$
$$+ a_2x^2(b_0 + b_1x + b_2x^2 + \ldots + b_nx^n) + \ldots$$
$$+ a_mx^m(b_0 + b_1x + b_2x^2 + \ldots + b_nx^n)$$
$$= a_0b_0 + (a_0b_1 + a_1b_0)x + (a_0b_2 + a_1b_1 + a_2b_0)x^2$$
$$+ \ldots + a_mb_nx^{m+n}$$

Thus, the product of a polynomial of degree m *and a polynomial of degree* n *is a polynomial of degree* m + n.

The multiplication is performed by repeated use of the distributive law and by combining coefficients of like powers of x, as illustrated in the following example.

Example 2.13. Multiply $5x^2 - 2x + 3$ by $-x + 7$.

Solution:

$$(5x^2 - 2x + 3) \cdot (-x + 7) = 5x^2(-x + 7) - 2x(-x + 7) + 3(-x + 7)$$
$$= -5x^3 + 35x^2 + 2x^2 - 14x - 3x + 21$$
$$= -5x^3 + 37x^2 - 17x + 21$$

PROBLEMS A

1. Write each of the following expressions in the form $a_0 + a_1x + a_2x^2 + \cdots + a_nx^n$ and identify its degree.

(a) $(3 - 5x^2) + (2 - 3x^3)$ (b) $(x - 4x^3 + x^4) - (x^3 + x^4)$

(c) $x(3 - 4x - x^2) + x^2$ (d) $x^2(2 - 3x) - x(3 - 2x)$

(e) $(x + 1)(x - 1) - (x - 1)(x + 2)$

(f) $(2x + 3)(x^3 - 4x^2 + 1)$

(g) $(x - 4)^2(x + 1) + (x + 1)^2(x - 4)$

(h) $x(x^2 - 2x + 3) - (x + 3)(x^2 + 2)$

(i) $(3x^3 + 2x^2 + x + 1)(x^2 - 3x + 7)$

(j) $(2x^2 + x - 5)(5x^3 - x + 1)$

(k) $(x + 1)(x^2 + 1)(x^3 + 1)$ (l) $x(x^2 - 1)(x^3 - 2)(x^4 - 3)$

2. Let $P(x) = 5x^3 - 7x^2 + 3x - 1$.   Find

(a) $P(1)$ (b) $P(-2)$

(c) $[P(x)]^2$ (d) $P(x + 1)$

(e) $P(-x)$ (f) $P(x) - P(-x)$

3. If $P(x)$ is a polynomial of degree m and $Q(x)$ is a polynomial of degree n, where $m > n$, find the degree of

(a) $P(x) + Q(x)$ (b) $P(x)Q(x)$

(c) $xP(x)$ (d) $P(x^2)$

(e) $[P(x)]^2$ (f) $P(ax)$

PROBLEMS B

1. If $P(x) = x^2 - 2x + 3$ and $Q(x) = 5 - x^3$, find

(a) $P(x) - Q(-x)$ (b) $P[Q(x)]$

(c) $Q[P(x)]$ (d) $P(-x)Q(-x) - P(x)Q(x)$

2. If $P(x)$ is a polynomial of degree m and $Q(x)$ is a polynomial of degree n, prove that $P[Q(x)]$ and $Q[P(x)]$ are both polynomials of degree $m \cdot n$ (not necessarily the same polynomials).

2.7   Division of Polynomials

A careful study of the process of multiplication of two polynomials makes it possible to prescribe a simple scheme for undoing this process, that is, for dividing polynomials to obtain a quotient and a remainder. Without going into the details of the derivation, we give an example to remind the student of the process for dividing a polynomial by another polynomial of *lower degree.*

Example 2.14. Divide $15x^2 + 14x - 8$ by $5x - 2$.

Solution:

$$
\begin{array}{r}
3x + 4 \qquad \leftarrow \text{Quotient} \\
\text{Divisor} \to 5x - 2\,\big|\,15x^2 + 14x - 8 \;\leftarrow \text{Dividend} \\
15x^2 - 6x \\
\hline
20x - 8 \leftarrow \text{Remainder 1} \\
20x - 8 \\
\hline
0 \leftarrow \text{Remainder 2}
\end{array}
$$

Therefore,

$$\frac{15x^2 + 14x - 8}{5x - 2} = 3x + 4$$

In order to make use of the process illustrated in Example 2.14, it is desirable that each polynomial be written with the exponents of x in *descending* order. Furthermore, any term with a coefficient of zero should be written down explicitly, as shown in the following example.

Example 2.15. Divide $x^4 - x^3 - x + 1$ by $x^3 - 1$.

Solution:

$$
\begin{array}{r}
x - 1 \qquad\qquad \leftarrow \text{Quotient} \\
\text{Divisor} \to x^3 + 0x^2 + 0x - 1\,\big|\,x^4 - x^3 + 0x^2 - x + 1 \\
x^4 + 0x^3 + 0x^2 - x \\
\hline
-x^3 + 0x^2 + 0x + 1 \;\leftarrow \text{Remainder 1} \\
-x^3 + 0x^2 + 0x + 1 \\
\hline
0 \;\leftarrow \text{Remainder 2}
\end{array}
$$

Therefore,

$$\frac{x^4 - x^3 - x + 1}{x^3 - 1} = x - 1$$

In the preceding examples, we obtained a final remainder of zero, and the quotient of the given polynomials was also a polynomial. This is not always the case, as illustrated in the following example.

Example 2.16. Divide $2x^3 - x^2 + 4x + 5$ by $x^2 + 2x - 1$.

Solution:

$$
\begin{array}{r}
2x - 5 \qquad\qquad \leftarrow \text{Quotient} \\
\text{Divisor} \to x^2 + 2x - 1\,\big|\,2x^3 - x^2 + 4x + 5 \;\leftarrow \text{Dividend} \\
2x^3 + 4x^2 - 2x \\
\hline
-5x^2 + 6x + 5 \leftarrow \text{Remainder 1} \\
-5x^2 - 10x + 5 \\
\hline
16x + 0 \leftarrow \text{Remainder 2}
\end{array}
$$

Therefore, we write

$$\frac{2x^3 - x^2 + 4x + 5}{x^2 + 2x - 1} = 2x - 5 + \frac{16x}{x^2 + 2x - 1}$$

As illustrated in Example 2.16, we halt the formal process of division as soon as the degree of the remainder is less than that of the divisor. The result is written in the form of a polynomial quotient plus an additional term. The numerator of the additional term is the last remainder, and the denominator is the divisor itself. Thus, the degree of the numerator is less than that of the denominator.

We have seen that sums, differences, and products of two polynomials are also polynomials. However, Example 2.16 shows that quotients of two polynomials are not necessarily polynomials. Thus, the set of polynomials is closed under the operations of addition, subtraction, and multiplication, but, unlike the set of real numbers, the set of non-zero polynomials is *not* closed under the operation of division.

2.8 Synthetic Division

The labor of division can be shortened in the special case when the divisor is of the form $x - a$. For example, let us consider the problem of dividing

$$2x^3 - 9x^2 + 13x - 12 \quad \text{by} \quad x - 3$$

Performing the long division, we obtain

$$
\begin{array}{r}
2x^2 - 3x + 4 \\
x - 3 \enclose{longdiv}{2x^3 - 9x^2 + 13x - 12} \\
\underline{2x^3 - 6x^2} \\
-3x^2 + 13x \\
\underline{-3x^2 + 9x} \\
4x - 12 \\
\underline{4x - 12} \\
0
\end{array}
$$

We note that the first coefficient in the quotient equals the first coefficient in the dividend. Furthermore, each successive coefficient in the quotient equals the first coefficient in a corresponding remainder. (These coefficients are printed in bold face.) We also note that the first coefficient in any remainder can be obtained by adding to the corresponding coefficient of the dividend the product of 3 and the first coefficient of the preceding remainder. Thus,

$$-3 = -9 + 3 \cdot 2, \quad 4 = 13 + 3(-3), \quad \text{and} \quad 0 = -12 + 3 \cdot 4$$

This procedure, known as synthetic division can be schematized as follows.

$$3 \mid \begin{array}{rrrr} 2 & -9 & 13 & -12 \\ & 6 & -9 & 12 \\ \hline 2 & -3 & 4 & 0 \end{array}$$

To summarize, we may divide any polynomial of degree greater than 1 by a polynomial of degree 1 and in the form $x - a$ as follows.

(1) Write down the coefficients of the dividend polynomial in the order of descending powers of x. (Do not forget to include any zero coefficients.)

(2) Write down the number a to the left of these coefficients.

(3) Bring down the first coefficient of the dividend.

(4) Multiply this number by a.

(5) Add the result to the second coefficient of the dividend.

(6) Repeat this process until no more coefficients of the dividend remain.

(7) The last result so obtained is the remainder.

Synthetic division is further illustrated in the following example.

Example 2.17. Divide $x^4 - 7x^2 + 29x - 13$ by $x + 4$.

Solution: Note that $a = -4$. We have

$$-4 \mid \begin{array}{rrrrr} 1 & 0 & -7 & 29 & -13 \\ & -4 & 16 & -36 & 28 \\ \hline 1 & -4 & 9 & -7 & 15 \end{array}$$

Thus,

$$\frac{x^4 - 7x^2 + 29x - 13}{x + 4} = x^3 - 4x^2 + 9x - 7 + \frac{15}{x + 4}$$

PROBLEMS A

1. Use long division to find the quotient and the remainder when

(a) $x^2 - 2x + 1$ is divided by $x - 1$.

(b) $x^2 + 3x - 5$ is divided by $x + 4$.

(c) $x^3 - 3x^2 + 7x - 4$ is divided by $x^2 - 2x + 2$.

(d) $x^4 - 3x + 2$ is divided by $x^2 + 1$.

(e) $4y^6 + 5y^3 - 6$ is divided by $3 - 4y^3$

(f) $u^4 - 4u^3 + 3u^2 - 4u + 12$ is divided by $u - 3$.

2. Divide $x^{3n} + x^{2n} + x^n + 1$ by $x^n - 1$.

3. Use synthetic division to find the quotient and the remainder when

(a) $3x^2 - 2x - 4$ is divided by $x - 3$.

(b) $x^5 - 4x^3 + 5x^2 - 5$ is divided by $x + 1$.

(c) $-2x^3 - 4x^2 + 3x - 5$ is divided by $x - 3$.
(d) $3x^4 + 22x^3 - 19x^2 - 22x + 16$ is divided by $x + 8$.
(e) $2x^3 + 5x^2 - 4x - 5$ is divided by $x + \frac{1}{2}$.
(f) $2x^4 - 10x^3 + 2x^2 - 12$ is divided by $2x - 2$.

PROBLEMS B

1. If we divide the polynomial $A(x)$ by the polynomial $B(x)$ we may write the quotient as the polynomial $Q(x)$ and the remainder as the polynomial $R(x)$. Show that

$$A(x) = B(x)Q(x) + R(x)$$

2. Show that when $x^{100} + 1$ is divided by $x - 1$, the remainder is 2.

2.9   Factoring Polynomials; Polynomial Fractions

In Section 2.1 we observed that certain positive integers could not be expressed as a product of positive integers other than themselves and 1, and we called these integers prime numbers. Furthermore, we said that any positive integer greater than 1 is factored completely if it is written as a product of prime factors only. It is possible also to define a prime polynomial, but a precise definition cannot be given in this book. In practice, we attempt to factor a polynomial so that each of its factors cannot be expressed as the product of two nonconstant polynomials in the same variable or variables. For example, we would not factor the polynomial $x - y$, although it is possible to write it in the form

$$(\sqrt{x} - \sqrt{y})(\sqrt{x} + \sqrt{y})$$

or in the form

$$2\left(\frac{x}{2} - \frac{y}{2}\right).$$

In the first case, the expressions $\sqrt{x} - \sqrt{y}$ and $\sqrt{x} + \sqrt{y}$ are not polynomials in x and y, and in the second case one of the factors is a constant.

The art of factoring polynomials is best learned through practice. We shall restrict ourselves to factors that are polynomials in one or two variables having *rational coefficients*. Thus, $x^2 - 2$, for example, will not be factored, even though it may be written as $(x + \sqrt{2})(x - \sqrt{2})$. It is helpful in such factoring of polynomials to remember the following standard products.

(1) $a(x \pm y) = ax \pm ay$
(2) $(x + y)(x - y) = x^2 - y^2$
(3) $(ax + b)(cx + d) = acx^2 + (ad + bc)x + bd$

(4) $(x \pm y)^2 = x^2 \pm 2xy + y^2$
(5) $(x \pm y)^3 = x^3 \pm 3x^2y + 3xy^2 \pm y^3$
(6) $(x \pm y)(x^2 \mp xy + y^2) = x^3 \pm y^2$

In these formulas the symbol $\pm$ means plus or minus, and the symbol $\mp$ means minus or plus.   If the top symbol is used at any place in a formula, the top symbol must be used throughout the formula, and the same is true for the bottom symbol.   Thus,

$$a(x \pm y) = ax \pm ay$$

really expresses the two formulas

$$a(x + y) = ax + ay \quad \text{and} \quad a(x - y) = ax - ay$$

The following examples illustrate the use of these products in factoring polynomials.

Example 2.18. Factor completely: $3xy - 4x^2y^3$.

Solution:
$$3xy - 4x^2y^3 = xy(3 - 4xy^2)$$

Example 2.19. Factor completely: $3x^2 - 13x - 10$.

Solution:
$$3x^2 - 13x - 10 = (3x + 2)(x - 5)$$

Example 2.20. Factor completely: $27 - x^6$.

Solution:
$$27 - x^6 = 3^3 - (x^2)^3 = (3 - x^2)(9 + 3x^2 + x^4)$$

Sometimes an expression containing several terms is most easily factored by grouping the terms as illustrated in the following examples.

Example 2.21. Factor completely: $ax + x + ay + y$.

Solution:
$$ax + x + ay + y = (ax + x) + (ay + y)$$
$$= x(a + 1) + y(a + 1)$$
$$= (x + y)(a + 1)$$

or:
$$ax + x + ay + y = (ax + ay) + (x + y)$$
$$= a(x + y) + (x + y)$$
$$= (a + 1)(x + y)$$

Example 2.22. Factor completely:

$$2x^3 + 3x^2y - 4x^2 - 2xy^2 - 3y^3 + 4y^2$$

Solution: The first three terms have the common factor x^2, and the last three terms have the common factor y^2. Thus, we have

$$(2x^3 + 3x^2y - 4x^2) + (-2xy^2 - 3y^3 + 4y^2) = x^2(2x + 3y - 4) - y^2(2x + 3y - 4)$$

$$= (x^2 - y^2)(2x + 3y - 4)$$

$$= (x + y)(x - y)(2x + 3y - 4)$$

Fractions involving polynomials may be added, subtracted, multiplied, and divided with the use of rules analogous to those given for fractions involving real numbers described in Section 2.2. It is often convenient to factor any composite polynomials prior to combining them with the use of these rules. These operations are illustrated in the following examples.

Example 2.23. Reduce to lowest terms. $\dfrac{x + 1}{x^2 + 3x + 2}$ $(x \neq -1, -2)$

Solution:

$$\frac{x + 1}{x^2 + 3x + 2} = \frac{x + 1}{(x + 1)(x + 2)}$$

$$= \frac{1}{x + 2}$$

Example 2.24. Add $\dfrac{1}{x + 1} + \dfrac{2}{x^2 + 3x + 2}$ $(x \neq -1, -2)$

Solution:

$$\frac{1}{x + 1} + \frac{2}{x^2 + 3x + 2} = \frac{1}{x + 1} + \frac{2}{(x + 1)(x + 2)}$$

$$= \frac{x + 2}{(x + 1)(x + 2)} + \frac{2}{(x + 1)(x + 2)}$$

$$= \frac{x + 4}{(x + 1)(x + 2)}$$

Example 2.25. Perform the indicated operations and reduce to lowest terms.

$$\frac{4xy}{x + 3} \cdot \frac{3x^2 + 9x}{16y^2} - \frac{7x}{y^2 + xy}   (x \neq -3, y \neq 0, x \neq -y)$$

Solution:

$$\frac{4xy}{x+3} \cdot \frac{3x^2+9x}{16y^2} - \frac{7x}{y^2+xy} = \frac{4xy \cdot 3x(x+3)}{(x+3)16y^2} - \frac{7x}{y^2+xy}$$

$$= \frac{3x^2}{4y} - \frac{7x}{y(x+y)}$$

$$= \frac{3x^2(x+y)}{4y(x+y)} - \frac{28x}{4y(x+y)}$$

$$= \frac{3x^2(x+y) - 28x}{4y(x+y)}$$

Example 2.26. Reduce to a simple fraction in lowest terms.

$$\frac{1 + \dfrac{1}{x} + \dfrac{1}{x^2}}{\dfrac{1}{x^2}} \qquad (x \neq 0)$$

Solution: The LCD of the simple fractions $1/x$ and $1/x^2$ is x^2. After multiplying the numerator and denominator of the complex fraction by x^2 we obtain

$$\frac{1 + \dfrac{1}{x} + \dfrac{1}{x^2}}{\dfrac{1}{x^2}} = \frac{x^2 + x + 1}{1} = x^2 + x + 1$$

PROBLEMS A

1. Factor completely.

(a) $6x + 12$

(b) $ax - bx^2$

(c) $8xy - 2x^2y^2 + 4xy^2$

(d) $abc - a^2b^2c^2 + ab^2c$

(e) $a^2 - 4b^2$

(f) $36 - 4x^4$

(g) $y^2 + 7y + 10$

(h) $2x^2 - 12x + 16$

(i) $6x^2 - 13x - 5$

(j) $5x^2 - 24x - 5$

(k) $27 + 27y + 9y^2 + y^3$

(l) $8a^3 - 36a^2b + 54ab^2 - 27b^3$

(m) $u^3 - (x + 2y)^3$

(n) $x^9 - 64$

(o) $6rs - 6rt - 10us + 10ut$

(p) $abc + bcx + acy + cxy + abz + bxz + ayz + xyz$

(q) $w^2 + 2wx + x^2 - y^2 + 2yz - z^2$

(r) $x^2 + x - y^2 - y$

(s) $u^4 - 2u^2v^2 + v^4$

(t) $r^4 - 64$

(u) $x^{3a} + 8y^{9b}$

(v) $\dfrac{1}{x^6} - \dfrac{9}{y^8}$

(w) $\dfrac{9u^2 - 4v^2}{a^2 - 2ab + b^2} - \dfrac{9u + 6v}{a - b}$

(x) $\dfrac{a^2 + abx - ab - b^2x}{ac + bcx + aby + b^2xy}$

2. Reduce to simple fractions in lowest terms.

(a) $\dfrac{y - x}{x^2 - y^2}$

(b) $\dfrac{y^2 - x^2}{x^4 - y^4}$

(c) $\dfrac{x^4 - 6x^2}{3x^3 - 18x}$

(d) $\dfrac{x^2y^3 - x^3y^2}{x - y}$

(e) $\dfrac{6x^2 - 5x - 6}{4x^2 + 10x - 24}$

(f) $\dfrac{u^2 + 2uv}{u^2 + u + 2v - 4v^2}$

(g) $\dfrac{(1/x) - (1/y)}{x^2 - y^2}$

(h) $\dfrac{x^2 - y^2}{(1/x) + (1/y)}$

(i) $\dfrac{(x - 1)^2/(x^4 - 1)}{(x - 1)/(x^2 + 1)}$

(j) $\dfrac{(x^3 + y^3)/(x^3 - y^3)}{(x^2 + xy)/(xy - y^2)}$

(k) $\dfrac{1 + 1/(x^3 - y^3)}{1 - 1/(x - y)}$

(l) $\dfrac{1/(x^3 + 3x^2y + 3xy^2 + y^3)}{1/(x^2 + 2xy + y^2)}$

3. Perform the indicated operations and reduce your answer to a simple fraction in lowest terms.

(a) $\dfrac{3}{x} - \dfrac{5}{7x^2}$

(b) $\dfrac{1}{x - 4} + \dfrac{x + 3}{x^2 - 4x}$

(c) $\dfrac{1}{x} - \dfrac{1}{x^2} + \dfrac{1}{x^3} - \dfrac{1}{x^4}$

(d) $\dfrac{x}{(y - 1)(z - 2)} + \dfrac{y}{(x - 3)(z - 2)} - \dfrac{z}{(x - 3)(y - 1)}$

(e) $\dfrac{3u}{u + 2} - \dfrac{2}{2 - u} - \dfrac{5u - 2}{u^2 - 4}$

(f) $\dfrac{1}{v} + \dfrac{3}{v^2 - 3v} - \dfrac{2}{v - 3}$

(g) $\dfrac{x - 1}{x^2 + 1} \cdot \dfrac{x^4 - 1}{(x - 1)^2}$

(h) $\dfrac{x^2 - 1}{2x - 3} \cdot \dfrac{4x^2 - 9}{2x^2 - x - 3}$

(i) $\dfrac{2y^2 - 3y - 9}{y^2 - 9} \cdot \dfrac{y^2 - 2y}{2y^2 + 5y + 3}$

(j) $\dfrac{x^2 - 5x - 14}{x^2 + x - 16} \cdot \dfrac{x^2 + 2x - 3}{(x - 7)^2}$

(k) $\left(\dfrac{x^2}{4y^2} - 1\right)\Big/\left(\dfrac{x}{2y} - 1\right)$

(l) $\left(\dfrac{1 + x}{1 - x} + \dfrac{1 - x}{1 + x}\right)\Big/\left(\dfrac{1 + x}{-1 + x} - \dfrac{-1 + x}{1 + x}\right)$

PROBLEMS B

1. Factor the following second-degree polynomial in x.

$$ax^2 - (a^2 - 1)x - a$$

2. Express xy as the difference between two squares.

3. Could you factor $x^2 + y^2$ if the restriction that the coefficients of the factors are real numbers were dropped? How?

4. Determine k so that $x - 1$ is a factor of

$$2x^2 + (k - 2)x - 8$$

3

The Complex
Numbers

3.1 Definition of Complex Numbers

When we defined the symbol a^n for rational values of n (Section 2.4) we
pointed out that $a^{1/q}$ is not a real number when a is negative and q is an
even integer.   In particular, we proved that $\sqrt{-1}$ is not a real number.
This suggests that we define a new set of numbers to give meaning to
symbols like $\sqrt{-1}$.

Before characterizing this new set of numbers, let us take a second look
at our definition of the rational numbers.   After we noted that the set of
integers is not closed under the operation of division, we introduced
rational numbers that can be written in the form a/b where a and b are
integers and $b \neq 0$.   We may also regard the rational numbers as *ordered
pairs* of integers written in the form (a, b) rather than a/b.   As before,
a is called the numerator and b is called the denominator.   Then we may
define the ordered pairs (a, b) and (c, d) to be equal if and only if $ad = bc$.
With this notation, we may write the addition rule given on page 32 in
the form

$$(a, c) + (b, c) = (a + b, c)$$

and the multiplication rule (page 31) may be written in the form

$$(a, b) \cdot (c, d) = (ac, bd)$$

Can you obtain similar formulas for subtraction and division of rational numbers?

This concept of ordered pairs of numbers may be used to define a new set of numbers. Let a and b be any *real* numbers and consider the ordered pair (a, b). We shall abbreviate $\sqrt{-1}$ by the symbol i and interpret the ordered pair $(0, 1)$ to mean i. (The symbol i comes from the word "imaginary" because it was thought that $\sqrt{-1}$ did not really exist, but was merely a figment of man's imagination. Actually, all of the real numbers were *defined by man* and are no less imaginary than the number i.)

Consistent with the interpretation of these new numbers as ordered pairs of real numbers, we state the following definition.

Definition 3.1. *The ordered pair* $z = $ (a, b), *where* a *and* b *are real numbers, is called a* **complex number** *if the following rules of equality, addition, and multiplication hold:*

(1) (a, b) = (c, d) *if and only if* a = c *and* b = d

(2) (a, b) + (c, d) = (a + c, b + d)

(3) (a, b) · (c, d) = (ac − bd, ad + bc)

The real number a *is called the* **real part** *of* z, *and the real number* b *is called the* **imaginary part** *of* z.

The adoption of these particular rules was no accident. An alternative way to write the complex number $z = (a, b)$ is $z = a + bi$, where we interpret the product bi and the sum $a + bi$ in the same way that we interpret these operations for the real numbers. As in the case of the real numbers, we shall require that the associative, commutative, and distributive laws hold for numbers of the form $a + bi$. Thus, the sum of two such numbers must be

$$(a + bi) + (c + di) = (a + c) + (b + d)i$$

Recalling that $i^2 = -1$, the product of two such numbers must be

$$(a + bi) \cdot (c + di) = ac + adi + bci + bdi^2$$
$$= (ac - bd) + (ad + bc)i$$

Thus, if we allow $a + bi$ to behave like any other algebraic quantity, and if we define (a, b) according to Definition 3.1, we see that the two expressions (a, b) and $a + bi$ are equivalent.

The following examples illustrate the rules of addition and multiplication of complex numbers.

Example 3.1. Add: $(3 - 4i) + (2 + i)$.

Solution:

$$(3 - 4i) + (2 + i) = (3 + 2) + (-4 + 1)i = 5 - 3i$$

Example 3.2. Multiply: $(6 - i) \cdot (2 + \sqrt{2}\, i)$.

Solution:

$$(6 - i) \cdot (2 + \sqrt{2}\, i) = 12 + 6\sqrt{2}\, i - 2i - \sqrt{2}\, i^2$$
$$= (12 + \sqrt{2}) + (6\sqrt{2} - 2)i$$

Example 3.3. Find the value of i^{10}.

Solution:

$$i^2 = -1,$$

thus

$$i^3 = -i, \quad i^4 = 1, \quad i^5 = i, \quad \text{etc.}$$

We see that *the positive integer powers of* i *repeat in cycles of four.* Therefore, to find i^n, find the remainder when n is divided by 4. If the remainder is 0, $i^n = 1$; if it is 1, $i^n = i$; if it is 2, $i^n = -1$; and if it is 3, $i^n = -i$. Since 10 divided by 4 leaves a remainder of 2, $i^{10} = -1$.

As we have seen, the definition of complex numbers is consistent with the associative, commutative, and distributive laws — Axioms 3, 4, and 5 for a field. Definition 3.1 can also be used to establish that the remaining axioms for a field are satisfied by the set of complex numbers. To establish that Axiom 1 holds, we note that sums and products of complex numbers are also complex numbers, having real and imaginary parts given by Definition 3.1. These real and imaginary parts consist of sums and products of real numbers which are uniquely defined by Axiom 1 for the set of real numbers. Thus, to each pair of complex numbers, there corresponds a unique sum and a unique product which is also a complex number. To establish that Axiom 2 holds, we merely note that the complex numbers $(0, 0)$ and $(1, 0)$ satisfy

$$(a, b) + (0, 0) = (a + 0, b + 0) = (a, b)$$

and

$$(a, b) \cdot (1, 0) = (a \cdot 1 - b \cdot 0, a \cdot 0 + b \cdot 1) = (a, b)$$

by Axiom 2 for the set of real numbers. Thus, $(0, 0)$ is the additive identity and $(1, 0)$ is the multiplicative identity for the set of complex numbers.

In order for Axiom 6 to hold, we need to define an additive inverse and a multiplicative inverse of (a, b) so that these inverses are unique complex numbers. These inverses must also be defined consistently with the rules for addition and multiplication of complex numbers. If we let (c, d) be the additive inverse of (a, b), for Axiom 6a and the rule of addition of complex numbers to hold, we have

$$(a, b) + (c, d) = (a + c, b + d) = (0, 0)$$

Thus, $c = -a$ and $d = -b$, by Axiom 6a for the set of real numbers and the definition of equality of two complex numbers. Similarly, if we let (e, f) be the multiplicative inverse of (a, b) we have

$$(a, b) \cdot (e, f) = (ae - bf, af + be) = (1, 0)$$

Thus,

$$ae - bf = 1 \quad \text{and} \quad af + be = 0$$

It can be shown that these equations are satisfied if and only if

$$e = \frac{a}{a^2 + b^2} \quad \text{and} \quad f = \frac{-b}{a^2 + b^2}$$

Thus, the additive inverse of the complex number (a, b) is the complex number $(-a, -b)$ and its multiplicative inverse is

$$\left(\frac{a}{a^2 + b^2}, \frac{-b}{a^2 + b^2} \right)$$

Note that the multiplicative inverse of $(0, 0)$ is not defined because if $a = b = 0$, then $ae - bf$ cannot equal 1.

An important relation between the real numbers and the complex numbers may now be obtained. First, we may prove that $0 \cdot i = 0$ using exactly the same steps that were used to prove Theorem 1.2. Now, we note that the complex number $(a, 0) = a + 0 \cdot i = a$, and, therefore, it is equivalent to the real number a. Thus, every real number can be regarded as a special complex number whose imaginary part is zero. In other words, *the set of real numbers is a subset of the set of complex numbers.*

PROBLEMS A

1. Perform the indicated operations and write your answer in the form $a + bi$.

(a) $(2 + 3i) + (3 - 4i)$ (b) $(6 - i) + (3 + 5i)$

(c) $(4 - i) + (4 + i)$ (d) $(\sqrt{3} + \sqrt{2}\,i) + (\sqrt{12} - \sqrt{8}\,i)$

(e) $(2 + 3i)(3 - 4i)$ (f) $(-2 + \sqrt{3}\,i)(2 + \sqrt{3}\,i)$

(g) $i(9 - 5i)(6 + i)$ (h) $(i - 1)(i + 2)(i - 3)$

(i) $(2i - 3)^2$ (j) $(1 - i)^3$

(k) $\left(\dfrac{1}{2} + \dfrac{i\sqrt{3}}{2}\right)^2$

(l) $\left(\dfrac{1}{3} - \dfrac{2i}{3}\right) + \left(\dfrac{5}{6} + \dfrac{i}{6}\right)i$

(m) $(a + bi)(a - bi) + (a + bi)(-a + bi)$

(n) $(i + 1)\left[i - \dfrac{i^3}{4} + i(3 - 4i)\right]$

(o) $(1 - i)[(2 + 3i) + (5 - 6i)]$

(p) $\left(-\dfrac{1}{2} + \dfrac{i\sqrt{3}}{2}\right)\left[\left(\dfrac{1}{2} - \dfrac{i\sqrt{3}}{2}\right) + \left(-\dfrac{1}{2} - \dfrac{i\sqrt{3}}{2}\right)^2\right]$

2. Find i^n if n equals

(a) 6   (b) 32
(c) 57   (d) 1743

3. Perform the indicated operations without using the form $z = a + bi$, and express your answer in the form $z = (a, b)$.

(a) $(1, 3) + (7, 9)$ (b) $(-2, \sqrt{5}) - (3, -\sqrt{20})$
(c) $(7, -4)(-6, 3)$ (d) $(-1, -3)(0, 12)$
(e) $(1, 1)[(-1, 2) + (3, -4)]$ (f) $[(0, 1) + (1, 0)]^2$

PROBLEMS B

1. If $z_1 = 1 + i$ and $z_2 = 1 - i$, prove that

$$z_1^2 - 2z_1 + 2 = z_2^2 - 2z_2 + 2 = 0$$

2. Use the definition of z^{-1} to write

$$z = \frac{1 + 2i}{3 + 4i}$$

in the form $a + bi$.

3. Prove that the negative of the complex number $z = (a, b)$ is $-(a, b) = (-a, -b)$. *Hint:* First prove that $kz = (ka, kb)$ where k is any real number; then let $k = -1$.

3.2 Properties of Complex Numbers

The **difference** $z_1 - z_2$ of two complex numbers may be defined in terms of a sum, similar to the way that we defined the difference of two real numbers. If $w + z_2 = z_1$, then w is the difference between z_1 and z_2. Writing

$$z_1 = a_1 + b_1 i \quad \text{and} \quad z_2 = a_2 + b_2 i$$

we have

$$z_1 - z_2 = (a_1 - a_2) + (b_1 - b_2)i$$

The following example illustrates this definition.

Example 3.4. Find the difference: $(8 - 9i) - (-3 + 4i)$.

Solution:
$$(8 - 9i) - (-3 + 4i) = (8 - (-3)) + (-9 - 4)i$$
$$= 11 - 13i$$

If $z_1 = wz_2$, then w is called the **quotient** of z_1 and z_2, or $w = z_1/z_2$. In order to evaluate quotients of complex numbers, it is useful first to define the **conjugate** of the complex number $a + bi$.

Definition 3.2. *The* **conjugate** *of the complex number* $z = a + bi$ *is the complex number* $\bar{z} = a - bi$.

If we evaluate the sum $z + \bar{z}$ and the product $z \cdot \bar{z}$, we obtain
$$z + \bar{z} = (a + bi) + (a - bi) = 2a$$
$$z \cdot \bar{z} = (a + bi)(a - bi) = a^2 + b^2$$

Thus, the sum and product, respectively, of a complex number and its conjugate is a real number.

Two important properties of the complex conjugate are given in the following theorems.

Theorem 3.1. $\overline{z_1 + z_2} = \bar{z}_1 + \bar{z}_2$.

Proof: Let $z_1 = a_1 + b_1i$ and $z_2 = a_2 + b_2i$. Then
$$z_1 + z_2 = (a_1 + a_2) + (b_1 + b_2)i$$
and
$$\overline{z_1 + z_2} = (a_1 + a_2) - (b_1 + b_2)i$$
$$= (a_1 - b_1i) + (a_2 - b_2i)$$
$$= \bar{z}_1 + \bar{z}_2$$

Theorem 3.2. $\overline{z_1 \cdot z_2} = \bar{z}_1 \cdot \bar{z}_2$.

Proof: The proof is left as an exercise. (See Problem A-2.)

Now let us evaluate the quotient $(a_1 + b_1i)/(a_2 + b_2i)$. If we multiply the numerator and denominator of this fraction by the conjugate of the denominator, the resulting denominator will be a real number. We obtain

$$\frac{a_1 + b_1i}{a_2 + b_2i} \cdot \frac{a_2 - b_2i}{a_2 - b_2i} = \frac{(a_1a_2 + b_1b_2) + (a_2b_1 - a_1b_2)i}{a^2 + b^2}$$

$$= \frac{a_1a_2 + b_1b_2}{a_2^2 + b_2^2} + \frac{a_2b_1 - a_1b_2}{a_2^2 + b_2^2}i$$

This formula for the quotient of two complex numbers, like that for their product, is rather complicated. If the reader remembers that the four fundamental operations with complex numbers have the same properties that they do with real numbers, it will not be necessary for him to commit these formulas to memory. The following example illustrates this statement.

Example 3.5. Write the quotient $\dfrac{-2 + 3i}{4 - i}$ in the form $a + bi$.

Solution: The conjugate of the denominator is $4 + i$. Multiplying both numerator and denominator by $4 + i$, we obtain

$$\frac{(-2 + 3i)(4 + i)}{(4 - i)(4 + i)} = \frac{-11 + 10i}{16 + 1} = -\frac{11}{17} + \frac{10}{17}i$$

PROBLEMS A

1. Perform the indicated operations and write your answer in the form $a + bi$.

(a) $(\sqrt{5} - 2\sqrt{20}\,i) - (\sqrt{20} - 2\sqrt{5}\,i)$

(b) $-i(3 + 4i) - i(4 - 3i)$

(c) $\dfrac{2i - 5}{i + 1}$

(d) $\dfrac{3 + 5i}{7 - \sqrt{3}\,i}$

(e) $(1 + i)^{-1}$

(f) $\overline{3i}$

(g) $\overline{(2 + i) - (3i - 1)}$

(h) $\overline{(3i + 9)} - \overline{(7 + 3i)}$

(i) $\overline{\left(\dfrac{12 + i}{i - 1}\right)}$

(j) $\dfrac{1 - 4i}{3 + 8i}$

(k) $\left(\dfrac{1}{3} - \dfrac{\sqrt{3}}{3}i\right)(3 + i)$

(l) $\overline{(2 - \sqrt{2}\,i)(\sqrt{3} + 3i)}$

(m) $\overline{(6 - 5i)^{-1}}$

(n) $\overline{(6 - 5i)}^{-1}$

2. Prove that $\overline{z_1 z_2} = \overline{z_1} \cdot \overline{z_2}$

3. Prove that $\overline{\left(\dfrac{z_1}{z_2}\right)} = \dfrac{\overline{z_1}}{\overline{z_2}}$

PROBLEMS B

1. For what complex numbers z does $z^{-1} = \overline{z}$?

2. For what complex numbers z does $z = \overline{z}$? $z = -\overline{z}$?

3. What numbers have their reciprocal equal to their negative?

4. Prove that $\overline{\overline{z}}$ (the conjugate of $\overline{z}$) equals z.

3.3 The Complex Plane

Analogous to the geometric interpretation of the real numbers by means of a real line, we may interpret the complex numbers geometrically by means of a plane. Since every complex number is an ordered *pair* of real numbers, we may use *two* lines to represent complex numbers. By convention, these two lines are chosen to intersect at right angles (Figure 3.1).

The horizontal line is called the **real axis,** and the vertical line is called the **imaginary axis.** The point of intersection of these axes is called the **origin.** Thus, these axes are real lines having a common origin, and we choose the same unit for both axes. As before, the positive direction on the real axis is to the right, and the negative direction is to the left. The positive direction on the imaginary axis is the upward direction, and the negative direction is downward.

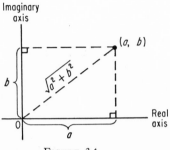

FIGURE 3.1

The real part of the complex number (a, b) is located on the real axis in the same way that we locate the real number a on the real line. The imaginary part b is located on the imaginary axis in a similar way. The point corresponding to the complex number (a, b) is located at the intersection of two lines, one perpendicular to the real axis and passing through the point a, and the other perpendicular to the imaginary axis and passing through the point b. The plane determined by the real and imaginary axes, containing all such points, is called the **complex plane.**

The ordering of the real numbers was derived by considering the distance and direction from the origin of points on the real line. Since there are only two points having a given distance from the origin, a complete ordering of the real numbers was made possible simply by specifying that the point to the left is less than the point to the right. In the complex plane, however, there are arbitrarily many complex points at a given distance from the origin. (In fact, they all lie on a circle having the origin as its center and the given distance as its radius.) For this reason, it is not fruitful to try to order the set of complex numbers, and we shall refrain from using the symbols $<$ or $>$ in connection with nonreal complex numbers. Thus, the terms "positive" and "negative" have no meaning in connection with nonreal complex numbers.

From Figure 3.1 we see that the distance of the complex point (a, b) from the origin is $\sqrt{a^2 + b^2}$. The real number $\sqrt{a^2 + b^2}$ is called the **absolute value** or **magnitude** of the complex number $z = (a, b)$ and is written $|z|$. From the discussion of the preceding paragraph, we see that all complex numbers having the same absolute value lie on a circle with its center at the origin and having a radius equal to the common absolute value. The following examples illustrate this definition.

Example 3.6. Find $|3 - 4i|$.

Solution:

$$|3 - 4i| = \sqrt{3^2 + (-4)^2} = \sqrt{9 + 16} = 5$$

Example 3.7. Prove that $|\bar{z}| = |z|$.

Solution: Let $z = a + bi$. Then $\bar{z} = a - bi$. By the definition of $|z|$, we have

$$|z| = \sqrt{a^2 + b^2}$$

and

$$|\bar{z}| = \sqrt{a^2 + (-b)^2}$$
$$= \sqrt{a^2 + b^2}$$
$$= |z|$$

which completes the proof.

Complex numbers may be given another important geometric interpretation in connection with the complex plane. Consider a *directed line segment* having its initial point at the origin of the complex plane and its terminal point at (a, b). This directed line segment is called a **vector,** and its direction is indicated by the arrow in Figure 3.2. Thus, we may refer to any vector having its initial point at the origin of the complex plane simply by giving the complex number corresponding to its terminal point. The real and imaginary parts of this complex number are called the **components** of the vector, and its absolute value is called the **length** of the vector.

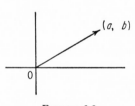

FIGURE 3.2

To define the sum of the vectors (a, b) and (c, d) we shall be consistent with the definition of the sum of two complex numbers. Since the sum of the *complex numbers* (a, b) and (c, d) is the *complex number* $(a + c, b + d)$, we define the sum of the *vectors* (a, b) and (c, d) to be the *vector* having components $(a + c, b + d)$. Similarly, the components of the vector $(a, b) - (c, d)$ are $(a - c, b - d)$.

We may use the definition of addition of vectors to add two vectors graphically, as shown in Figure 3.3. To add the vectors (a, b) and (c, d) we draw a parallelogram having these vectors as two adjacent sides. The sum $(a, b) + (c, d)$ is the vector having its initial point at the origin and its terminal point at the opposite vertex of the parallelogram. Can you prove from the geometry of Figure 3.3 that this construction is consistent with the definition $(a, b) + (c, d) = (a + c, b + d)$?

The difference $(a, b) - (c, d)$ can be regarded as the sum of the vectors (a, b) and $-(c, d)$. The vector $-(c, d)$ has components $(-c, -d)$, and is constructed by continuing the vector (c, d) through the origin in the

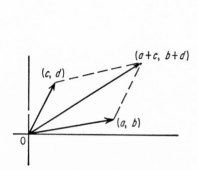

FIGURE 3.3

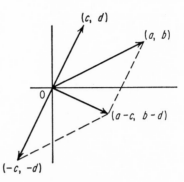

FIGURE 3.4

opposite direction for a distance equal to the length of (c, d). The difference $(a, b) - (c, d)$ is found by vector addition, as shown in Figure 3.4. Can you prove from the geometry of Figure 3.4 that this construction is consistent with the definition

$$(a, b) - (c, d) = (a - c, b - d)?$$

PROBLEMS A

1. Locate on the complex plane and find the absolute value.

(a) $3 - 4i$ (b) $12 + 5i$
(c) $\frac{1}{2} + \frac{1}{3}i$ (d) $-7 + \frac{1}{2}i$
(e) -2 (f) $3i$
(g) $1 + i$ and $\overline{1 + i}$ (h) $\frac{3}{4} - \frac{1}{2}i$ and $\overline{\frac{3}{4} - \frac{1}{2}i}$

2. Find the following sums and differences by graphic addition of vectors.

(a) $(1, 1) + (2, 3)$ (b) $(-1, 4) + (\frac{1}{2}, -2)$
(c) $(-1, 2) - (3, 5)$ (d) $(\frac{1}{2}, -\frac{1}{4}) - (\frac{3}{4}, \frac{7}{2})$
(e) $(3, 0) + (0, 3)$ (f) $(0, 1) - (0, -4)$

3. Prove that $|z_1 z_2| = |z_1| \, |z_2|$.

PROBLEMS B

1. Prove that $|z_1 + z_2| \leq |z_1| + |z_2|$.

2. For what z does $|z| = \bar{z}$?

3. Find two complex numbers (not conjugates) having the common magnitude 10.

4. Show that the vector representing the difference $z_1 - z_2$ forms the third side of the triangle having the vectors z_1 and z_2 as its other two sides. What is its direction?

5. Locate the vector $2[(1, 1) + (-2, 3) + (3, -1)]$ by graphic addition.

PART 2

Functions

The purpose of Part II is to study certain relationships between the elements of two sets. The reader already is familiar with many physical examples of relationships. There is the relationship between the distance through which a body falls and its velocity, the speed of an automobile and its gasoline consumption, the experience of a salesman and his sales ability, etc.

In mathematics we study certain kinds of relationships, called **functions.** We shall embark on a systematic study of functions by defining the concept of a function rigorously and by studying the properties of several special functions. These special functions have important applications to physics, biology, accounting, etc. Some of these applications will be considered in the course of studying the functions themselves; many others must be deferred until you study the particular subject of application.

In the study of functions, the reader has an opportunity to understand much of the beauty of mathematics, and to get a glimpse of how purely mathematical ideas may be used to describe physical phenomena.

4

The Function
Concept

4.1 Definitions

Suppose we have two sets; the first set consisting of m elements and the
second set consisting of n elements.   Let us consider the problem of associating with each element of the first set exactly one element of the second
set.   If $m = n$ we can always make such an association.   For example,
we can imagine lining up the elements of the two sets in two parallel
columns and associate elements that occupy the same position in each
column.   If $m > n$ we run out of elements of the second set but we can
still make the assignment by using some elements of the second set over
again.   If $m < n$ we run out of elements of the first set.   We cannot use
elements of the first set over again because each element of the first set
must be associated with *exactly* one element of the second set.   Although
the two sets may be fixed, many different assignments are possible.
Therefore, we shall be interested not only in the elements of the two sets,
but also in the way that they are associated with one another.

Let us call the first set the **domain** and the second set the **range.** To
every element of the domain, we associate exactly one element of the
range.   Such an association is also called a **correspondence.** It is a
one-to-one correspondence if to each element of the domain there corresponds a unique element of the range, and vice versa.   If an element of
the range corresponds to more than one element of the domain, we have

a **many-to-one correspondence.** We shall exclude from consideration one-to-many correspondences; that is, correspondences in which more than one element of the range is associated with one element of the domain.

To construct an example of a one-to-one correspondence, write down the letters of the alphabet in a column and then put down a second column consisting of the integers from 1 to 26, in that order. To the letter A corresponds the number 1 and vice versa, to the letter B corresponds the number 2 and vice versa, etc. To construct an example of a many-to-one correspondence, let the domain consist of the letters of the alphabet, as before, but now let the range consist of the integers 1, 2, and 3 only. To establish the correspondence, write 1, 2, 3, 1, 2, 3, . . . , etc. in the second column until you have 26 numbers. (The column should end with a 2.) Now, to every element of the domain there corresponds exactly one integer, but to every element of the range there correspond several letters. For example, to the letter A there corresponds only the integer 1, but to the integer 1 there correspond the letters A, D, G, J, M, P, S, V, and Y.

The range and the domain also may contain arbitrarily large sets of elements. For example, let the domain be a set X, consisting of real numbers, and let the range be a set Y, also consisting of real numbers. A correspondence between elements x of X and elements y of Y could be established as follows: "To every element x in the domain X there corresponds an element y in the range Y such that y equals twice x."   There are many other possible correspondences. Can you think of some?

Using the ideas of a correspondence between the elements of two sets, we now give a formal definition of a function.

Definition 4.1 *A* **function** *is a correspondence that assigns to each element* x *of a set* X, *called the domain, exactly one element* y *of a set* Y, *called the range.*

According to this definition, a function is either a one-to-one correspondence or a many-to-one correspondence between elements of the domain and the range. We exclude one-to-many correspondences for technical reasons that cannot be explained here.

In Definition 4.1, the letters x and y are variables, standing for some element of the domain and range, respectively. We call x the **independent variable** and y the **dependent variable** because the value of y *depends* upon the choice of x.   In order to emphasize the correspondence between x and y, we often denote the element y that corresponds to a specific element x by the symbol $f(x)$. For example, the value of y that corresponds to $x = 2$ is denoted by $f(2)$. We shall use the symbol **f** to

denote the function itself.   Symbols other than **f** also can be used to
represent a function.   Commonly used letters are **F**, **g**, **φ**, etc.

It is not necessary that the variables x and y stand for numbers.   For
example, the following table defines a function having a domain and a
range that are sets of abstract symbols.

x	!	#	$	%	*
y	?	/	σ	#	%

Furthermore, note that the following table *does not define a function*
because there are two values of y corresponding to $x = 1$.

x	0	1	1	2	3
y	-2	3	4	-6	5

If the domain and range of **f** consist of numbers, it may be possible to
express the correspondence between x and y by some equation.   For
example, the equation $f(x) = x^2$ says that the function **f** assigns to each x
in X the number y in Y such that $y = x^2$.   Note that this equation does
not completely specify the function **f** because the domain X is not given.
For example, the function **f**, where $f(x) = x^2$, defined on the domain
$x \geq 0$ is different from the function **f**, where $f(x) = x^2$, defined on the
domain $x < 0$.   The following example further illustrates the use of
functional notation.

Example 4.1. If $f(x) = x^3 - x^2 + x + 1$, find $f(2)$, $f(-1)$, $f(\sqrt{3})$, and $f(2x)$.

Solution:

$$f(2) = 2^3 - 2^2 + 2 + 1 = 7$$
$$f(-1) = (-1)^3 - (-1)^2 + (-1) + 1 = -2$$
$$f(\sqrt{3}) = (\sqrt{3})^3 - (\sqrt{3})^2 + (\sqrt{3}) + 1 = -2 + 4\sqrt{3}$$
$$f(2x) = (2x)^3 - (2x)^2 + (2x) + 1 = 8x^3 - 4x^2 + 2x + 1$$

The following example illustrates how we may find the range of a function when the domain and an equation for the correspondence are given.

Example 4.2. If $f(x) = |x|$, find the range of **f** if the domain is given by
(a) $x \geq 0$, (b) $x \leq -3$.

Solution:
(a) If $x \geq 0$, then $|x| \geq 0$. Thus, Y is the set of all non-negative real numbers.
(b) If $x \leq -3$, then $|x| \geq 3$. Thus, Y is the set of all real numbers greater
than or equal to 3.

So far, our examples of functions have involved domains that could adequately be described by a single variable.   If we consider the problem of representing the area A of a rectangle, for example, we find that A depends upon two quantities, the length l and the width w.   Corresponding to each number pair (l, w) there is one and only one area A, and we can say that there is a function $\mathbf{f}$ with $A = f(l, w)$.   (In fact, the correspondence may be given by the equation $f(l, w) = l \cdot w$.)   In this example, the domain of $\mathbf{f}$ consists of pairs of real numbers (l, w) and the range consists of numbers A.   In general, if the domain of $\mathbf{f}$ involves n variables $x_1, x_2, \ldots, x_n$, then these variables are called the independent variables, and $f(x_1, x_2, \ldots, x_n)$ is called the dependent variable.

We shall confine ourselves, in the remainder of this book, to functions having domains and ranges that are sets of real numbers.   In this sense, we may say, for example, that the function $\mathbf{f}$, where $f(x) = \sqrt{x}$ is *not defined* when $x < 0$.   On what domain is the function $\mathbf{g}$ undefined, where $g(x) = \sqrt{-x}$?

PROBLEMS A

1. For the functions described, find the domain and the range, and establish the correspondence by means of a formula or a table.

(a) To each real number there corresponds its negative.

(b) To each integer there corresponds a number equal to half its value.

(c) Mary, Joan, and Sally are married to Tom, Dick, and Harry, respectively.

(d) Each person in my family has a birth date.

2. Find the range of the functions described.

(a) $f(x) = x - 1,\ x = 0, 1, 2$ (b) $g(x) = -x,\ x > 0$

(c) $\phi(x) = |x|,\ x$ is any real number

(d) $F(x) = (x - 1)^2,\ x$ is any real number

(e) $h(x) = \dfrac{1}{x - 1},\ x > 1$ (f) $f(y) = \dfrac{y}{|y|},\ y = 1, 2, 3, 4$

(g) $f(u) = 1 - u^2,\ 0 \le u \le 1$ (h) $G(v) = \dfrac{1}{1 + v^{-1}},\ v > 0$

3. If $f(x) = x^2 - 2x + 1$, find

(a) $f(1)$ (b) $f(-3)$

(c) $f(y)$ (d) $f(2z)$

(e) $f(x + h) - f(h)$ (f) $3f(2) - 2f(3)$

(g) $f(-x)$ (h) $f(x^2 + 1)$

4. Find the domain so that the range consists of real numbers only.

(a) $f(x) = \sqrt{(x - 1)}$ (b) $f(x) = \sqrt[3]{x}$

(c) $f(x) = \sqrt{x^2 - 2x + 1}$ (d) $f(x) = x + x^{1/2} + x^{1/4}$

(e) $f(x) = (-x)^{3/2}$ (f) $f(x) = \sqrt{-x^4}$

5. If $f(x, y) = x^2 + 2xy - y^3$, find

(a) $f(1, 1)$　　　　　　　　　　　　(b) $f(-3, 4)$

(c) $f(x, 0)$　　　　　　　　　　　　(d) $f(z, 2z)$

PROBLEMS B

1. Tabulate the function represented by

$$y = |x|, \quad x = 0, \pm 1, \pm 2$$

2. Find an equation representing the function

x	0	1	2	3	4	5
y	1	2	5	10	17	26

3. If $f(x) = x^2 + 1$ and $g(x) = |x|$, find

(a) $f[g(x)]$

(b) $g\{1 + [f(x)]^2\}$

(c) $g\left[\dfrac{f(x)}{g(-x)}\right]$　When is this function undefined?

4.2　Variation and Other Examples of Functions

A famous law of physics, known as Hooke's law, states that the force on a spring varies *directly* with the displacement. A fundamental law of gravitation states that the gravitational attraction between two bodies of known mass varies *inversely* with the square of the distance between them. Let us translate these statements into the language of functions.

Definition 4.2. *If a function* **f** *assigns to each* x *of some real domain the value* y, *such that* y = kx, *we say that* **y varies directly with x.** *If* y = k/x, *we say that* **y varies inversely with x.** *(The letter* k *stands for a constant called the* **constant of proportionality.***)*

Thus, Hooke's law states that $F = kx$, where x is the displacement of the spring (the distance through which it is stretched) and F is the force tending to return it to its original position. The law of gravity stated above can be written

$$F = \frac{k}{x^2}$$

where x is the distance between the two bodies and F is the gravitational force. A more sophisticated law of gravitation also takes into account the masses of the two bodies and states: "The gravitational attraction is directly proportional to the product of the masses of the two bodies and inversely proportional to the square of the distance between them." If m_1 and m_2 are the masses of the two bodies, then this law states that

$$F = \frac{km_1m_2}{x^2}$$

The proportionality constants k in these examples can be evaluated only when specific conditions are given. For example, if it is known that the return force on a spring is 10 pounds when the spring has been stretched 2 feet, then

$$10 = k \cdot 2 \quad \text{or} \quad k = 5 \text{ lb/ft}$$

In this particular instance, k is called the *spring constant* and its value depends upon the construction of the spring. The following are further examples of the concept of variation.

Example 4.3. If the electromotive force E in a circuit varies directly with the current I and is equal to 12 volts when the current is 5 amperes, find E when $I = 2$ amperes.

Solution: Since $E = kI$, and $E = 12$ when $I = 5$, we have

$$12 = 5k \quad \text{or} \quad k = \tfrac{12}{5} = 2.4$$

Thus, we can write $E = 2.4I$ and, when $I = 2$,

$$E = 2.4 \cdot 2 = 4.8 \text{ volts}$$

(This particular proportionality constant is called the resistance.)

Example 4.4. The stiffness of a beam varies directly with the product of its breadth and its depth and inversely with the square of its length. What is the change in the stiffness of a beam when its length is halved and its breadth is doubled?

Solution: The relation is $S = kBD/L^2$, where B is the breadth of the beam, D is its depth, L is its length, and S is its stiffness. Let us denote the original values of these variables by B_0, D_0, L_0, and S_0. The final values are $B_1 = 2B_0$, $D_1 = D_0$, $L_1 = \tfrac{1}{2}L_0$, and S_1 is to be determined relative to S_0. Since

$$S_1 = \frac{kB_1D_1}{L_1^2} = \frac{k \cdot 2B_0 \cdot D_0}{\tfrac{1}{4}L_0^2} = \frac{8kB_0D_0}{L_0^2} = 8S_0$$

we conclude that the stiffness is 8 times as great.

We now consider some further examples of functions that arise from physical problems.

Example 4.5. A rectangular area of 1000 square feet is to be fenced in with material costing $0.75 per linear foot. Find an equation to express the cost C in terms of the length of a side x of the rectangle.

Solution: Since one side of the rectangle is x, the other side must be $1000/x$. (The area is the product of the sides.) The perimeter of the rectangle is therefore $2x + \dfrac{2000}{x}$, and the cost to fence this perimeter is

$$C = .75\left(2x + \frac{2000}{x}\right) \qquad \text{where } x > 0$$

Example 4.6. An automobile travels due north from a certain intersection at a speed of 30 miles per hour. Five minutes later another automobile travels due east from this intersection at a speed of 40 miles per hour. Find an equation to express the distance d between these automobiles in terms of time. What restrictions should be placed on the domain of this function?

Solution: Let t represent the time (in hours) since the first automobile left the intersection; let d_1 represent the distance travelled in time t by this automobile, and let d_2 represent the distance travelled during the same period of time by the second automobile, measured from the instant the first automobile left the intersection. Then,

$$d_1 = 30t \quad \text{and} \quad d_2 = 40\left(t - \frac{5}{60}\right)$$

Since $d^2 = d_1^2 + d_2^2$, we have

$$d = \sqrt{900t^2 + 1600\left(t - \frac{1}{12}\right)^2}$$

This formula makes no sense unless the second car has passed the intersection, so we must restrict the domain of the function to $t \geq 1/12$ hr.

PROBLEMS A

1. If y varies directly with x, and $y = 2$ when $x = 4$, find y when $x = 5$.

2. If z varies directly with the square root of x and inversely with y, find an equation to express z in terms of x and y.

3. If v varies inversely with u, and $f(2) = 3$, find $f(4)$.

4. If r varies directly with the product of s and t, and $r = \frac{1}{2}$ when $s = 1/t$, find r when $s = \sqrt{2}$ and $t = \sqrt{8}$.

5. The resistance of a round wire varies directly with its length and inversely with the square of its radius. If the length is increased by 10 per cent, by what percentage does the resistance change?

6. According to Boyle's law, the pressure varies inversely with the volume of a confined gas. If the gas is confined to a cylindrical container and the length of the container is decreased by 25 per cent, what is the corresponding percentage increase in pressure?

7. Find an equation to express the sum of the reciprocals of two numbers in terms of their sum and the reciprocal of their product.

8. If the quotient of two numbers is a constant, how does one number vary with the other?

9. If the product of two numbers is a constant, how does one number vary with the other?

10. Find an equation to express the product of two numbers in terms of their squares and their difference.

11. An airplane leaves the airport at 6 P.M. traveling due south at the speed of 300 mph. At 6:30 P.M. another airplane leaves the airport travelling due west at 250 mph. Find an equation to express the distance s between the airplanes in terms of the time t after the second airplane took off.

12. A ship 10 nautical miles east of a dye marker steams toward the marker at 20 knots. Another ship 5 miles south of the marker steams toward it at 15 knots. Find an equation to express the distance between the ships in terms of the distance of the first ship from the marker.

PROBLEMS B

1. An automobile passes the point P at the speed r_1. A pursuing motorcycle patrolman reaches his maximum speed r_2 after the car has travelled a distance s from the motorcycle, and catches up with the car after travelling an additional distance d. Find an equation to express the speed r_2 of the motorcycle in terms of r_1, s, and d.

2. The symbol $[x]$ denotes the greatest integer less than or equal to x. Thus,

$$[\tfrac{5}{3}] = 1 \quad \text{and} \quad [-\tfrac{1}{2}] = -1$$

What is the range of the function **f**, where $f(x) = [x]$ on the domain

$$-\frac{2}{5} \le x \le \frac{17}{2}$$

4.3 The Geometry of Functions

The association between numbers and points on a line or points in a plane is not new to us. We now consider the problem of how to represent functions by points in a plane. Again, let us point out that we shall consider only the case where x and $f(x)$ represent real numbers.   We shall further restrict ourselves to functions having domains that can be described by a single variable.

Any geometric representation of a function **f** must take into account its domain, its range, and the correspondence between elements of these sets.   Since we are limiting ourselves to real variables, the domain and the range of **f** are sets of real numbers.   Each such set can be represented by points on a line.   Thus, to represent **f** geometrically we introduce two perpendicular lines, called the **coordinate axes.**   The elements x of the domain X are represented by points on the horizontal axis, called the **X-axis,** as shown in Figure 4.1.   The elements y of the range Y are represented by points on the vertical axis, called the **Y-axis.** The point of intersection 0 of the coordinate axes is called the **origin.**   Any point in the plane determined by these axes corresponds to a pair of real numbers (x, y) called its **coordinates.**   The number x **abscissa** represents the distance of the point (x, y) from the Y-axis,

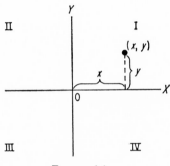

FIGURE 4.1

and the number y **ordinate** represents the distance of this point from the X-axis.   Any point on the X-axis to the right of the origin has a positive x-value, and any point to the left of 0 has a negative x-value.   Any point on the Y-axis above the origin has a positive y-value, and any point below 0 has a negative y-value. Thus, any point on the Y-axis has the coordinates $(0, y)$, any point on the X-axis has the coordinates $(x, 0)$, and the coordinates of the origin are $(0, 0)$.   The coordinate axes divide the plane into four distinct parts, called **quadrants.**   The quadrants are referred to by number, as shown in Figure 4.1.   This system of coordinates is called a **rectangular,** or **Cartesian coordinate system,** after its inventor René Descartes (1596–1650).

A function **f** is a correspondence between elements x and $f(x)$.   If we construct a geometric figure using points in a Cartesian coordinate system to display this correspondence, we have an adequate geometric representation of a function.

Definition 4.3.   *The **graph** of the function **f** is the totality of all points having coordinates* (x, f(x)) *in a Cartesian coordinate system.*

Accordingly, if one member of the pair $(x, f(x))$ is not a real number, the graph does not exist at that point.   As an illustration of Definition

4.3, let us construct the graph of the function **f**, where $f(x) = \sqrt{x}$, defined on the domain $x \geq 0$.   If we make a table of values of $f(x)$ corresponding to several conveniently-chosen values of x, we shall have the coordinates of some points on the graph of this function.   Thus, we have the table

x	0	1	4	9	16
y	0	1	2	3	4

for a start.   These points are shown in Figure 4.2, where x is located on the X-axis and $f(x)$ is plotted on the Y-axis.   This figure shows only a partial graph of **f**; to complete the graph, we would have to find the y-value corresponding to *every* x-value in the domain $x \geq 0$; an impossible task.   Intuition tells us, however, that we can approximate this graph by connecting the points already located with a smooth curve, as done in Figure 4.2.   (We have not really completed the graph because the domain extends indefinitely to the right of the origin, but we shall rely upon our imagination for the rest.)   Note that the graph would remain the same if the domain were extended to include all real numbers because $\sqrt{x}$ is not a real number when $x \leq 0$, and the graph does not exist at such points.

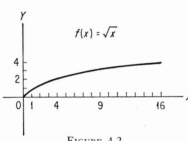

FIGURE 4.2

Nothing but intuition has given us the right to connect the points in Figure 4.2 with a smooth curve.   In fact, the study of why we can do this sort of thing and why it may lead us into trouble is a very lengthy and difficult one, taking us into the calculus.   The following example illustrates some of these difficulties.

Example 4.7. Graph the function **f**, where $f(x) = 1/x$, defined on the domain of all real numbers except 0.

Solution: Note that $f(-x) = -f(x)$ and that we need only construct a table of values for $x > 0$.   We have

x	$\frac{1}{4}$	$\frac{1}{2}$	1	2	3	4
y	4	2	1	$\frac{1}{2}$	$\frac{1}{3}$	$\frac{1}{4}$

These points are plotted in Figure 4.3 and are connected by a smooth curve. Since **f** is not defined at $x = 0$, there is no point on the graph with $x = 0$. However, we note that $f(x)$ becomes larger as x approaches zero from the right (through positive values of x).   Since $f(-x) = -f(x)$, $f(x)$ becomes smaller as x approaches zero from the left, and we complete the graph as shown in Figure 4.3. This example shows that we must be especially careful when drawing a graph in the neighborhood of a point where the function is undefined.

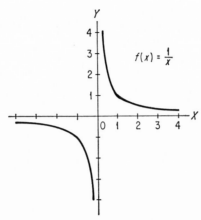

FIGURE 4.3

PROBLEMS A

1. Graph the functions described.   (The domain is the set of all real numbers, unless otherwise specified.)

(a) $f(x) = x + 1$

(b) $f(x) = -x + 1$

(c) $f(u) = \sqrt{u + 3}$

(d) $g(x) = \sqrt{4 - x}$

(e) $f(x) = x^2 - 2x + 1$

(f) $\phi(x) = 3x^2 + x - 5$

(g) $h(x) = |x|$

(h) $f(v) = |2v - 1|$

(i) $F(x) = \dfrac{1}{x - 1}, \; x \neq 1$

(j) $f(z) = \dfrac{1}{1 + z^{-1}}, \; z \neq 0$

2. For what values of x do the following described functions (defined on the domain of all real numbers) fail to have a graph?

(a) $f(x) = \sqrt{x + 1}$

(b) $f(x) = \sqrt{x^2 - 4}$

(c) $\phi(x) = x^2 - x\sqrt{x - 1}$

(d) $F(x) = \dfrac{1}{\sqrt{x^2 - 2}}$

PROBLEMS B

1. Graph the function **f** where

$$f(x) = \begin{cases} x, & 0 \leq x < 1 \\ x - 1, & 1 \leq x < 2 \\ x - 2, & 2 \leq x < 3 \\ 0 & \text{elsewhere} \end{cases}$$

2. Graph the function **f** where $f(x) = [x]$. (See Problem B-2, end of Section 4.2.)

4.4 Linear and Quadratic Functions

When discussing variation in Section 4.2, we introduced the constant of proportionality k and noted that its value may vary from problem to problem. Any "constant" that remains fixed in a particular problem, but may assume a different value in another problem, is called a **parameter.** Often it is convenient to define sets of functions by displaying their correspondences in equations containing one or more parameters. Such sets of functions are called **families.** In this section, we shall study two important families of functions.

First, we consider the function **f**, where

$$(4.1) \qquad f(x) = ax + b$$

In Equation 4.1, a and b are real parameters and **f** is defined on the domain of all real numbers. Every function whose correspondence may be expressed by an equation of the form (4.1) is called a **linear function.** The following example illustrates the properties of the family of linear functions by considering a particular member.

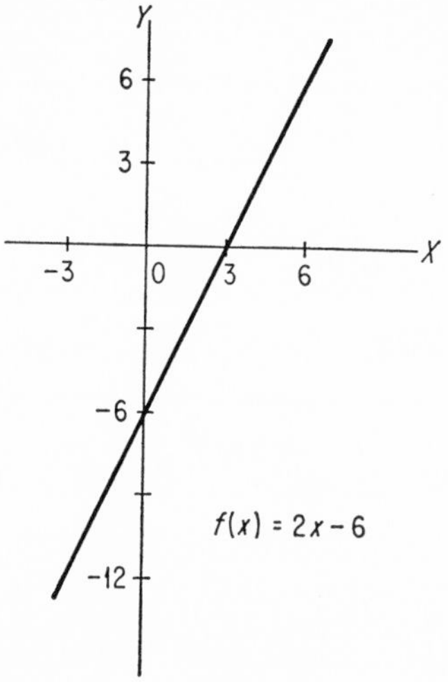

Example 4.8. Graph the function **f**, where $f(x) = 2x - 6$.

Solution: A table of values of this function is

x	-3	0	3	6
y	-12	-6	0	6

These points are plotted in Figure 4.4 and, apparently, they may be joined by a straight line.

$f(x) = 2x - 6$

FIGURE 4.4

Example 4.8 raises the question of whether the graph of each linear function is a straight line. Although we shall not prove this assertion here, it can be shown that the graph of each linear function is a nonvertical straight line, and, conversely, each nonvertical straight line is represented by a linear function.

Second, we consider the function **f**, where

$$(4.2) \qquad f(x) = ax^2 + bx + c \quad (a \neq 0)$$

a, b, and c are real parameters, and **f** is defined on the domain of all real numbers. Every function whose correspondence can be represented by an equation of the form (4.2) is called a **quadratic function.**

To understand better the nature of this family of functions, and to facilitate the graphing of such functions, we shall rewrite the expression for $f(x)$ given by (4.2). To do this, we employ a process called "completing the square." First, we write

$$f(x) = a\left(x^2 + \frac{b}{a}x + \frac{c}{a}\right)$$

so that the coefficient of x^2 in the quadratic expression in parentheses is 1. (Why do we not have to be concerned about the possibility that $a = 0$?) Then, inside the parentheses, we *add and subtract the square of half the coefficient of* x, to obtain

$$f(x) = a\left[\left(x^2 + \frac{b}{a}x + \frac{b^2}{4a^2}\right) + \left(\frac{c}{a} - \frac{b^2}{4a^2}\right)\right]$$

The first expression in parentheses is the perfect square $\left(x + \frac{b}{2a}\right)^2$, and we may write

$$f(x) = a\left[\left(x + \frac{b}{2a}\right)^2 + \left(\frac{c}{a} - \frac{b^2}{4a^2}\right)\right]$$

or

(4.3) $$f(x) = a\left(x + \frac{b}{2a}\right)^2 + \left(c - \frac{b^2}{4a}\right)$$

Equation 4.3 gives the correspondence of any quadratic function as the sum of a square term involving x and a term made up entirely of constants. This equation may be used to determine the value of x for which $f(x)$ takes on its largest (maximum) or smallest (minimum) value. First, note that $\left(x + \frac{b}{2a}\right)^2$ is the square of some real number and must always be positive or zero. Thus, $a\left(x + \frac{b}{2a}\right)^2$ is greater than or equal to zero when $a > 0$, and it is less than or equal to zero when $a < 0$. Thus, if $a > 0, f(x)$ is at least equal to $c - \frac{b^2}{4a}$. On the contrary, if $a < 0, f(x)$ is at most equal to this quantity. Therefore, if x is chosen so that $\left(x + \frac{b}{2a}\right)^2 = 0, f(x)$ takes on its minimum value when $a > 0$, and it takes on its maximum value when $a < 0$. Since $x = -b/2a$ makes this quantity equal to zero, we conclude that *the maximum or minimum value of* f(x) *occurs at* x $= -b/2a$, f(x) *being a minimum if* a > 0 *and a maximum if* a < 0. The following example illustrates the use of this conclusion in graphing quadratic functions.

Example 4.9. Graph the function **f**, where $f(x) = x^2 - 4x + 7$.

Solution: This is a quadratic function with $a = 1$, $b = -4$, and $c = 7$. Since $a > 0$, $f(x)$ will have its minimum value at

$$x = -\frac{(-4)}{2(1)} = 2$$

This minimum value is $f(2) = 3$. We now construct a table of values of **f** for $x \geq 2$.

x	2	3	4	5	6
y	3	4	7	12	19

It is easy to verify by substitution that the values of y corresponding to values of x to the left of $x = 2$ equal those corresponding to values of x the same distance to the right of $x = 2$. For example,

$$f(1) = f(3) = 4, \quad f(0) = f(4) = 7, \quad \text{etc.}$$

(Can you prove this in general; that is, can you prove that

$$f\left(-\frac{b}{2a} + x\right) = f\left(-\frac{b}{2a} - x\right)$$

for any quadratic function?) A sketch of the graph of this function is shown in Figure 4.5.

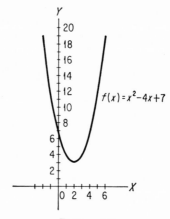

FIGURE 4.5

PROBLEMS A

1. Graph the functions described.

(a) $f(x) = 2x + 5$

(b) $f(x) = -3x + 1$

(c) $f(x) = \dfrac{x - 4}{3}$

(d) $f(x) = \dfrac{3 - 2x}{5}$

(e) $f(x) = 2x^2 - 3x + 7$

(f) $f(x) = -x^2 + 2x - 1$

(g) $f(x) = \frac{1}{2}x^2 - \frac{2}{3}x + \frac{1}{5}$

(h) $f(x) = 4 - 3x^2$

2. Describe the graph of **f**, where $f(x) = b$.

3. Describe the graphs of the family of functions having the equation $f(x) = ax$. Sketch some members of this family on the same set of coordinate axes.

4. "Complete the square" by writing each of the following expressions as a square term involving x plus a constant.

(a) $x^2 + 2x$

(b) $x^2 - 6x + 3$

(c) $-x^2 + 2x - 1$

(d) $3 - 4x - x^2$

(e) $5x^2 - 10x + 15$

(f) $3x^2 - 7x + 5$

PROBLEMS B

1. If $f(x) = ax^2 + bx + c$, prove that

$$f\left(-\frac{b}{2a} + x\right) = f\left(-\frac{b}{2a} - x\right)$$

What can you conclude about the graph of **f**?

2. Use the Pythagorean theorem to prove that the distance d between the points P_1 with coordinates (x_1, y_1) and P_2 with coordinates (x_2, y_2) satisfies the equation

$$d^2 = (x_1 - x_2)^2 + (y_1 - y_2)^2$$

3. If three points P_1, P_2, and P_3 are colinear, then the sum of two of the distances $\overline{P_1P_2}$, $\overline{P_1P_3}$, and $\overline{P_2P_3}$ equals the third, and conversely. Use this fact together with the result of Problem 2 to prove that the graph of any linear function is a straight line. *Hint:* Let P_1, P_2, and P_3 be any points on the graph, with P_2 lying between P_1 and P_3. Prove that $\overline{P_1P_2} + \overline{P_2P_3} = \overline{P_1P_3}$.

5

The Exponential and Logarithmic Functions

5.1 The Exponential Function

In our discussion of exponents in Chapter 2 we defined the expression a^n and showed that it represents a real number when $a > 0$ and n is any rational number. (If $a < 0$, a^n was shown to be real only for certain rational numbers n; and if $a = 0$, we excluded $n \leq 0$.) It was also stated in Chapter 2 that the definition of a^n, for $a > 0$, could be extended to include irrational values of n employing successive approximations. To illustrate how this may be done, consider the expression $2^{\sqrt{2}}$. The irrational number $\sqrt{2}$ can be approximated by rational numbers, using its decimal representation $\sqrt{2} = 1.41421 \ldots$. If we choose to approximate $\sqrt{2}$ by the rational number 1.4, then $2^{\sqrt{2}}$ is approximately equal to $2^{1.4}$, which is defined. A better rational approximation to $\sqrt{2}$ is 1.41; thus, $2^{\sqrt{2}}$ is better approximated by $2^{1.41}$, etc. In this way, the expression a^n, where $a > 0$, can be given meaning for any real number n.

Any nonalgebraic expression in some variable is called a **transcendental** expression in that variable. The expression a^x is, therefore, a transcendental expression. If $f(x)$ is expressible only as a transcendental expression in x, then the function **f** is called a **transcendental function.** We now define the transcendental function **f**, where

(5.1) $$f(x) = b^x \quad (b > 0)$$

on the domain of all real numbers. Any function belonging to this family

84

of functions is called an **exponential function.** The restriction $b > 0$ is made in order that the range of an exponential function includes only real numbers. A further restriction that should, perhaps, be made on the parameter b is $b \neq 1$. The reason for this restriction becomes clear when we realize that if b were allowed to equal 1, the function **f**, where $f(x) = 1^x = 1$, would be a member of the family of exponential functions. Since this function is, in fact, a constant, we wish to exclude it from the exponential family.

The real number b is called the **base** of the exponential function. As we have seen, if b is varied, subject to the restrictions that $b > 0$ and $b \neq 1$, we obtain a family of exponential functions with b as its parameter. We now examine some of the properties of this family of functions by sketching the graphs of two particular exponential functions, having the bases 2 and $\frac{1}{2}$, respectively. Tables of selected points (x, y) for these two functions are shown below. The resulting graphs are shown in Figure 5.1.

$b = 2$						$b = \frac{1}{2}$					
x	-2	-1	0	1	2	x	-2	-1	0	1	2
y	$\frac{1}{4}$	$\frac{1}{2}$	1	2	4	y	4	2	1	$\frac{1}{2}$	$\frac{1}{4}$

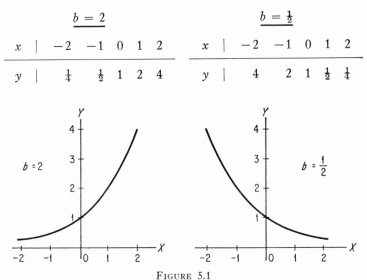

FIGURE 5.1

Figure 5.1 illustrates the following important properties of the exponential function. First, *the range of the exponential function is restricted to the set of positive real numbers.* Second, f(x) *increases as* x *increases when* b > 1, *and it decreases as* x *increases when* b < 1. Proofs of the foregoing assertions for any value of b require concepts that we cannot go into here but the student is urged to support these statements by working additional examples.

A final observation is that f(0) = 1 *for all positive* b. This conclusion follows from the definition of b^0.

PROBLEMS A

1. Graph the functions described.

(a) $f(x) = 4^x$

(b) $g(x) = (\frac{2}{3})^x$

(c) $F(x) = 2^{-x}$

(d) $h(x) = 3(\frac{1}{2})^{-x}$

(e) $\phi(x) = 2 \cdot 2^{x/2}$

(f) $G(x) = -\frac{1}{2} \cdot (\frac{1}{3})^{2x}$

(g) $f(x) = 1 - 4^{-x}$

(h) $f(x) = 2^{x^2}$

2. Graph the function **f**, where $f(x) = 2^x$ and obtain approximate values of the following numbers from this graph.

(a) $2^{.301}$

(b) $\sqrt[4]{2}$

(c) $2^{\sqrt{2}}$

(d) $2^{-\sqrt{2}}$

(e) $(\frac{1}{2})^{1/2}$

(f) $(\frac{1}{4})^{-3/5}$

3. Use properties of the graphs of exponential functions to demonstrate the following.

(a) $3^{\sqrt{3}} > 3^{\sqrt{2}}$

(b) $5^{-\sqrt{10}} > 0$

(c) $4^{\sqrt{5}} < 2^5$

(d) $(\frac{1}{4})^{\sqrt{5}} > (\frac{1}{2})^5$

4. The pressure p (in atmospheres) and altitude y (in centimeters) of a pure gas in equilibrium at uniform temperature are related by the equation

$$p = A \cdot 10^{-By}$$

For a certain gas $A = 1$ and $B = .0000005$. Graph the function represented and use this graph to find the pressure in atmospheres at an altitude of 10^6 centimeters.

5. When a capacitor is discharged through a resistance, the current flowing in the circuit at time t is given by

$$I = I_0 e^{-t/RC}$$

where I_0 is the current at which the capacitor begins to discharge, R is the resistance, C is the capacity of the capacitor, and e is a constant approximately equal to 2.7. If $I_0 = .5$ ampere, $R = 12$ ohms, and $C = 10$ microfarads, graph the function described in this problem and use this graph to find the current (in amperes) flowing in the circuit after 60 seconds.

PROBLEMS B

1. Prove the following properties of the exponential function.

(a) $f(u + v) = f(u)f(v)$

(b) $f(u - v) = \dfrac{f(u)}{f(v)}$

(c) $f(uv) = [f(u)]^v = [f(v)]^u$

(d) $f\left(\dfrac{u}{v}\right) = [f(u)]^{1/v}$

2. The half-life of a radioactive substance is the time required for one-half of the substance to decay. If a radioactive substance has a half-life of 5 minutes, what proportion of the substance remains after 1 hour?

5.2 The Logarithmic Function

A transcendental function closely related to the exponential function may be obtained by interchanging the roles of the range and the domain of the exponential function. Since the domain of the exponential function is the set of all real numbers and its range is the set of all positive numbers, the domain of this new function must exclude negative real numbers and zero, but its range consists of all real numbers. Any function defined in this way, that is, by preserving the correspondence of another function but interchanging its domain and its range, is called the **inverse** of the original function. A more general discussion of inverse functions will be postponed until Chapter 8.

Whenever possible, we have expressed the correspondence of a given function by an equation in which the dependent variable was denoted by $f(x)$ or y. Suppose we could obtain such an equation for the inverse of the exponential function by "solving" the equation $y = b^x$ for x, and then interchanging x and y. To indicate that this has been done, let the equation

$$(5.2) \qquad\qquad y = \log_b x \quad (b > 0)$$

represent the inverse of the exponential function. The symbol "$\log_b x$" stands for "the logarithm to the base b of x," and the function so defined is called the **logarithmic function.** The restriction $b > 0$ was required in the definition of the exponential function; therefore, it must be preserved in the definition of the logarithmic function. For the same reason, we should also require that $b \neq 1$.

The foregoing discussion shows that the equation $y = \log_b x$ *is merely another way of writing the equation* $x = b^y$. Thus, if we wish to evaluate an expression such as $\log_2 8$, we can write the equation $y = \log_2 8$ in the form $8 = 2^y$, from which we conclude that $y = 3$.

Example 5.1. Evaluate $\log_{\sqrt{3}} 9$.

Solution: Let $y = \log_{\sqrt{3}} 9$. Then

$$(\sqrt{3})^y = 9 \quad \text{or} \quad 3^{y/2} = 3^2$$

from which we conclude that

$$\frac{y}{2} = 2 \quad \text{or} \quad y = 4$$

A table of values of a given member of the family of logarithmic functions can be obtained from a table of the corresponding exponential function by interchanging x and y. Thus, tables of values of **f** and **g**, where

$$f(x) = \log_2 x \quad \text{and} \quad g(x) = \log_{1/2} x$$

are obtained from the tables shown on page 85, and are shown below.

<table>
<tr><td colspan="6" align="center">$y = \log_2 x$</td><td colspan="6" align="center">$y = \log_{1/2} x$</td></tr>
<tr><td>x</td><td>$\frac{1}{4}$</td><td>$\frac{1}{2}$</td><td>1</td><td>2</td><td>4</td><td>x</td><td>4</td><td>2</td><td>1</td><td>$\frac{1}{2}$</td><td>$\frac{1}{4}$</td></tr>
<tr><td>y</td><td>-2</td><td>-1</td><td>0</td><td>1</td><td>2</td><td>y</td><td>-2</td><td>-1</td><td>0</td><td>1</td><td>2</td></tr>
</table>

The graphs of **f** and **g** are shown in Figure 5.2. What is the relationship of these graphs to those shown in Figure 5.1?

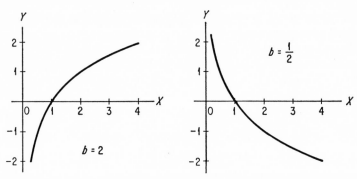

FIGURE 5.2

We shall now prove three fundamental properties of the logarithmic function. The method of proof will involve translation of the equations from the logarithmic to the exponential form. This will put us in a position to make use of the properties of exponents proved in Section 2.3.

Theorem 5.1. $\log_b uv = \log_b u + \log_b v$.

Proof: Let

$$x = \log_b u \quad \text{and} \quad y = \log_b v$$

Thus, $u = b^x \quad \text{and} \quad v = b^y$

and $uv = b^x \cdot b^y = b^{x+y}$

However the equation $uv = b^{x+y}$ can also be written as

$$\log_b uv = x + y = \log_b u + \log_b v$$

which completes the proof.

Theorem 5.1 establishes that the logarithm of a product is the *sum* of the logarithms of the factors. Its use is illustrated in the following example.

Example 5.2. If $\log_b 3 = 1.099$ and $\log_b 5 = 1.609$, find $\log_b 15$.

Solution: Since $15 = 3 \cdot 5$, we have

$$\log_b 15 = \log_b 3 + \log_b 5$$
$$= 1.099 + 1.609 = 2.708$$

We now prove that the logarithm of a quotient is the *difference* of the logarithms of the numerator and the nominator.

Theorem 5.2. $\log_b \dfrac{u}{v} = \log_b u - \log_b v.$

Proof: Let

$$x = \log_b u \quad \text{and} \quad y = \log_b v$$

Thus,
$$u = b^x \quad \text{and} \quad v = b^y$$

and
$$\frac{u}{v} = \frac{b^x}{b^y} = b^{x-v}$$

But the equation $u/v = b^{x-v}$ can also be written as

$$\log_b \frac{u}{v} = x - y = \log_b u - \log_b v$$

which completes the proof.

An application of Theorem 5.2 is illustrated in the following example.

Example 5.3. If $\log_b 12 = 1.079$ and $\log_b 2 = 0.301$, find $\log_b 3$.

Solution: Since $3 = \frac{12}{4} = \frac{12}{2 \cdot 2}$, we have

$$\log_b 3 = \log_b 12 - \log_b 2 \cdot 2$$
$$= \log_b 12 - (\log_b 2 + \log_b 2)$$
$$= 1.079 - 2(0.301) = 0.477$$

Finally, we prove that the logarithm of the power of a number is the *product* of the exponent and the logarithm of the number.

Theorem 5.3. $\log_b u^n = n \log_b u \ (u > 0).$

Proof: Let

$$y = \log_b u$$

Then
$$u = b^y$$

and
$$u^n = (b^y)^n = b^{ny}$$

However, the equation $u^n = b^{ny}$ can also be written as

$$\log_b u^n = ny = n \log_b u$$

which completes the proof.

An application of Theorem 5.3 is illustrated in the following example.

Example 5.4. If $\log_b 8 = 2.079$, find $\log_b 2$.

Solution: Since $8 = 2^3$, we have

$$\log_b 8 = 3 \log_b 2$$

or

$$\log_b 2 = \tfrac{1}{3} \log_b 8$$

$$= \frac{2.079}{3} = 0.693$$

There are many useful special properties of the logarithmic function that can be derived from Equation 5.2 and Theorems 5.1–5.3. Three important ones are stated below and several others are contained in prob-- lems at the end of this section. Can you prove the following relations?

(5.3) $\log_b 1 = 0 \quad (b > 0, b \neq 1)$

(5.4) $\log_b b = 1 \quad (b > 0, b \neq 1)$

(5.5) $b^{\log_b u} = u \quad (b > 0, b \neq 1, u > 0)$

PROBLEMS A

1. Find the value of x in the following equations.
   (a) $x = \log_8 64$ (b) $x = \log_2 64$
   (c) $4 = \log_3 x$ (d) $3 = \log_{10} x$
   (e) $4 = \log_x 16$ (f) $-2 = \log_x .01$
   (g) $-\tfrac{2}{3} = \log_x 4$ (h) $x = \log_7 \tfrac{1}{7}$

2. Given that $\log_b 2 = 0.301$, $\log_b 3 = 0.477$, and $\log_b 5 = 0.699$, find
   (a) $\log_b 6$ (b) $\log_b 10$ (c) $\log_b 2.5$
   (d) $\log_b 1.5$ (e) $\log_b 1.2$ (f) $\log_b 7.5$
   (g) $\log_b 125$ (h) $\log_b 24$ (i) $\log_b 1$
   (j) $\log_b 6b$ (k) $\log_b \sqrt{\tfrac{3}{5}}$ (l) $\log_b \sqrt[3]{1.5}$
   (m) $\log_b \dfrac{1}{b}$ (n) $\log_b 0.2$ (o) $(\log_b 5)/(\log_b 3)$
   (p) $(\log_b 3)^2$ (q) $\log_b 50$ (r) $\log_b 80$

3. Graph the functions described.
   (a) $f(x) = \log_3 x$ (b) $g(x) = \log_{10} x$
   (c) $F(x) = \log_4 (x - 5)$ (d) $h(x) = \log_2 (-x)$

4. Prove that $\log_b \sqrt[q]{u^p} = \dfrac{p}{q} \log_b u$

5. Generalize Theorem 5.1 to include the product of three factors, and prove the resulting theorem.

6. Prove that $\log_b 1 = 0$, $b > 0$, $b \neq 1$.

7. Prove that $\log_b b = 1$, $b > 0$, $b \neq 1$.

8. Prove that $b^{\log_b u} = u$, $b > 0$, $b \neq 1$, $u > 0$.

PROBLEMS B

1. Consider the function **f**, where $f(x) = ab^{cx}$. Show that **g** is a linear function, where $g(x) = \log_b f(x)$.

2. Prove that the inverse of any nonconstant linear function is also a linear function.

3. Prove that the sign of $\log_b x$ is the same as the sign of the product $(b - 1)(x - 1)$.

5.3 Common Logarithms

The methods introduced in Section 5.2 do not enable us to find the logarithm of any number to a given base conveniently. For this reason, it is useful to have tables of logarithms; that is, tables of the logarithmic function having a given base b. Fortunately, it is not necessary to tabulate this function separately for every value of b. Given the logarithm of some number x to the base b, it is possible to find the logarithm of x to any other base a by means of the following theorem.

Theorem 5.4. $\log_a x = \log_b x / \log_b a$.

Proof: By Equation 5.5

$$x = a^{\log_a x}$$

Thus, $$\log_b x = \log_b (a^{\log_a x})$$
$$= (\log_a x)(\log_b a)$$

by Theorem 5.3. If we solve this last equation for $\log_a x$, the proof is complete.

A commonly used base for tables of the logarithmic function is the number 10; chosen because 10 is the base of our number system. Logarithms of numbers to the base 10 are called **common logarithms.** We shall abbreviate the phrase "common logarithm" by the word "log" and use the symbol $\log N$ to stand for $\log_{10} N$.

To describe the tables of logs, we note that every positive number can be written as an integer power of 10 multiplied by some number M, with $1 \leq M < 10$. For example,

$$.0251 = 2.51 \cdot 10^{-2}$$
$$.251 = 2.51 \cdot 10^{-1}$$
$$2.51 = 2.51 \cdot 10^{0}$$
$$25.1 = 2.51 \cdot 10^{1}$$
$$251 = 2.51 \cdot 10^{2}$$

.

.

.

In general, we may write the number N in the form

$$N = M \cdot 10^{c}$$

where $1 \leq M < 10$ and c is an integer. This notation, called **scientific notation**, is often used in physical calculations.

If N is a positive number, and it is written in the form $N = M \cdot 10^{c}$, then the common logarithm of N has the form

$$\log N = \log M + c$$
$$= m + c$$

where $m = \log M$. The number m is called the **mantissa** of $\log N$, and the integer c is called its **characteristic**. Since $1 \leq M < 10$, evidently m lies between $\log 1$ and $\log 10$, or $0 \leq m < 1$.

Given a number N, it is necessary to tabulate only the mantissa of $\log N$ because the characteristic may be obtained by inspection. Table I contains the mantissa of the common logarithm of every number from 1.00 to 9.99 in intervals of .01 correct to four decimal places. This table may be used to find the log of *any* number having up to three digits, to four decimal places. For example, to find $\log 4$, we have $4 = 4 \cdot 10^{0}$. Thus, the characteristic of $\log 4$ is 0. From Table I we find the mantissa to be .6021. Thus, $\log 4 = 0 + .6021 = 0.6021$. The following examples further illustrate the use of Table I.

Example 5.5. Find $\log 3450$.

Solution: Since

$$3450 = 3.45 \cdot 10^{3} \qquad c = 3$$

To find m, locate the entry in Table I corresponding to 3.45. Thus, $m = .5378$, and

$$\log 3450 = 3 + .5378 = 3.5378$$

Example 5.6. Find log .00215.

Solution·
$$.00215 = 2.15 \cdot 10^{-3}$$

Thus, $c = -3$

and $m = \log 2.15 = .3324$ (From Table I)

Finally, $\log .00215 = -3 + .3324 = -2.6676.$

(A common mistake would have been to write this log as -3.3324.)

When $\log N$ is a negative number, it is usually more convenient to write this log as a positive number minus some suitable integer. Thus, $\log .00215 = -2.6676$, which can also be written in the form $7.3324 - 10$. This notation saves the trouble of subtracting the mantissa from 1 and is useful in calculations. A more general rule for writing a negative logarithm in this form is: if $-10 < log\ N < 0$, *subtract the absolute value of the logarithm from* 10, *and append* -10 *to the resulting number.* This procedure is further illustrated in the following example.

Example 5.7. Find log .0175.

Solution:
$$.0175 = 1.75 \cdot 10^{-2}$$

Thus, $c = -2$

and $m = \log 1.75 = .2430$

Since
$$10 - |-2| = 8$$

we have $\log .0175 = 8.2430 - 10$

The rule for writing negative logs can be extended to include cases where $\log N < -10$. For example, if

$$-20 < \log N < -10$$

we may subtract the absolute value of $\log N$ from 20 and append -20. Thus,

$$\log 2.15 \cdot 10^{-12} = -12 + .3324$$

and this log can be written in the form $8.3324 - 20$. Can you further extend this rule to include *any* negative log?

Table I also may be used to find N when $\log N$ is given. First, identify the mantissa of $\log N$. Second, find the entry in Table I closest to the

given mantissa.   Third, write down the corresponding number and locate
the decimal point with the use of the characteristic of log N.   The
following example illustrates this process.

Example 5.8. Evaluate $10^{-2.0612}$.

Solution: Let $N = 10^{-2.0612}$.   Then

$$\log N = -2.0612 = 7.9388 - 10$$

Thus, the mantissa of log N is .9388, *not* .0612.   The closest mantissa in
Table I is .9390, corresponding to the number 8.69.   Since the characteristic
of log N is $7 - 10 = -3$ (*not* -2), the required number is

$$N = 8.69 \cdot 10^{-3} = .00869$$

Example 5.8 shows the usefulness of writing a negative log such as
-2.0612 in the form $7.9388 - 10$.   In this form, the mantissa is displayed
and the characteristic is obtained immediately to be $7 - 10 = -3$.

PROBLEMS A

1. Rewrite the following numbers, using scientific notation.
(a) 25   (b) 125
(c) 3,476,000   (d) 85,000,000,000
(e) .015   (f) .000254
(g) 5   (h) $\sqrt{2500}$
(i) -37.005 (j) $-.00005$

2. Find the logs of the following numbers.
(a) 127   (b) 3720
(c) .354   (d) .159
(e) 6200   (f) .000254
(g) .00219   (h) .0000795
(i) 65.3^7 (j) $(-7.6)^{12}$

3. Find the numbers having the following logs.
(a) 2.8768   (b) 1.4057
(c) $7.7430 - 10$ (d) -0.5498
(e) $5.6592 - 20$ (f) $8.3763 - 30$

4. Approximate the value of $10^{\sqrt{2}}$ to three digits.

PROBLEMS B

1. Construct a pair of coordinate axes and space the divisions on the Y-axis
so that the logs of the corresponding numbers are equally spaced. Using this
scale, graph the function **f**, where $f(x) = 10^{2x}/25$.   Why is the resulting graph
a straight line?

5.4 Interpolation

It is sometimes necessary to estimate the logarithm of a number containing more digits than are included in a given table. Although five-place, six-place, and higher-place tables are available for this purpose, an approximation to the correct result can be obtained from a four-place table by a process called **interpolation.** Interpolation consists of approximating $f(x)$ at some point x in the domain of **f** by $g(x)$, where **g** is a simpler function than **f.** For our purposes, **f** will be the log function, and **g** will be a suitably-chosen *linear* interpolation function.

To illustrate the process of **linear interpolation,** let us find the value of log 7814. The procedure will be to find the logs of the two closest numbers to 7814 from Table I and to find the linear function having the same values as the log function at these two points. The approximate value of log 7814 is the value of the linear function at $x = 7814$.

First, we observe that log 7810 = 3.8927, and log 7820 = 3.8932. A sketch of the graph of the log function from $x = 7810$ to $x = 7820$ is shown in Figure 5.3. The graph of the linear interpolation function is

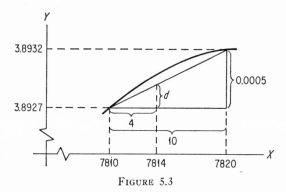

FIGURE 5.3

also shown in the figure. You can see that the straight line gives a reasonable approximation to the arc made by the graph of the log function in this small interval. To find the approximation for log 7814, we note that the two similar right triangles in Figure 5.3 have legs equal to .0005 and 10, and d and 4, respectively. Since corresponding legs of similar triangles are proportional we have

$$\frac{d}{4} = \frac{.0005}{10}$$

or

$$d = 4 \cdot \frac{.0005}{10} = .0002$$

From the figure it is evident that the required approximation is given by log 7814 = 3.8927 + .0002 = 3.8929.

The interpolation could have been made more accurate if we had used a polynomial of higher degree to approximate the arc of the graph of the log function. The process of linear interpolation used here should not be used when the number N has more than four digits. In general, when a p-place table is used, you may use linear interpolation to find the log of any number containing up to $p + 1$ digits.

It is not necessary to make a sketch like Figure 5.3 whenever you wish to interpolate. Can you verify that the scheme used in the following example is equivalent to what we have just done?

Example 5.9. Find log .3294.

Solution: Since

$$.3294 = 3.294 \cdot 10^{-1} \qquad c = -1$$

To find m, we use the following scheme.

$$\frac{d}{.004} = \frac{.0013}{.010}$$
$$d = .0005 \qquad \text{(to four decimal places)}$$
$$m = .5172 + .0005 = .5177$$

Thus, $\log .3294 = 9.5177 - 10$

A similar procedure can be used to find a number when its logarithm is given. Can you verify the procedure shown in the following example?

Example 5.10. Find N when $\log N = 0.8771$.

Solution:

$$\frac{d}{.0003} = \frac{.01}{.0006}$$
$$d = .005$$
$$M = 7.530 + .005 = 7.535$$

Since $c = 0$, $N = M \cdot 10^0 = 7.535$.

Table I may be used in conjunction with Theorem 5.4 to find the logarithm of a number to any base, as shown in the following example.

Example 5.11. Evaluate $\log_{6.2} 8.965$.

Solution: From Theorem 5.4 we have

$$\log_{6.2} 8.965 = \frac{\log 8.965}{\log 6.2}$$

Interpolating in Table I, we have

$$\log 8.965 = 0.9526$$

$$\log 6.2 = 0.7924$$

Therefore, $\log_{6.2} 8.965 = 0.9526/0.7924 = 1.202$.

PROBLEMS A

1. Find the logs of the following numbers.

(a) 1.825   (b) 7.456

(c) 3795   (d) 9874

(e) 19.68   (f) .3071

(g) 10.02   (h) 403.3

(i) .04237   (j) .001999

2. Find the numbers having the following logs.   (Use linear interpolation.)

(a) 1.5058   (b) 0.8576

(c) 3.6770   (d) 2.1194

(e) $9.7999 - 10$ (f) $7.4618 - 10$

(g) $9.1754 - 20$ (h) $6.5009 - 30$

(i) -0.1268 (j) -2.6219

3. Evaluate the following numbers.

(a) $\log_5 16$ (b) $\log_2 0.134$

(c) $\log_{12} 0.01932$ (d) $\log_{\sqrt{3}} 4$

4. Given $\log 4.50 = 0.6532$ and $\log 4.60 = 0.6628$. Find $\log 452$ by linear interpolation and compare your answer with the value of $\log 452$ shown in Table I.

PROBLEMS B

1. Use linear interpolation (do not use logarithms) to approximate $\sqrt[3]{11}$, given that $\sqrt[3]{8} = 2$ and $\sqrt[3]{27} = 3$. Now, use logs to evaluate $\sqrt[3]{11}$ and compare the two answers.

2. Use a quadratic interpolation together with Table I to find $\log 7812.5$. *Hint:* Find the quadratic function having a graph that passes through three points near 7812.5. What three points would you use?

5.5 Computation With Logarithms

Although the role of logarithms in computation has been greatly diminished in recent years by the development of automatic calculators, this does not diminish the importance of the logarithmic function in mathematics. The following examples apply Theorems 5.1, 5.2, and 5.3 and are intended to reinforce your knowledge of these theorems as well as to acquaint you with the use of logarithms in computation.

Example 5.12. Compute $\dfrac{(15.20)(176.2)}{.01950}$.

Solution: Let y stand for the quantity to be evaluated.

Then
$$\log y = \log 15.2 + \log 176.2 - \log .0195$$
From Table I

$$\log 15.2 = 1.1818$$
$$\log 176.2 = \underline{2.2460} \quad \text{(after linear interpolation)}$$
$$3.4278 \quad \text{(Sum)}$$
$$\log .0195 = \underline{8.2900 - 10}$$
$$-4.8622 + 10 \quad \text{(Difference)}$$

Therefore,
$$\log y = 5.1378$$
After interpolation in Table I, we find
$$y = 137,400$$
correct to four digits.

Example 5.13. Compute $12.3^{8.92}$.

Solution: Let $y = 12.3^{8.92}$.

$$\log y = 8.92 \log 12.3$$
$$\log 12.3 = 1.0899$$
$$8.92 \log 12.3 = 9.7219 = \log y$$

After interpolation in Table I, we find

$$y = 5,271,000,000 \ (\text{or } y = 5.271 \cdot 10^9)$$

An alternate solution that does not require multiplication of 8.92 by 1.0899 makes use of the fact that

$$\log (8.92 \log 12.3) = \log 8.92 + \log (\log 12.3)$$
$$= \log 8.92 + \log 1.0899$$
$$= 0.9504 \quad + 0.0374$$
$$= 0.9878$$

Thus, $\log y = 9.723$

and $y = 5.28 \cdot 10^9$

The slight discrepancy in the two answers results from the fact that the mantissa of log y could be obtained to three decimal places only.

Example 5.14. Compute $\sqrt[4]{1291}$.

Solution: Let $y = \sqrt[4]{1291} = 1291^{1/4}$.

$$\log y = \tfrac{1}{4} \log 1291$$
$$\log 1291 = 3.1109 \quad \text{(After linear interpolation)}$$
$$\log y = \tfrac{1}{4} \log 1291 = 0.7777$$
$$y = 5.994 \quad \text{(After linear interpolation)}$$

PROBLEMS A

1. Compute the following by use of Table I.

(a) $(8.76)(86.2)$

(b) $(3610)(.785)$

(c) $(17.62)(1980)$

(d) $(.00598)(62,470)$

(e) $(17,420)(168,300)$

(f) $(.001985)(.00003781)$

(g) $(785)(4936)(.0130)$

(h) $(.0517)(.1797)(10.34)$

(i) $\dfrac{(16.4)(1781)}{34,720}$

(j) $\dfrac{(.01985)(.0941)}{.00762}$

(k) $\dfrac{3.862}{(815.7)(.08362)}$

(l) $\dfrac{23,290}{(18.25)(.4133)}$

(m) $(176.5)^{.1746}$

(n) $(6.217)^{-1.792}$

(o) $(28.43)(9.047)^{-4.763}$

(p) $\dfrac{(64.7)(32.98)^{-3.67}}{(918)^{-1.835}}$

PROBLEMS B

1. Define $n!$ (n-factorial) by

$$n! = n(n - 1)(n - 2) \cdot \ldots \cdot 3 \cdot 2 \cdot 1$$

where n is a natural number. (Thus, $1! = 1$, $2! = 2 \cdot 1 = 2$, $3! = 3 \cdot 2 \cdot 1 = 6$, etc.) Use logs to construct a table of factorials from $n = 10$ to $n = 20$, correct to 3 digits.

The Trigonometric
Functions

6.1 Angles

In this chapter, we shall define a set of transcendental functions called the trigonometric functions. These functions may be defined on a domain consisting of a set of real numbers, or on a domain of angles. In this section we shall define an angle and introduce a common measure of an angle.

A line (as opposed to a line segment) is of indefinite extent in either direction. A **half-line**, or **ray**, has a terminal- or end-point, but extends indefinitely in one direction. An **angle** is a geometric figure formed by a pair of half-lines meeting in a common end-point, called the **vertex** of the angle. An angle might also be regarded as the figure that results from rotating a given half-line about its end-point. The original half-line is called the **initial side** of the angle, and the half-line into which the initial side rotates is called the **terminal side** of the angle.

The **measure of an angle** is the amount of rotation of the terminal side from the initial side. Hereafter, we shall give the word "angle" a dual meaning, using this word in reference to the geometric figure itself, as well as to the measure of the angle.

A common measure of an angle is derived by placing its vertex at the center of a circle of some fixed radius. We divide the circumference of the circle into 360 equal parts, called **degrees**, and let the intersection of the initial side of the angle with the circumference of the circle correspond to zero degrees. The number of degrees θ between the initial and terminal sides of an angle is its degree measure. For additional precision, each degree is subdivided into 60 equal parts, called **minutes**, and each minute is subdivided into 60 equal parts, called **seconds**. The symbol ° is used to denote degrees, ′ is used to denote minutes, and ″ is used to denote seconds. Thus, 36° 15′ 45″ means 36 degrees, 15 minutes, and 45 seconds.

The **sense** of an angle is derived from the direction of rotation of the initial side into the terminal side. If this direction is counterclockwise, the sense of the angle is defined to be positive, and if this direction is clockwise, the sense is negative. The measure of an angle having the positive sense is positive, and the measure of an angle having the negative sense is negative. The following example illustrates degree measure.

Example 6.1. Draw angles measuring (a) $\theta = 45°$, (b) $\theta = -60°$, (c) $\theta = 420°$.

Solution: See Figure 6.1.

FIGURE 6.1

PROBLEMS A

1. Sketch the following angles.

(a) 30°   (b) 120°   (c) −45°
(d) 150°   (e) 630°   (f) −420°

2. Convert the following to degrees, minutes, and seconds.

(a) 24.3°   (b) 185.27°
(c) −87.68°   (d) 58.135°

PROBLEMS B

1. Angles measuring 80° and 440° look the same. How do they differ?

2. Find the angle between the minute hand of a clock and the hour hand when the time is 7:20.

6.2   Radian Measure

The degree measure of an angle represents a part of the circumference of a circle.   Although 30 is a number, 30° is a geometric entity, not a number. To express the measure of an angle as a real number, we introduce **radian measure,** based upon the fact that the ratio of the circumference of any circle to its diameter is a constant.   This constant π is an irrational number having the decimal representation $\pi = 3.14159\ldots$.   As shown in

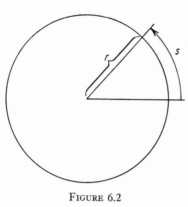

Figure 6.2, we place the vertex of an angle at the center of a circle of radius r. The angle subtends an arc of length s, and we define the radian measure of the angle as follows.

Definition 6.1. *The* **radian measure** t *of an angle is the ratio of the length* s *of the arc subtended by that angle to the length of the radius* r *of the circle centered at the vertex of the angle.   In symbols,*

FIGURE 6.2

$$t = \frac{s}{r}$$

Thus, the radian measure of an angle formed by rotating its initial side through the entire circumference of a circle with radius r (and circumference $2\pi r$) is

$$t = \frac{2\pi r}{r} = 2\pi \text{ radians}$$

Definition 6.1 also may be used to find s, given t and r, as shown in the following example.

Example 6.2. Find the length of the arc subtended by a central angle of 2 radians in a circle of radius 4 inches.

Solution: Since $t = s/r$, we have

$$s = tr$$

$$= 2 \cdot 4$$

$$= 8 \text{ inches}$$

We can find the degree measure of an angle with given radian measure, and vice versa, using the fact that 360° corresponds to 2π radians, as illustrated in the following examples.

Example 6.3. Find t if $\theta = 60°$.

Solution: Since $60°$ is $\frac{1}{6}$ of $360°$, then t is $\frac{1}{6}$ of 2π, or $t = \pi/3$. Expressing this as a proportion, we have

$$\frac{60}{360} = \frac{t}{2\pi}$$

$$t = \frac{120\pi}{360} = \frac{\pi}{3}$$

Example 6.4. Find θ if $t = 1$ radian.

Solution:

$$\frac{1}{2\pi} = \frac{\theta}{360}$$

$$\theta = \frac{360}{2\pi} = \frac{180}{\pi} = \frac{180}{3.1416} = 57.296°$$

If we wish, we may convert $.296°$ into minutes and seconds, as follows. Since 1 minute equals $1/60$ of a degree, if m is the number of minutes in $.296°$, then

$$m = (.296)(60) = 17.76'$$

Since 1 second equals $1/60$ of a minute, if s is the number of seconds in $.76'$, then

$$s = (.76)(60) = 45.6''$$

Thus, $\theta = 57° \ 17' \ 46''$

to the nearest second.

As defined, the radian measure of an angle does not depend upon the radius of the circle chosen. If we choose a circle of radius $r = 1$, called the **unit circle**, then $t = s/1 = s$. Thus, *the radian measure of any angle equals the length of the arc subtended by that angle in the unit circle.*

Now, consider the central angle t of the unit circle shown in Figure 6.3. The directed line segment along the terminal side of the angle, from its vertex to the circumference of the unit circle, is a vector T, having components (x, y). This vector, which

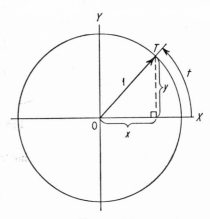

FIGURE 6.3

we shall denote by $T(x, y)$, is called the **unit radius vector** corresponding to the angle t. *To each angle t there corresponds exactly one unit radius vector T.* The terminal point of this vector is found by proceeding from the point $(1, 0)$ along the arc of the unit circle in the positive sense through a distance t.

Given an angle t, we can find the components of T. First, we note that the point (x, y) lies on the circumference of the unit circle, and from the right triangle in Figure 6.3, and the Pythagorean theorem we see that x and y are related by the equation

(6.1) $$x^2 + y^2 = 1$$

Geometric arguments may be used to find an additional relation between the components of T when t is given, so that you can find x and y. The following examples illustrate the use of plane geometry to find the second relation in three important cases.

Example 6.5. Find the components of T when $t = \pi/2$ radians.

Solution: Since $t = \pi/2$ is a right angle (Figure 6.4) its terminal side is along the Y-axis. Thus, the x component of T is $x = 0$. Using Equation 6.1 and noting from the figure that $y > 0$, we have $y = 1$.

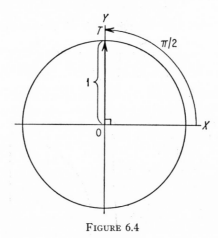

FIGURE 6.4

Example 6.6. Find the components of T when $t = \pi/4$ radians.

Solution: From Figure 6.5, we note that

$$\angle\, POT \,=\, \angle\, OTP \,=\, \frac{\pi}{4}$$

$(\overline{TP} \perp \overline{OA}$, and the sum of the angles of a triangle is π.) Thus, $\triangle OPT$ is an isosceles triangle, and $\overline{OP} = \overline{PT}$. Using the definition of the components of T, we have

$$x = y$$

Using Equation 6.1, together with the above equation, we have

$$x^2 + x^2 = 1$$

or

$$x^2 = \frac{1}{2}$$

From Figure 6.5 we note that both x and y are positive, and conclude that

$$x = y = \frac{\sqrt{2}}{2}$$

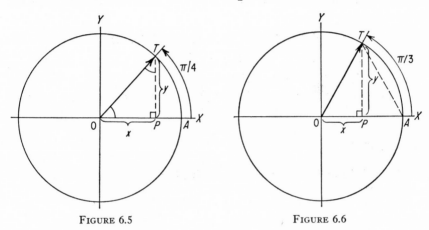

FIGURE 6.5   FIGURE 6.6

Example 6.7. Find the components of T when $t = \pi/3$ radians.

Solution: From Figure 6.6, we note that

$$\angle\,OTP = \angle\,PTA = \frac{\pi}{6}$$

($\overline{TP} \perp \overline{OA}$, and the sum of the angles of a triangle is π.) Thus, $\triangle OTA$ is an equilateral triangle, and the altitude $\overline{TP}$ bisects the base $\overline{OA}$. Since $\overline{OA} = 1$ and $\overline{OP} = x$, we have

$$x = \frac{1}{2}$$

Using Equation 6.1 together with the above equation, we have

$$\left(\frac{1}{2}\right)^2 + y^2 = 1$$

or

$$y^2 = \frac{3}{4}$$

From Figure 6.6 we note that y is positive, and conclude that

$$y = \frac{\sqrt{3}}{2}$$

We have illustrated how to obtain the components of T when the angle t is given. If the components of T are given, it is not possible to find t uniquely. For example, we know from Example 6.5 that $t = \pi/2$ corresponds to $T(0, 1)$. But, the angle

$$t = \frac{\pi}{2} + 2\pi = \frac{5\pi}{2}$$

has the same terminal side as $t = \pi/2$. Therefore, both these angles correspond to the unit radius vector $T(0, 1)$. In general, any angle of the form

(6.2) $t' = t + 2k\pi \quad (k = 0, \pm 1, \pm 2, \ldots)$

has the same unit radius vector as the angle t. We may conclude from this discussion that *to every unit radius vector* T(x, y) *there correspond an unlimited number of angles that differ from each other by integer multiples of 2π.*

PROBLEMS A

1. Find the radian measure corresponding to the following degree measures.

(a) 30°   (b) 60°   (c) 270°
(d) 135°   (e) 15°   (f) 22° 30′
(g) 8°   (h) 340°   (i) −120°
(j) −15°   (k) −360°   (l) −7.5°

2. Find the degree measure corresponding to the following radian measures.

(a) $\pi/6$ (b) $\pi/12$ (c) $2\pi/3$
(d) $-5\pi/6$ (e) 2   (f) $\frac{1}{3}$
(g) .815   (h) −.013   (i) −1.876

3. Find the components of T corresponding to the given value of t.

(a) π (b) 0   (c) $3\pi/4$
(d) 2π (e) $-\pi/4$ (f) $2\pi/3$
(g) $\pi/6$ (h) $5\pi/6$ (i) $7\pi/3$
(j) $-\pi/3$ (k) $27\pi/4$ (l) $-11\pi/2$

4. Find the length of the arc subtended by a central angle of 15° in a circle of radius 5 inches.

5. A bicycle with 26 inch wheels travels 10 feet. Through what angle have the wheels turned?

PROBLEMS B

1. Prove that the area A of a sector of a circle of radius r is $A = \frac{1}{2}r^2|t|$, where t is the radian measure of the central angle of the sector.

2. Two gears are meshed, one with a radius of 6 inches, and the other with a radius of 2 inches. How far does a point on the circumference of the large gear travel when the small gear makes 2 revolutions?

6.3 The Trigonometric Functions

Consider a function whose domain is the set of real numbers, whose range is the set of all y-components of the unit radius vectors $T(x, y)$, and which associates with each real number t the y-component of the corresponding T. In this way, we introduce a particular **trigonometric function**, called the **sine function**. By associating with each t the x-component of T, or some other unique number calculated from x and y, we can introduce additional trigonometric functions. There are six basic functions in all, each defined on a domain of real numbers. The range of each function is a set of real numbers constructed from the components of T according to the following definition.

Definition 6.2. *The six* **trigonometric functions** *have the correspondences*

$$\sin t = y \qquad\qquad \csc t = \frac{1}{y} \quad (y \neq 0)$$

$$\cos t = x \qquad\qquad \sec t = \frac{1}{x} \quad (x \neq 0)$$

$$\tan t = \frac{y}{x} \quad (x \neq 0) \qquad\qquad \cot t = \frac{x}{y} \quad (y \neq 0)$$

where x *and* y *are the components of the unit radius vector* T *corresponding to the radian measure* t. *These functions are defined on the domain of all real numbers* t, *except those corresponding to the components excluded above.*

In Definition 6.2, the abbreviations *sin, cos, tan, csc, sec,* and *cot* stand for the words *sine, cosine, tangent, cosecant, secant,* and *cotangent,* respectively. The domains of the tangent and secant functions exclude all values of t for which $x = 0$; that is, all numbers of the form $\pi/2 + k\pi$, where k is an integer. The domains of the cosecant and cotangent functions exclude all values of t for which $y = 0$, that is, all numbers of the form $k\pi$, where k is an integer. Since neither x nor y can be less than -1 or exceed 1, the range of the sine and cosine functions consists of all real numbers between -1 and 1, inclusive. The range of the tangent and cotangent functions is the set of all real numbers, and the range of the cosecant and secant functions includes all real numbers greater than or equal to 1 or less than or equal to -1.

The value of a trigonometric function for some t is found by determining the coordinates of the corresponding unit radius vector and applying Definition 6.2, as shown in the following examples.

Example 6.8. Find the values of the six trigonometric functions when $t = \pi/3$.

Solution: In Example 6.7, the components of T, when $t = \pi/3$, were found to be $(1/2, \sqrt{3}/2)$. Thus,

$$\sin \frac{\pi}{3} = \frac{\sqrt{3}}{2} \qquad\qquad \csc \frac{\pi}{3} = \frac{2}{\sqrt{3}} = \frac{2}{3}\sqrt{3}$$

$$\cos \frac{\pi}{3} = \frac{1}{2} \qquad\qquad \sec \frac{\pi}{3} = \frac{2}{1} = 2$$

$$\tan \frac{\pi}{3} = \frac{\sqrt{3}/2}{\frac{1}{2}} = \sqrt{3} \qquad\qquad \cot \frac{\pi}{3} = \frac{\frac{1}{2}}{\sqrt{3}/2} = \frac{\sqrt{3}}{3}$$

Example 6.9. Find $\sin\left(-\dfrac{11\pi}{2}\right)$.

Solution: If we take $k = 3$ in Equation 6.2, we see that the unit radius vector corresponding to $t = -11\pi/2$ is identical to that corresponding to

$$-\frac{11\pi}{2} + 6\pi = \pi/2$$

In Example 6.5, the components of T when $t = \pi/2$ were found to be $(0, 1)$, and we have

$$\sin\left(-\frac{11\pi}{2}\right) = \sin\frac{\pi}{2} = 1$$

Using methods similar to Example 6.8, we can find the values of the six trigonometric functions at several points in the interval from 0 to $\pi/2$. The results are summarized in the following table. The (—) means that

t	$\sin t$	$\cos t$	$\tan t$	$\csc t$	$\sec t$	$\cot t$
0	0	1	0	—	1	—
$\pi/6$	1/2	$\sqrt{3}/2$	$\sqrt{3}/3$	2	$2\sqrt{3}/3$	$\sqrt{3}$
$\pi/4$	$\sqrt{2}/2$	$\sqrt{2}/2$	1	$\sqrt{2}$	$\sqrt{2}$	1
$\pi/3$	$\sqrt{3}/2$	1/2	$\sqrt{3}$	$2\sqrt{3}/3$	2	$\sqrt{3}/3$
$\pi/2$	1	0	—	1	—	0

the function is undefined at the given point. The student is urged to verify as many of the values in this table as possible.

PROBLEMS A

1. Find the values of the six trigonometric functions when the components of T are

(a) $(\frac{3}{5}, \frac{4}{5})$ (b) $(-\frac{1}{2}, \sqrt{3}/2)$

(c) $(0, 1)$ (d) $(-1, 0)$

2. Find the values of the six trigonometric functions when t equals

(a) π (b) 0 (c) $3\pi/4$

(d) 2π (e) $-\pi/4$ (f) $2\pi/3$

(g) $5\pi/6$ (h) $7\pi/3$ (i) $27\pi/4$

(j) $-11\pi/2$ (k) $-13\pi/6$ (l) 55π

3. For what values of t $(0 \leq t \leq 2\pi)$ does T lie in

(a) the first quadrant.   (b) the second quadrant.

(c) the third quadrant.   (d) the fourth quadrant.

4. Complete the following table.

SIGNS OF THE FUNCTIONS

Quadrant	sin	cos	tan	csc	sec	cot
I	+	+	+	+	+	+
II						
III						
IV						

PROBLEMS B

1. List all the values of t on the interval $-\pi \leq t \leq \pi$ for which $\sin t = 0$.

2. The graph of a function $\mathbf{f}$ is symmetric about the Y-axis if $f(-x) = f(x)$ for all x. Which of the trigonometric functions have this property?

3. The graph of a function $\mathbf{f}$ is symmetric about the origin if $f(-x) = -f(x)$ for all x. Which of the trigonometric functions have this property?

4. A function $\mathbf{f}$ is said to be periodic with period p if p is the smallest positive number such that $f(x + p) = f(x)$ for all x. Is the sine function periodic? If so, find the smallest positive number p for which $\sin(x + p) = \sin x$ for all x.

6.4   Relations Among the Trigonometric Functions

It is evident from Definition 6.2 that the six trigonometric functions are related. Such relations may be brought out by deriving equations linking the values of these functions at some arbitrary t. The following theorem gives the **six elementary trigonometric relations.**

Theorem 6.1.

$$\cos^2 t + \sin^2 t = 1$$

$$\tan t = \frac{\sin t}{\cos t} \qquad \left(t \neq \frac{\pi}{2} + k\pi \right)$$

$$\csc t = \frac{1}{\sin t} \qquad (t \neq k\pi)$$

$$\sec t = \frac{1}{\cos t} \qquad \left(t \neq \frac{\pi}{2} + k\pi \right)$$

$$\cot t = \frac{\cos t}{\sin t} \qquad (t \neq k\pi)$$

$$\cot t = \frac{1}{\tan t} \qquad (t \neq k\pi)$$

where k *is any integer.*

Proof: According to Definition 6.2, we can substitute $\cos t$ for x and $\sin t$ for y in Equation 6.1 to obtain $\cos^2 t + \sin^2 t = 1$. Similarly, we can make the same substitutions and use Definition 6.2 to prove the remaining formulas comprising this theorem.

Other relations among the trigonometric functions can be proved with the use of Theorem 6.1, as shown in the following example.

Example 6.10. Prove that $1 + \cot^2 t = \csc^2 t$, $(t \neq k\pi)$.

Solution:

$$1 + \cot^2 t = 1 + \frac{\cos^2 t}{\sin^2 t}$$

$$= \frac{\sin^2 t + \cos^2 t}{\sin^2 t}$$

$$= \frac{1}{\sin^2 t}$$

$$= \csc^2 t$$

It is convenient to be able to express the values of trigonometric functions for any t in their domain in terms of values of functions where t lies between 0 and $\pi/2$, inclusive. There are many relations that make this possible; the following theorems give some of the more useful ones.

Theorem 6.2. *If* $0 \leq t \leq \dfrac{\pi}{2}$*, then*

$$\sin\ (-t) = -\sin t \qquad\qquad \csc\ (-t) = -\csc t$$
$$\cos\ (-t) = \cos t \qquad\qquad \sec\ (-t) = \sec t$$
$$\tan\ (-t) = -\tan t \qquad\qquad \cot\ (-t) = -\cot t$$

Proof: In Figure 6.7 we observe that triangles OPT and OPT_1 have two sides and the included angle in common. Therefore, they are congruent, and $\overline{PT} = \overline{T_1P}$. If the components of the unit radius vector T are (x, y), we have

$$\overline{PT} = y, \quad \overline{PT_1} = -y, \quad \text{and} \quad \overline{OP} = x$$

Thus, the components of the radius vector T_1, corresponding to $-t$, are $(x, -y)$. Application of Definition 6.2 completes the proof.

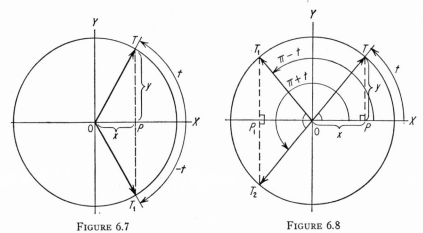

FIGURE 6.7   FIGURE 6.8

Theorem 6.3. *If* $0 \leq t \leq \dfrac{\pi}{2}$*, then*

$$\sin\ (\pi \pm t) = \mp \sin t \qquad\qquad \csc\ (\pi \pm t) = \mp \csc t$$
$$\cos\ (\pi \pm t) = -\cos t \qquad\qquad \sec\ (\pi \pm t) = -\sec t$$
$$\tan\ (\pi \pm t) = \pm \tan t \qquad\qquad \cot\ (\pi \pm t) = \pm \cot t$$

Proof: In Figure 6.8 we observe that right triangles OPT, OP_1T_1, and OP_1T_2 have equal acute angles and equal hypotenuses. Therefore, they are congruent, and

$$\overline{OP} = \overline{P_1O}, \quad \text{and} \quad \overline{PT} = \overline{P_1T_1} = \overline{T_2P_1}$$

If the components of the unit radius vector T are (x, y), we have

$$\overline{OP} = x, \quad \overline{OP_1} = -x, \quad \overline{PT} = y, \quad \overline{P_1T_1} = y, \quad \text{and} \quad \overline{P_1T_2} = -y$$

Thus, the components of the unit radius vector T_1, corresponding to $\pi - t$, are $(-x, y)$, and the components of the unit radius vector T_2, corresponding to $\pi + t$, are $(-x, -y)$. Application of Definition 6.2 completes the proof.

Theorem 6.4. *If* $0 \leq t \leq \dfrac{\pi}{2}$, *then*

$$\sin\left(\frac{\pi}{2} \pm t\right) = \cos t \qquad \csc\left(\frac{\pi}{2} \pm t\right) = \sec t$$

$$\cos\left(\frac{\pi}{2} \pm t\right) = \mp\sin t \qquad \sec\left(\frac{\pi}{2} \pm t\right) = \mp\csc t$$

$$\tan\left(\frac{\pi}{2} \pm t\right) = \mp\cot t \qquad \cot\left(\frac{\pi}{2} \pm t\right) = \mp\tan t$$

Proof: In Figure 6.9 we observe that right triangles OPT, OP_1T_1. and OP_2T_2 have common acute angles and common hypotenuses. Therefore, they are congruent, and

$$\overline{OP} = \overline{P_1T_1} = \overline{P_2T_2} \quad \text{and} \quad \overline{PT} = \overline{OP_1} = \overline{P_2O}$$

If the components of the unit radius vector T are (x, y), we have

$$\overline{OP} = x, \quad \overline{P_1T_1} = x, \quad \overline{P_2T_2} = x, \quad \overline{PT} = y, \quad \overline{OP_1} = y, \quad \text{and} \quad \overline{OP_2} = -y$$

Thus, the components of the unit radius vector T_1, corresponding to $\pi/2 - t$, are (y, x), and the components of the unit radius vector T_2, corresponding to $\pi/2 + t$, are $(-y, x)$. Application of Definition 6.2 completes the proof.

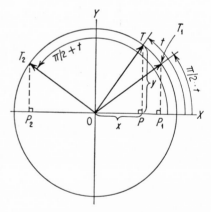

FIGURE 6.9

These theorems may be extended to include values of t outside the interval $0 \leq t \leq \pi/2$. This restriction has been made here only to simplify the proof. It is not necessary (or even advisable) to attempt to memorize these theorems. Figures 6.7, 6.8, and 6.9 are easily reconstructed, and any of the formulas comprising these theorems may be obtained by inspection of the appropriate figure.

Theorems 6.1 through 6.4 can be used to find values of the trigonometric functions when t is outside the interval $0 \leq t \leq \pi/2$, given suitable values inside this interval. The following example illustrates this procedure.

Example 6.11. Find $\cos \dfrac{5\pi}{3}$.

Solution:

$$\cos \frac{5\pi}{3} = \cos\left(\pi + \frac{2\pi}{3}\right) = -\cos \frac{2\pi}{3}$$

$$\cos \frac{2\pi}{3} = \cos\left(\frac{\pi}{2} + \frac{\pi}{6}\right) = -\sin \frac{\pi}{6} = -\frac{1}{2}$$

Therefore, $\cos \dfrac{5\pi}{3} = \dfrac{1}{2}$

PROBLEMS A

1. Prove the following relations.

(a) $1 + \tan^2 t = \sec^2 t$ (b) $(\cos t)(\csc t) = \cot t$

(c) $\cos^2 t - \sin^2 t = 2\cos^2 t - 1$

(d) $(\sin t + \cos t)^2 = 1 + 2(\sin t)(\cos t)$

(e) $\cos\left(\dfrac{3\pi}{2} + t\right) = \sin t$ (f) $\sin(t - \pi) = -\sin t$

(g) $\tan\left(\dfrac{5\pi}{2} - t\right) = \cot t$ (h) $\sec\left(t - \dfrac{7\pi}{2}\right) = -\csc t$

PROBLEMS B

1. Prove Theorem 6.2 if t is in the interval $\pi/2 \le t \le \pi$.

2. Prove Theorem 6.3 if t is in the interval $\pi \le t \le 3\pi/2$.

3. Prove Theorem 6.4 if t is in the interval $3\pi/2 \le t \le 2\pi$.

6.5   Tables of the Trigonometric Functions

Values of the six trigonometric functions are tabulated in Table 2. This table gives four-place values of the functions for t in the interval $0 \le t \le \pi/2$, together with the degree measure corresponding to each radian measure. The table is read in two ways. For t in the interval $0 \le t \le \pi/4$, we use the headings at the left and on the top. For t in the interval $\pi/4 \le t \le \pi/2$, we use the headings at the right and on the bottom. Thus, from Table 2 we read

$$\sin .3927 = 0.3827, \quad \tan 1.1199 = 2.066, \quad \text{etc.}$$

This space-saving arrangement of the trigonometric tables is made possible by the relations given in Theorem 6.4. For example, if values of $\sin t$ are tabulated from $t = 0$ to $t = \pi/4$, we also have values of $\cos (\pi/2 - t)$ from $t = 0$ to $t = \pi/4$; that is, we have values of the cosine function on the interval $\pi/4 \leq t \leq \pi/2$. From Theorem 6.4 and the arrangement of Table 2, we see that the radian measures on the left- and right-hand sides of any given line in Table 2 add to $\pi/2 = 1.5708$.

Note that Table 2 really serves several purposes. It provides values of the trigonometric functions for angle measures in radians, and it enables you to convert from radians to degrees, and vice versa. In addition, it provides tables of values of trigonometric functions defined on domains consisting of angles, measured in degrees. We shall introduce such functions in Section 6.6, and make use of this feature of Table 2 in that section.

In connection with any of the purposes described, you can use linear interpolation in exactly the same way that you interpolated in the table of logarithms (Table 1). The following examples illustrate some of the uses of Table 2.

Example 6.12. Find cos .5521.

Solution: From Table 2,

$$\cos .5498 = .8526, \quad \text{and} \quad \cos .5527 = .8511$$

The scheme for interpolation is as follows.

$$\frac{d}{.0023} = \frac{-.0015}{.0029}$$

$$d = -.0012$$

Thus, cos .5521 = .8526 − .0012 = .8514.

Example 6.13. Convert 56° 14′ to radians.

Solution: From Table 2,

$$56° \ 10' = .9803 \text{ radian}, \quad \text{and} \quad 56° \ 20' = .9832 \text{ radian}$$

The scheme for interpolation is as follows.

$$\theta \qquad\qquad t$$

$$10'\left[\; 04'\left[\begin{array}{l} 56°\,10' \\[6pt] 56°\,14' \end{array}\right.\begin{array}{l}\left.\begin{array}{l}.9803 \\[6pt] - \end{array}\right]d \\[6pt] .9832 \end{array}\right].0029$$

$$\frac{d}{4} = \frac{.0029}{10}$$

$$d = .0012$$

Thus, 56° 14' is equivalent to .9803 + .0012 = .9815 radian.

Table 2 can be used also to find values of the trigonometric functions corresponding to values of t outside the interval $0 \leq t \leq \pi/2$. To find such values, we use an appropriate relation from Theorems 6.2 through 6.4, as illustrated in the following example.

Example 6.14. Find sec 4.1467.

Solution: From Theorem 6.3, we have

$$\sec(\pi + t) = -\sec t$$

Therefore,

$$\sec 4.1467 = \sec(3.1416 + 1.0051)$$

$$= -\sec 1.0051$$

The interpolation scheme for finding sec 1.0051 is as follows.

$$t \qquad\qquad \sec t$$

$$.0029\left[\; .0015\left[\begin{array}{l} 1.0036 \\[6pt] 1.0051 \end{array}\right.\begin{array}{l}\left.\begin{array}{l}1.861 \\[6pt] - \end{array}\right]d \\[6pt] 1.870 \end{array}\right].009$$

$$\frac{d}{.0015} = \frac{.009}{.0029}$$

$$d = .005$$

Thus,

$$\sec 1.0051 = 1.861 + .005 = 1.866$$

and

$$\sec 4.1467 = -1.866$$

PROBLEMS A

1. Use Table 2 to evaluate.

(a) sin .5469   (b) sec .0058   (c) tan 1.2828

(d) cos 1.1868   (e) sec .4027   (f) cot 1.3628

(g) cos $\frac{5}{4}$ (h) csc $\frac{1}{8}$ (i) tan 7.415

(j) sin (−.0159)   (k) csc (−3.4851)   (l) cot 4.9520

2. Use Table 2 to convert the following degree measures to radians.

(a) 24°   (b) 53°   (c) 10° 25′

(d) 86° 05′   (e) 8° 15′ 17″   (f) 37° 20′ 12″

3. Use Table 2 to convert the following radian measures to degrees.

(a) 1.3   (b) .1   (c) 6.28

(d) 11.5   (e) 3.1427   (f) .0175

PROBLEMS B

1. On what interval on t is the approximation sin $t \simeq t$ valid to within an error of less than .01? Does it make sense to use the approximation sin $\theta \simeq \theta$ over a like interval? Why?

2. If $3\pi/2 \leq t \leq 2\pi$, and cos t = .6851, find sin t.

3. Use the results of Problem B-1 to find a good approximation to cos t.

6.6   Right-Triangle Functions

The trigonometric functions were defined in Section 6.3 on domains of real numbers. In this section, we shall define a set of functions consistent with the trigonometric functions, but on domains of angles.

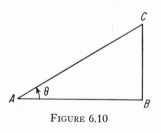

These functions are based upon relations among the sides of a right triangle. Consider the right triangle ABC of Figure 6.10, where the acute angle BAC has degree measure θ. The side opposite this angle is BC, the side adjacent to this angle is AB, and the hypotenuse of the right triangle is AC. We shall use the same terminology to mean the *lengths* of these sides. We now define six right-triangle functions on domains of positive acute angles, with reference to the sides of the right triangle.

FIGURE 6.10

Definition 6.3. *The six* **right-triangle functions** *have the correspondences*

$$\sin \theta = \frac{\text{side opposite}}{\text{hypotenuse}} \qquad \csc \theta = \frac{\text{hypotenuse}}{\text{side opposite}}$$

$$\cos \theta = \frac{\text{side adjacent}}{\text{hypotenuse}} \qquad \sec \theta = \frac{\text{hypotenuse}}{\text{side adjacent}}$$

$$\tan \theta = \frac{\text{side opposite}}{\text{side adjacent}} \qquad \cot \theta = \frac{\text{side adjacent}}{\text{side opposite}}$$

We must exclude the angles measuring $\theta = 0°$ and $\theta = 90°$ because the geometric figure is no longer a triangle in these cases. Note also that the hypotenuse is always greater than either leg of a right triangle, thus, the ranges of the sine and cosine functions defined here are restricted to the set of real numbers greater than 0 and less than 1. Similarly, the ranges of the cosecant and secant functions consist of all real numbers greater than 1, and the ranges of the tangent and cotangent functions include all positive real numbers.

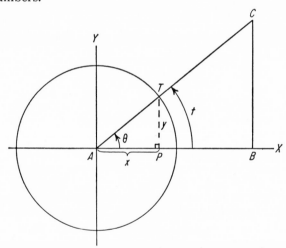

FIGURE 6.11

We have used the same names for the right-triangle functions and the trigonometric functions. To justify this usage, we must show that Definitions 6.2 and 6.3 are consistent; that is, that we obtain the same value, for example, for $\sin \theta$ and $\sin t$ when θ and t correspond. To demonstrate consistency, let us refer $\triangle ABC$ to a pair of coordinate axes with the vertex A at the origin and the side AB along the positive half of the X-axis, as shown in Figure 6.11. Now, we draw a circle with center at A and unit radius, labelling the point T at the intersection of AC and the circumference of the circle.   If we draw a perpendicular from T to AB, the right triangle APT has an acute angle in common with $\triangle ABC$, and we conclude that these triangles are similar.   Since corresponding sides of similar triangles are proportional, we obtain the same values for $\sin \theta$, $\cos \theta$, . . . , whether we refer to $\triangle APT$ or to $\triangle ABC$.   But the x-component of the unit radius vector T equals the side adjacent to $\angle PAT$ in $\triangle APT$, and the y-component of this vector equals the side opposite.   A comparison of Definitions 6.2 and 6.3 verifies that

$$\sin \theta = \sin t, \quad \cos \theta = \cos t, \quad \text{etc.}$$

(In Figure 6.11, $\overline{AC} > \overline{AT}$.   Note that this entire argument is still valid if $\overline{AC} \leq \overline{AT}$.)

The definition of the right-triangle functions can be extended to include angles other than acute angles by taking advantage of the parallel between these functions and the trigonometric functions.   Any angle θ may be placed so that its vertex lies at the center of the unit circle.   Thus, to every angle θ there corresponds an arc t of the unit circle.   We may define the **trigonometric functions on domains of angles** by equating their values with those of the corresponding trigonometric functions defined on domains of real numbers.   For example, the angle $\theta = 135°$ corresponds to the arc $t = 3\pi/4$, and we define

$$\tan 135° = \tan \frac{3\pi}{4} = -1$$

Since certain trigonometric functions are undefined for some values of t, they are likewise undefined for the corresponding angles θ.

Definition 6.3 can be used together with Table 2 to find any sides or angles of a right triangle when the length of a side and an acute angle are given, or when the lengths of two sides are given.   The following examples illustrate the calculations involved, as well as some of the physical applications to which these calculations may be applied.

Example 6.15. A right triangle with an angle measuring 24° has an hypotenuse measuring 6 inches.   What are the measures of the three unknown parts of the triangle?

Solution: From Figure 6.12 we have

$$\sin 24° = \frac{y}{6}, \quad \text{or} \quad y = 6 \sin 24°$$

$$\cos 24° = \frac{x}{6}, \quad \text{or} \quad x = 6 \cos 24°$$

$$90° + 24° + \alpha = 180°, \quad \text{or} \quad \alpha = 66°$$

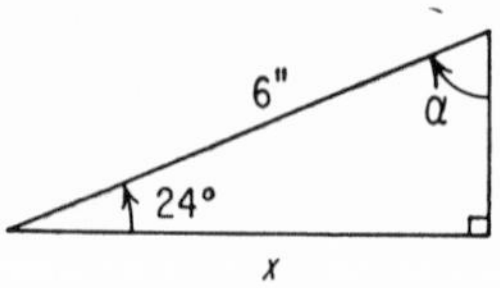

FIGURE 6.12

From Table 2, we find sin 24° = .4067 and cos 24° = .9135, thus

$$y = 6(.4067) = 2.4402 \text{ inches}$$

$$x = 6(.9135) = 5.4810 \text{ inches}$$

Example 6.16. A guy wire is to be stretched from the top of a vertical 40-foot pole to the ground to make an angle of 32° with the ground. What length wire is required?

Solution: From Figure 6.13 we have

$$\csc 32° = \frac{h}{40}, \quad \text{or} \quad h = 40 \csc 32°$$

From Table 2, csc 32° = 1.887, thus

$$h = 40(1.887) = 75.48 \text{ feet}$$

FIGURE 6.13

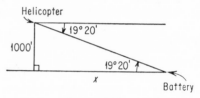

FIGURE 6.14

Example 6.17. A helicopter flying at 1000 feet observes an artillery battery making an angle of depression of 19° 20'. How far from the battery is a point on the ground directly beneath the helicopter?

Solution: From Figure 6.14 we have

$$\cot 19° 20' = \frac{x}{1000}, \quad \text{or} \quad x = 1000 \cot 19° 20'$$

From Table 2, cot 19° 20' = 2.850, thus

$$x = 1000(2.850) = 2850 \text{ feet}$$

In solving these problems, other trigonometric functions than those chosen could have been used. For example, in Example 6.16 we could have used the equation sin 32° = 40/h, obtaining $h = 40/\sin 32°$. The cosecant function was chosen instead so that the labor of division could be avoided.

PROBLEMS A

1. Referring to the notation of the accompanying figure, two parts of a right triangle are given. Find the other parts.

(a) $a = 12$, $A = 33°$

(b) $b = 78.2$, $A = 43° 17'$

(c) $a = 9.86$, $A = 36° 21'$

(d) $a = 124$, $b = 78$

(e) $b = 8.3$, $c = 96.4$

(f) $a = 14.1$, $c = 15.5$

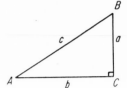

2. A ladder 25 feet long rests against a vertical wall. If its foot is 4 feet from the base of the wall, what angle does it make with the ground?

3. The *grade* of a hill is the tangent of the angle between the hill and a horizontal line. Find the grade of a hill that rises 240 feet and is 550 feet long.

4. A pendulum 8 inches in length swings through an angle measuring 25°. What is the minimum width of a case used to house this pendulum?

5. A man 69 inches tall stands near an 11-foot lamp post. His shadow is 4 feet long. How far from the post is he?

6. One side of a regular octagon is 12 inches. What is the radius of the circumscribed circle?

7. Find the radius of the circle inscribed in the octagon of Problem 6.

8. From a certain point on a level street, the angle of elevation of the top of a building is 50°. From another point 100 yards away, the angle of elevation is 38°. Find the height of the building.

9. A flag pole on top of a building makes an angle of depression of 62° with a point on the ground 500 feet from the base of the building. The top of the building makes an angle of depression of 58° with the same point. How high is the flagpole?

10. The height of an inaccessible mountain is found by measuring its angles of elevation from two different points on level ground at a known distance apart. If the angles of elevation are α and β and the distance between the two points is d, find an equation for the height h of the mountain in terms of α, β, and d.

PROBLEMS B

1. A certain tower leans at an angle of 5° from the vertical. At a point 50 feet from the base of the tower, perpendicular to the direction of leaning, the angle of elevation of its top is 20°. How high is the top of the tower from the ground?

2. Solve Problem 1 if the angle of lean is α, the angle of elevation is β, and the distance from the base is d.

$$7$$

The Algebra of Trigonometric Functions

7.1 Addition Formulas

Given some function **f**, a formula that relates $f(u + v)$ to $f(u)$ and $f(v)$ is called an **addition formula.** For example, an addition formula for the exponential function is

$$f(u + v) = f(u) \cdot f(v), \quad \text{because} \quad b^{u+v} = b^u \cdot b^v$$

In this section we shall derive the important addition formulas for the sine, cosine, and tangent functions.

These addition formulas may be derived directly from a formula expressing $\cos (u - v)$ in terms of $\cos u$, $\cos v$, $\sin u$, and $\sin v$. To establish this formula, we shall need a result expressing the distance between two points in terms of their coordinates. It was shown on page 25 that the distance d between two points a and b on the real line is given by $d = |a - b|$. The following theorem generalizes this result to include any two points in a plane.

Theorem 7.1. *If* P_1 *has coordinates* (x_1, y_1) *and* P_2 *has coordinates* (x_2, y_2), *then the distance* d *between* P_1 *and* P_2 *is given by*

$$d = \sqrt{(x_1 - x_2)^2 + (y_1 - y_2)^2}$$

Proof: In Figure 7.1 the right triangle P_1AP_2 is formed by drawing a line perpendicular to the X-axis from P_1 and another line perpendicular to the Y-axis through P_2, meeting the first perpendicular at A. The length of the hypotenuse P_1P_2 of this triangle equals the distance d between P_1 and P_2. From the property of absolute values given on page 25, the distance $\overline{AP_1}$ equals $|y_1 - y_2|$ and the distance $\overline{P_2A}$ equals $|x_1 - x_2|$. From the Pythagorean theorem, we have

$$\overline{P_1P_2}^2 = \overline{P_2A}^2 + \overline{AP_1}^2$$

if $\overline{P_1P_2}$ is not parallel to the x- or y-axis.

Thus,
$$d^2 = |x_1 - x_2|^2 + |y_1 - y_2|^2$$
$$= (x_1 - x_2)^2 + (y_1 - y_2)^2$$

By convention, d is non-negative, and we have

$$d = \sqrt{(x_1 - x_2)^2 + (y_1 - y_2)^2}$$

which completes the proof in this case. Can you complete the proof if $\overline{P_1P_2}$ is parallel to either axis?

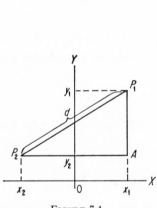

FIGURE 7.1

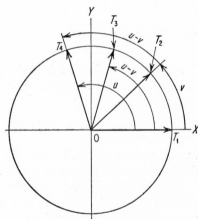

FIGURE 7.2

Using Theorem 7.1 and the definition of $\sin t$ and $\cos t$, we prove the following theorem.

Theorem 7.2. *If* u *and* v *are any real numbers, then*

$$\cos (u - v) = \cos u \cos v + \sin u \sin v$$

Proof: According to Definition 6.2, the x-component of the unit radius vector T equals $\cos t$ and the y-component of T equals $\sin t$. Thus, the components of T_2, T_3, and T_4 in Figure 7.2 are

$$(\cos v, \sin v), \quad [\cos (u - v), \quad \sin (u - v)], \quad \text{and} \quad (\cos u, \sin u)$$

respectively. Note that the arc of the unit circle joining T_1 and T_3 equals the arc joining T_2 and T_4. Therefore, the chords $\overline{T_1 T_3}$ and $\overline{T_2 T_4}$ are equal in length; that is,

$$\overline{T_1 T_3} = \overline{T_2 T_4}$$

From Theorem 7.1 we have

$$\overline{T_1 T_3}^2 = [\cos (u - v) - 1]^2 + [\sin (u - v) - 0]^2$$
$$= 2 - 2 \cos (u - v)$$

after using the fact that $\cos^2 (u - v) + \sin^2 (u - v) = 1$. Using Theorem 7.1 again, we have

$$\overline{T_2 T_4}^2 = (\cos u - \cos v)^2 + (\sin u - \sin v)^2$$
$$= 2 - 2(\cos u \cos v + \sin u \sin v)$$

Equating $\overline{T_1 T_3}^2$ and $\overline{T_2 T_4}^2$, we have

$$2 - 2 \cos (u - v) = 2 - 2(\cos u \cos v + \sin u \sin v)$$

Thus,

$$\cos (u - v) = \cos u \cos v + \sin u \sin v$$

which completes the proof.

Having established the necessary preliminary results, we now prove the following theorem, giving the addition formulas for the sine, cosine, and tangent functions.

Theorem 7.3. *If u and v are any real numbers, subject to the restrictions given, then*

(1) $\sin (u + v) = \sin u \cos v + \cos u \sin v$

(2) $\cos (u + v) = \cos u \cos v - \sin u \sin v$

(3) $\tan (u + v) = \dfrac{\tan u + \tan v}{1 - \tan u \tan v}$ $\left. \begin{array}{l} u \neq \dfrac{\pi}{2} + k\pi \\[2mm] v \neq \dfrac{\pi}{2} + k\pi \\[2mm] u + v \neq \dfrac{\pi}{2} + k\pi \end{array} \right.$

where k is any integer.

Proof:

(1) Applying Theorem 6.4, we have

$$\sin (u + v) = \cos \left[\frac{\pi}{2} - (u + v) \right]$$

$$= \cos \left[\left(\frac{\pi}{2} - u \right) - v \right]$$

Applying Theorem 7.2, we have

$$\cos \left[\left(\frac{\pi}{2} - u \right) - v \right] = \cos \left(\frac{\pi}{2} - u \right) \cos v + \sin \left(\frac{\pi}{2} - u \right) \sin v$$

But we proved that $\cos \left(\frac{\pi}{2} - u \right) = \sin u$, and $\sin \left(\frac{\pi}{2} - u \right) = \cos u$, in Theorem 6.4, and the proof of part (1) is complete.

(2) Substituting $-v$ for v in Theorem 7.2, we have

$$\cos [u - (-v)] = \cos u \cos (-v) + \sin u \sin (-v)$$

In Theorem 6.2, we proved that

$$\cos (-v) = \cos v \quad \text{and} \quad \sin (-v) = -\sin v$$

Since

$$\cos [u - (-v)] = \cos (u + v)$$

the proof is complete.

(3) Applying Theorem 6.1, we have

$$\tan (u + v) = \frac{\sin (u + v)}{\cos (u + v)}$$

$$= \frac{\sin u \cos v + \cos u \sin v}{\cos u \cos v - \sin u \sin v}$$

If neither u nor v equals $\pi/2 + k\pi$, $\cos u \cos v$ cannot equal zero and we may divide numerator and denominator of this last expression by $\cos u \cos v$ to obtain

$$\tan (u + v) = \frac{\dfrac{\sin u}{\cos u} + \dfrac{\sin v}{\cos v}}{1 - \dfrac{\sin u \sin v}{\cos u \cos v}}$$

Again using the relation $\tan t = \dfrac{\sin t}{\cos t}$, we obtain the required result.

You may have noticed that the formulas of Theorem 7.3-1 and 7.3-2 are not strictly addition formulas, because they involve more than one function. However, the formula for sin $(u + v)$, for example, can be put in the form

$$\sin (u + v) = \sin u \sin \left(\frac{\pi}{2} - v\right) + \sin \left(\frac{\pi}{2} - u\right) \sin v$$

which is an addition formula of the form

$$f(u + v) = f(u) \cdot f\left(\frac{\pi}{2} - v\right) + f\left(\frac{\pi}{2} - u\right) \cdot f(v)$$

Can you put the formula for cos $(u + v)$ in a similar form?

Theorem 7.3 can be used to find unknown values of the trigonometric functions when t is a sum or difference of two angle measures with known values, as shown in the following example.

Example 7.1. Find $\cos \dfrac{\pi}{12}$.

Solution:

$$\frac{\pi}{12} = \frac{\pi}{3} - \frac{\pi}{4}$$

$$\cos \frac{\pi}{12} = \cos \frac{\pi}{3} \cos \frac{\pi}{4} + \sin \frac{\pi}{3} \sin \frac{\pi}{4}$$

From the table on page 108, we have

$$\cos \frac{\pi}{3} = \frac{1}{2}, \quad \cos \frac{\pi}{4} = \frac{\sqrt{2}}{2}, \quad \sin \frac{\pi}{3} = \frac{\sqrt{3}}{2}, \quad \sin \frac{\pi}{4} = \frac{\sqrt{2}}{2}$$

Therefore,

$$\cos \frac{\pi}{12} = \frac{1}{2} \cdot \frac{\sqrt{2}}{2} + \frac{\sqrt{3}}{2} \cdot \frac{\sqrt{2}}{2} = \frac{\sqrt{2} + \sqrt{6}}{4}$$

Theorem 7.3 also can be used to find other relations among the trigonometric functions, as illustrated in the following example.

Example 7.2. Prove that $\sin \left(\dfrac{3\pi}{2} + t\right) = -\cos t$.

Solution:

$$\sin \left(\frac{3\pi}{2} + t\right) = \sin \frac{3\pi}{2} \cos t + \cos \frac{3\pi}{2} \sin t$$

$$= (-1) \cos t + (0) \sin t$$

$$= -\cos t$$

Note that it would not be correct to use Theorem 7.3 in a similar way to *prove* that $\cos\left(\dfrac{\pi}{2} - t\right) = \sin t$ or $\sin\left(\dfrac{\pi}{2} - t\right) = \cos t$ because these formulas were used in the proof of this theorem. However, this theorem is useful as a device to *remember* these and other results, such as those in Theorems 6.2-6.4.

PROBLEMS A

1. Find the exact values of the following.

(a) $\sin 105°$ (b) $\tan 75°$

(c) $\cot 15°$ (d) $\cos 135°$

(e) $\cos\dfrac{2\pi}{3}$ (f) $\sin\dfrac{\pi}{12}$

(g) $\tan\dfrac{7\pi}{12}$ (h) $\sec\dfrac{5\pi}{12}$

2. Use Theorem 7.3 to establish the following formulas.

(a) $\tan(-t) = -\tan t$ (b) $\cos(2\pi - t) = \cos t$

(c) $\tan\left(\dfrac{\pi}{2} - t\right) = \cotan t$ (d) $\sin(t - \pi) = -\sin t$

(e) $\cos\left(\dfrac{\pi}{2} + t\right) = -\sin t$ (f) $\csc\left(\dfrac{\pi}{2} - t\right) = \sec t$

(g) $\cot t = -\cot(-t)$ (h) $\sec t = -\csc\left(t - \dfrac{\pi}{2}\right)$

3. Express $\sin(u - v)$ in terms of $\sin u$, $\sin v$, $\cos u$, and $\cos v$.

4. Express $\tan(u - v)$ in terms of $\tan u$ and $\tan v$.

5. Find an addition formula for the cotangent function.

6. Prove the following *factoring formulas*.

(a) $\sin(u + v) + \sin(u - v) = 2\sin u \cos v$
(b) $\sin(u + v) - \sin(u - v) = 2\cos u \sin v$
(c) $\cos(u - v) + \cos(u + v) = 2\cos u \cos v$
(d) $\cos(u - v) - \cos(u + v) = 2\sin u \sin v$

PROBLEMS B

1. If a function **f** has the property $f(x) = f(-x)$ it is called an *even function.* If $f(x) = -f(-x)$, **f** is called an *odd function.* Which of the following functions are even, odd, or neither even nor odd?

(a) $f(x) = \sec x$ (b) $f(x) = x^4$
(c) $f(x) = x\cos x$ (d) $f(x) = x^2 - 1$
(e) $f(x) = \tan(-x)$ (f) $f(x) = x^3 + x$

2. Define the function **h** by $h(x) = f(x) \cdot g(x)$.   Prove

(a) **h** is even if and only if **f** and **g** are both even or both odd.

(b) **h** is odd if and only if **f** is even and **g** is odd, or **f** is odd and **g** is even.

3. Express $\sin(u + v + w)$ in terms of sines and cosines of u, v, and w.

4. Prove the following *reduction formulas.*

(a) $\sin\left(t + 2k\dfrac{\pi}{2}\right) = (-1)^k \sin t$ $(k = 0, \pm 1, \pm 2, \ldots)$

(b) $\cos\left(t + 2k\dfrac{\pi}{2}\right) = (-1)^k \cos t$ $(k = 0, \pm 1, \pm 2, \ldots)$

(c) $\sin\left[t + (2k + 1)\dfrac{\pi}{2}\right] = (-1)^k \cos t$ $(k = 0, \pm 1, \pm 2, \ldots)$

(d) $\cos\left[t + (2k + 1)\dfrac{\pi}{2}\right] = (-1)^{k+1} \sin t$ $(k = 0, \pm 1, \pm 2, \ldots)$

7.2 Values of the Functions at $2t$ and $\frac{1}{2}t$

In this section we shall derive formulas giving the values of the sine, cosine, and tangent functions at $2t$ and $\frac{1}{2}t$ in terms of the values of these functions at t.   These formulas are direct consequences of the addition formulas, and could well have been left as exercises.   However, their importance justifies their separate development.

First, we prove the following theorem, giving the values of the functions at $2t$ in terms of their values at t.

Theorem 7.4. *If* t *is any real number, subject to the restrictions given, then*

(1) $\sin 2t = 2 \sin t \cos t$

(2) $\cos 2t = \cos^2 t - \sin^2 t$

(3) $\tan 2t = \dfrac{2 \tan t}{1 - \tan^2 t}$ $\begin{cases} t \neq \dfrac{\pi}{2} + k\pi \\[2mm] 2t \neq \dfrac{\pi}{2} + k\pi \end{cases}$

Proof:

(1) Setting $u = v = t$ in the formula for $\sin(u + v)$, we have

$$\sin 2t = \sin t \cos t + \cos t \sin t$$

$$= 2 \sin t \cos t$$

(2) Setting $u = v = t$ in the formula for $\cos (u + v)$, we have

$$\cos 2t = \cos t \cos t - \sin t \sin t$$
$$= \cos^2 t - \sin^2 t$$

(3) Setting $u = v = t$ in the formula for $\tan (u + v)$, we have

$$\tan 2t = \frac{\tan t + \tan t}{1 - \tan t \tan t}$$

$$= \frac{2 \tan t}{1 - \tan^2 t}$$

Two other forms for $\cos 2t$ are useful. From the formula $\cos^2 t + \sin^2 t = 1$, we obtain

(7.1) $\qquad \cos 2t = \cos^2 t - (1 - \cos^2 t) = 2 \cos^2 t - 1$

and

(7.2) $\qquad \cos 2t = (1 - \sin^2 t) - \sin^2 t = 1 - 2 \sin^2 t$

Theorem 7.4 can be used conveniently to derive the following theorem, giving the values of the functions at $t/2$ in terms of their values at t.

Theorem 7.5. *If* t *is any real number, subject to the restrictions given, then*

(1) $\sin \dfrac{1}{2}t = \pm \sqrt{\dfrac{1 - \cos t}{2}}$

(2) $\cos \dfrac{1}{2}t = \pm \sqrt{\dfrac{1 + \cos t}{2}}$

(3) $\tan \dfrac{1}{2}t = \pm \sqrt{\dfrac{1 - \cos t}{1 + \cos t}}$ $\qquad \left\{ \begin{array}{l} t \neq \dfrac{\pi}{2} + k\pi \\[2mm] \dfrac{t}{2} \neq \dfrac{\pi}{2} + k\pi \end{array} \right.$

(4) $\tan \dfrac{1}{2}t = \dfrac{\sin t}{1 + \cos t} = \dfrac{1 - \cos t}{\sin t}$

where the sign is determined by noting in which quadrant the vector T, *corresponding to* $\frac{1}{2}$t, *is located.*

Proof:

(1) If we let $t = u$ in Equation 7.2, and solve for $\sin u$, we have

$$\sin u = \pm \sqrt{\frac{1 - \cos 2u}{2}}$$

This equation states that $\sin u$ may be expressed in terms of $\cos 2u$. To emphasize that the number u is half as large as $2u$, let $t = 2u$ and write

$$\sin \frac{1}{2} t = \pm \sqrt{\frac{1 - \cos t}{2}}$$

which is in the form stated in the theorem.

(2) Letting $t = u$ in Equation 7.1 and solving for $\cos t$, we have

$$\cos u = \pm \sqrt{\frac{1 + \cos 2u}{2}}$$

Substituting t for $2u$, we have

$$\cos \frac{1}{2} t = \pm \sqrt{\frac{1 + \cos t}{2}}$$

(3) Dividing $\sin \frac{1}{2}t$ by $\cos \frac{1}{2}t$, we have

$$\tan \frac{1}{2} t = \frac{\sin \frac{1}{2}t}{\cos \frac{1}{2}t} = \pm \sqrt{\frac{1 - \cos t}{1 + \cos t}}$$

(4) $$\tan \frac{1}{2} t = \frac{\sin \frac{1}{2}t}{\cos \frac{1}{2}t} = \frac{2 \sin \frac{1}{2}t \cos \frac{1}{2}t}{2 \cos^2 \frac{1}{2}t}$$

$$= \frac{\sin t}{1 + \cos t}$$

Can you prove that this last expression also equals

$$\left(\frac{1 - \cos t}{\sin t} \right)?$$

The following example illustrates the use of Theorems 7.4 and 7.5 in evaluating the functions at certain values of t.

Example 7.3. Find the exact values of (a) $\sin \dfrac{2\pi}{3}$, (b) $\cos \dfrac{\pi}{8}$, and (c) $\tan \left(-\dfrac{\pi}{16} \right)$.

Solution:

(a) $$\sin \frac{2\pi}{3} = 2 \sin \frac{\pi}{3} \cos \frac{\pi}{3}$$

$$= 2 \left(\frac{\sqrt{3}}{2} \right) \left(\frac{1}{2} \right) = \frac{\sqrt{3}}{2}$$

(b) $\cos \dfrac{\pi}{8} = \pm \sqrt{\dfrac{1 + \cos (\pi/4)}{2}}$

$= \pm \sqrt{\dfrac{1 + (\sqrt{2}/2)}{2}} = \pm \dfrac{1}{2} \sqrt{2 + \sqrt{2}}$

Since the unit radius vector corresponding to $t = \pi/8$ is in the first quadrant, and $\cos t > 0$ in this quadrant, we select the plus sign, and write

$$\cos \frac{\pi}{8} = \frac{1}{2} \sqrt{2 + \sqrt{2}}$$

(c) $\tan \left(-\dfrac{\pi}{16} \right) = \pm \sqrt{\dfrac{1 - \cos (-\pi/8)}{1 + \cos (-\pi/8)}}$

Since $\cos (-t) = \cos t$,

$$\cos \left(-\frac{\pi}{8} \right) = \frac{1}{2} \sqrt{2 + \sqrt{2}}$$

Also, the unit radius vector corresponding to $t = -\pi/16$ is in the fourth quadrant, where $\tan t < 0$. Thus,

$$\tan \left(-\frac{\pi}{16} \right) = -\sqrt{\frac{2 - \sqrt{2 + \sqrt{2}}}{2 + \sqrt{2 + \sqrt{2}}}}$$

PROBLEMS A

1. Find the exact values of the following.

(a) $\cos 15°$ (b) $\tan 22° \, 30'$

(c) $\sin 75°$ (d) $\csc 150°$

(e) $\sec \dfrac{3\pi}{8}$ (f) $\cot \left(-\dfrac{\pi}{12} \right)$

(g) $\sin \dfrac{\pi}{24}$ (h) $\cos \dfrac{5\pi}{16}$

2. Derive a formula expressing $\cos 3t$ in terms of $\cos t$.

3. Derive a formula expressing $\tan 4t$ in terms of $\tan t$.

4. Derive a formula expressing $\sin (t/4)$ in terms of $\cos t$, where $0 < t < \dfrac{\pi}{2}$.

5. Prove that $\tan \dfrac{1}{2} t = \dfrac{1 - \cos t}{\sin t}$.

PROBLEMS B

1. If $\cos t = 1$, prove that $\sin (2 \sin t) = \sin (\sin 2t)$.

2. Prove the following *factoring formulas*.

(a) $\sin u + \sin v = 2 \sin \frac{1}{2}(u + v) \cos \frac{1}{2}(u - v)$

(b) $\sin u - \sin v = 2 \cos \frac{1}{2}(u + v) \sin \frac{1}{2}(u - v)$

(c) $\cos u + \cos v = 2 \cos \frac{1}{2}(u + v) \cos \frac{1}{2}(u - v)$

(d) $\cos u - \cos v = -2 \sin \frac{1}{2}(u + v) \sin \frac{1}{2}(u - v)$

7.3 Graphs of the Trigonometric Functions

Using the table of values of the functions on page 108 and some of the relations derived in Theorems 6.3 and 6.4 we can graph the trigonometric functions with relative ease. Although the domains of these functions are of indefinite extent, we observed in Section 6.2 that the components of T repeat themselves when t increases beyond 2π. Thus, the values of the trigonometric functions repeat, and it will be adequate to graph these functions on the interval $0 \leq t \leq 2\pi$. (In fact, we could graph them on any interval of length 2π.)

We begin by graphing the sine function. From the table on page 108, we have

$$\sin 0 = 0, \quad \sin \frac{\pi}{6} = \frac{1}{2}, \quad \sin \frac{\pi}{4} = \frac{\sqrt{2}}{2} = .707,$$

$$\sin \frac{\pi}{3} = \frac{\sqrt{3}}{2} = .866, \quad \text{and} \quad \sin \frac{\pi}{2} = 1$$

We locate these points on the graph shown in Figure 7.3, joining them with the heavy curve shown. Now, from Theorem 6.3, we have

$$\sin (\pi - t) = \sin t$$

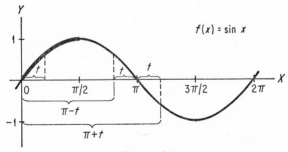

FIGURE 7.3

thus, the ordinate of any point on the sine curve t units to the left of π equals the ordinate on this curve at t. In other words, we can graph the sine function from $\pi/2$ to π by *reflecting* the heavy curve about a line through the point $t = \pi/2$ and perpendicular to the t-axis. To complete the graph of the sine function on the interval $0 \leq t \leq 2\pi$, we use the relation $\sin (\pi + t) = -\sin t$, proved in Theorem 6.3. Accordingly, the graph from $t = \pi$ to $t = 2\pi$ is the reflection about the t-axis of the curve already drawn from $t = 0$ to $t = \pi$.

The graph of the cosine function may be drawn with the aid of Figure 7.3 and the relation $\cos t = \sin \left(\dfrac{\pi}{2} + t\right)$, proved in Theorem 6.4. According to this relation, the graph of the cosine function is identical to that of the sine function shifted $\pi/2$ units to the left. This graph is shown in Figure 7.4.

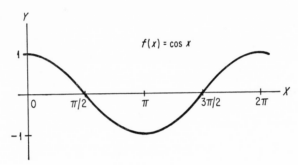

$$f(x) = \cos x$$

FIGURE 7.4

To graph the tangent function, we use the values

$$\tan 0 = 0, \quad \tan \frac{\pi}{6} = \frac{\sqrt{3}}{3} = 0.577, \quad \tan \frac{\pi}{4} = 1,$$

$$\text{and} \quad \tan \frac{\pi}{3} = \sqrt{3} = 1.732$$

given on page 108. Since $\tan (\pi/2)$ is undefined, we must be especially careful to study the behavior of $\tan t$ in the vicinity of $t = \pi/2$. Writing

$$\tan t = \frac{\sin t}{\cos t}$$

and noting that neither $\sin t$ nor $\cos t$ is negative on the interval $0 \leq t < \pi/2$, we conclude that the graph of the tangent function must remain above the t-axis as we approach $t = \pi/2$ from the left. Furthermore, $\cos t$ approaches zero as we approach $t = \pi/2$ from the left, while $\sin t$ remains positive (it becomes close to 1). Thus, the ratio $\dfrac{\sin t}{\cos t}$ must become an arbitrarily large positive number as t comes closer and closer to $\pi/2$ from the left. Now, we may complete the graph of the tangent function on the interval $0 \leq t < \pi/2$ with the heavy curve shown in Figure 7.5. Note that there is no point on the graph corresponding to $t = \pi/2$.

To continue the graph of the tangent function from $t = \pi/2$ to $t = \pi$ we use the relation $\tan (\pi - t) = -\tan t$, proved in Theorem 6.3. Thus, the graph in this interval is drawn by reflecting the heavy curve about a vertical line through $t = \pi/2$ perpendicular to the t-axis and then about the t-axis. Note the "jump" in this graph at $t = \pi/2$. Finally, we complete the graph in the interval from $t = \pi$ to $t = 2\pi$ by using the relation $\tan (\pi + t) = \tan t$, proved in Theorem 6.3. Thus, the curve already drawn from $t = 0$ to $t = \pi$ is repeated from $t = \pi$ to $t = 2\pi$.

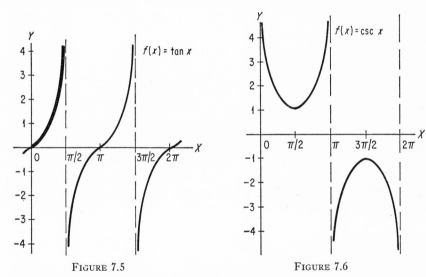

FIGURE 7.5   FIGURE 7.6

Similar techniques can be used to sketch the graphs of the cosecant, secant, and cotangent functions. Can you verify that the graph shown in Figure 7.6 is that of the cosecant function?

The graphs sketched in this section are useful devices to remember many of the facts, already proved, about the trigonometric functions. For example, Figure 7.3 reminds us that the range of the sine function consists of all real numbers from -1 to 1, inclusive. Also, a glance at the graph of the appropriate trigonometric function reminds us of the relations discovered in Theorems 6.2-6.4. For example, from Figure 7.6 we are reminded that $\csc (\pi + t) = -\csc t$, etc. In fact, the student need commit to memory only the definitions of $\sin t$ and $\cos t$, the six fundamental relations of Theorem 6.1, the values of $\sin (\pi/6)$, $\sin (\pi/4)$, and $\sin (\pi/3)$, and Theorem 7.2. All the remaining results can be obtained rapidly from these results.

PROBLEMS A

  1. Sketch the graph of the secant function from $t = 0$ to $t = 2\pi$.

  2. Sketch the graph of the cotangent function from $t = 0$ to $t = 2\pi$.

  3. Graph the functions defined on the intervals given.

  (a) $y = 3 \cos t$ $(0 \leq t \leq 2\pi)$

  (b) $y = \sin 2t$ $(0 \leq t \leq \pi)$

  (c) $y = \sin t + \cos t$ $(0 \leq t \leq 2\pi)$

  (d) $y = t - \sin t$ $(0 \leq t \leq \pi)$

PROBLEMS B

  1. Use the graph of the sine function to sketch a graph of **f**, where $f(t) = |\sin t|$ without using a table of values.

  2. Without using a table of values, sketch the graph of **f**, where $f(t) = \sqrt{1 - \sin^2 t}$.

7.4   Periodic Functions

In this section we shall discuss some of the properties of the graphs of the trigonometric functions that are of special importance in physical applications and in advanced mathematics. These properties are shared with other functions; therefore, we shall introduce them as general properties of a class of functions, rather than merely as oddities of the trigonometric functions.

In constructing the graphs of the trigonometric functions, it was emphasized that these graphs repeat in intervals of length 2π. This property of repetition, or **periodicity**, is one of the more useful properties of the trigonometric functions. We now define more rigorously what is meant by a periodic function in order that we may study this property more fully.

  Definition 7.1. *If a function* **f** *has the property*

$$f(x + a) = f(x)$$

for some nonzero real number a *and for all* x *on the domain of* **f**, *we say that function is* **periodic**. *If among all the numbers* a *such that* $\mathrm{f}(x + a) = \mathrm{f}(x)$ *there is a smallest positive number* p, *we say that* p *is the* **period** *of the function* **f**.

From Figures 7.3-7.5, we note that the period of the sine and cosine functions is 2π, and the period of the tangent function is π. What are the periods of the cosecant, secant, and cotangent functions?

Many periodic functions can be constructed from the trigonometric functions. For example, the function **f**, where $f(x) = \sin bx$ and $b \neq 0$, is a new trigonometric function that can be defined on the domain of all real numbers. It possesses many of the properties of the sine function; for example, its range is also restricted to the set of real numbers between -1 and 1, inclusive. Although it is periodic, its period is not necessarily 2π. The following theorem is useful in establishing the periods of functions like the one described.

Theorem 7.6. *If* **f** *is a periodic function with period* p, *then the function* g, *where* $g(x) = f(bx)$ *and* b > 0, *is also periodic, with period* p/b.

Proof: We must prove first that **g** is periodic; that is, we must prove that there exists some real number a such that $g(x + a) = g(x)$ for all x. By definition

$$g\left(x + \frac{p}{b}\right) = f\left[b\left(x + \frac{p}{b}\right)\right]$$

$$= f(bx + p)$$

However, **f** is periodic with period p, thus

$$f(bx + p) = f(bx)$$

However, $f(bx) = g(x)$ by hypothesis; thus, we have shown that $g(x + p/b) = g(x)$; that is, **g** is a periodic function. To establish that the period of **g** is p/b we would have to show that there is no positive number a, smaller than p/b, for which $g(x + a) = g(x)$. This proof is omitted.

The application of this theorem is illustrated in the following example.

Example 7.4. Find the period of **f**, where $f(x) = \sec (x/4)$ and graph this function.

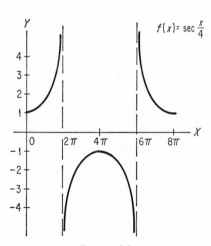

FIGURE 7.7

Solution: First we must find the period of the secant function. Since $\sec x = 1/\cos x$, if a is a positive number such that $\cos (x + a) = \cos x$ for all x, then it follows that $\sec (x + a) = \sec x$ for all x on the domain of the secant function. However, the period of the cosine function is 2π; thus, the smallest positive number for which $\sec(x + a) = \sec x$ is $a = 2\pi$. Now, we apply Theorem 7.6 to conclude that the period of $\mathbf{f}$ is

$$\frac{2\pi}{\frac{1}{4}} = 8\pi$$

The graph is shown in Figure 7.7.

Another property that is readily apparent from the graphs of some of the trigonometric functions is the property of "boundedness," illustrated by the fact that the range of the sine and cosine functions is limited to the set of real numbers between -1 and 1, inclusive. In general, a function $\mathbf{f}$ is said to be **bounded** if there exists a pair of numbers such that every element $f(x)$ in the range of $\mathbf{f}$ is contained between these numbers. Of the six trigonometric functions defined, only the sine and cosine functions are bounded; these functions have the maximum value 1 and the minimum value -1.

If a function is bounded, it is useful to define a number that expresses the variation in its range.

Definition 7.2. *The* **amplitude** *of a bounded function having the maximum value* M *and the minimum value* m *is* $\dfrac{M - m}{2}$.

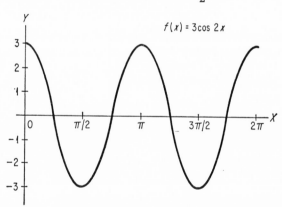

$f(x) = 3\cos 2x$

FIGURE 7.8

Thus, the amplitude of a bounded function is half the distance between its largest and its smallest value. For example, the sine and the cosine functions each have the amplitude 1. If a function $\mathbf{f}$ has the amplitude A, and $\mathbf{g}$ is defined so that $g(x) = a \cdot f(x)$, it follows from Definition 7.2 that the amplitude of $\mathbf{g}$ is $|a| \cdot A$. This result is illustrated in the following example.

Example 7.5. Find the amplitude of **f**, where $f(x) = 3 \cos 2x$ and graph this function.

Solution: Since the maximum value of $\cos 2x$ is 1 and the minimum value is -1, the maximum and minimum values of $3 \cos 2x$ are 3 and -3, respectively. Thus, the amplitude of **f** is

$$\frac{3 - (-3)}{2} = 3$$

The graph is shown in Figure 7.8.

If we are given some function **f** with $f(x)$ of the form $A \sin bx$, for example, we know that its graph behaves like that of the sine function, its period is $2\pi/b$, and its amplitude is A, and we can sketch the graph rapidly. Suppose, now, that we wish to graph the function **f**, where

$$f(x) = A \sin (bx + c)$$

If we shift the entire curve c/b units to the *left*, it is equivalent to using the new variable $u = x + c/b$, because every value of u is c/b less than the corresponding value of x. Substituting $u - c/b$ in the equation for $f(x)$, we obtain

$$f\left(u - \frac{c}{b}\right) = A \sin bu$$

We can conclude that the graph of **f** is identical with the graph of **g**, where

$$g(x) = A \sin bx$$

except that it is shifted c/b units to the left. The number $-c/b$ is called the **phase shift.** This result is used in the following examples.

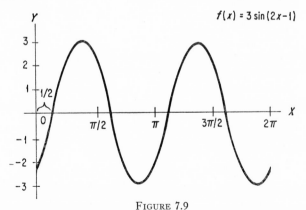

$$f(x) = 3 \sin (2x - 1)$$

FIGURE 7.9

Example 7.6. Graph the function **f**, where $f(x) = 3 \sin (2x - 1)$.

Solution: This function has the period π and the amplitude 3. The phase shift is $-(-1)/2 = \frac{1}{2}$. The graph is plotted on the interval from 0 to 2π in Figure 7.9.

Example 7.7. Graph the function **f**, where

$$f(x) = -\frac{1}{2}\cos\left(\frac{x}{2} + \pi\right)$$

Solution:

$$-\frac{1}{2}\cos\left(\frac{x}{2} + \pi\right) = -\frac{1}{2}\sin\left[\frac{\pi}{2} - \left(\frac{x}{2} + \pi\right)\right]$$

$$= -\frac{1}{2}\sin\left(-\frac{x}{2} - \frac{\pi}{2}\right)$$

$$= \frac{1}{2}\sin\left(\frac{x}{2} + \frac{\pi}{2}\right)$$

Thus, the graph is a sine curve with period 4π and amplitude $\frac{1}{2}$. The phase shift is $-\pi$. The graph is plotted on the interval from 0 to 4π in Figure 7.10.

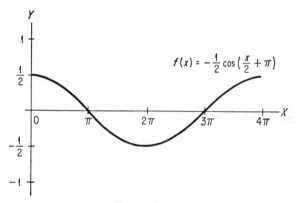

FIGURE 7.10

As shown in Examples 7.6 and 7.7, a sine curve should be plotted on a sufficiently long interval to show at least one full period.

In certain applications, it is useful to express $A \sin (bx + c)$ in an alternate form. From Theorem 7.3, we have

$$A \sin (bx + c) = A (\sin bx \cos c + \cos bx \sin c)$$

Letting $B = A \cos c$ and $C = A \sin c$, we have

$$A \sin (bx + c) = B \sin bx + C \cos bx$$

Thus, the graph of **f** can be obtained from graphs of sine and cosine functions. The method of graphing, known as *addition of ordinates*, requires that the appropriate sine and cosine functions be graphed on the same set of coordinate axes. The graph of **f** is obtained by adding the ordinates of these two graphs with the aid of dividers or some other convenient device. This procedure is illustrated in the following example.

Example 7.8. Graph the function **f**, where

$$f(x) = \cos 2x - 2 \sin x$$

Solution: Letting **g** be the function defined by

$$g(x) = \cos 2x$$

and **h** be the function defined by

$$h(x) = -2 \sin x$$

we graph **g** and **h** as shown in Figure 7.11. By adding the ordinates of **g** and **h**, we obtain the graph of **f**, shown by the heavy curve in the figure.

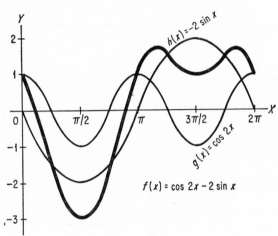

FIGURE 7.11

PROBLEMS A

1. Find the period and amplitude of the functions defined.

(a) $f(x) = \cos \dfrac{x}{2}$

(b) $f(x) = \tan 3x$

(c) $f(x) = 2 \sin (-2x)$

(d) $f(x) = -\csc \dfrac{x}{4}$

(e) $f(x) = 3 \sin (2x + 1)$

(f) $f(x) = -\cos \left(\pi - \dfrac{x}{2} \right)$

2. Sketch the graphs of the functions defined on an interval of length at least equal to the period of the function. Find the amplitude (if defined) and phase shift of each function.

(a) $f(x) = \sin 3x$

(b) $f(x) = \cos \dfrac{x}{2}$

(c) $f(x) = \sin \left(2x + \dfrac{\pi}{4} \right)$

(d) $f(x) = 3 \tan \left(x - \dfrac{\pi}{3} \right)$

(e) $f(x) = -5 \sin (\frac{1}{2}x - 1)$ (f) $f(x) = \dfrac{\sqrt{2}}{2} (\cos x + \sin x)$

(g) $f(x) = \cos 2x - \sin 3x$ (h) $f(x) = 3 \tan 2x - 2 \sec 3x$

3. If $h(x) = f(x) + g(x)$ and **f** and **g** both have period p, prove that **h** has period p.

4. Use the results of Problem 3 to find the period of **f**, where

(a) $f(x) = \sin 2x + \tan x$ (b) $f(x) = \tan x - \cot x$

PROBLEMS B

1. If $h(x) = f(x) + g(x)$, **f** has period p and **g** has period q, prove that $h(x + r) = h(x)$ for all x on the domain of **h**, where r is any common multiple of p and q.

2. Prove the converse of the theorem stated in Problem 1; that is, prove that $h(x + r) = h(x)$ for all x on the domain of **h** only if r is a common multiple of p and q.

3. Use the results of Problems 1 and 2 to prove that the period of **h** is the LCM of p and q. What is the period of **h**, where $h(x) = \tan 3x - \cot (x/2)$?

4. It is possible to approximate certain bounded periodic functions by sums of trigonometric terms. Such a sum is known as a *Fourier series*. The periodic function **f**, where

$$f(x) = \begin{cases} x & -\pi \le x < \pi \\ x - 2\pi & \pi \le x < 3\pi \\ x - 4\pi & 3\pi \le x < 5\pi \\ \cdot \\ \cdot \\ \cdot \\ \text{etc.} \end{cases}$$

has period 2π. Graph this function on the interval $-\pi \le x < \pi$. A four-term Fourier series approximation to this function on $-\pi \le x < \pi$ is

$$g(x) = 2 \sin x - \sin 2x + \tfrac{2}{3} \sin 3x - \tfrac{1}{2} \sin 4x$$

Show the successive stages of this approximation by plotting on the same set of axes:

$f_1(x) = 2 \sin x$

$f_2(x) = 2 \sin x - \sin 2x$

$f_3(x) = 2 \sin x - \sin 2x + \tfrac{2}{3} \sin 3x$

$f_4(x) = 2 \sin x - \sin 2x + \tfrac{2}{3} \sin 3x - \tfrac{1}{2} \sin 4x$

7.5 Polar Coordinates

The concepts of angle measure, discussed in Sections 6.1 and 6.2, also can be used to describe a new coordinate system. Given a point O, called the **origin**, and a half-line terminating at O, called the **reference line**, it is possible to describe the location of a point P in a plane by specifying its distance r from O and the measure θ of the angle made by the reference line and a line from O to P. These numbers (r, θ) are called the **polar coordinates** of P. Unlike the rectangular coordinates of P, its polar coordinates are not unique. For example, the point P having polar coordinates $(2, \pi/4)$ is located 2 units from the vertex O along the terminal side of an angle measuring $\pi/4$, as shown in Figure 7.12. This same angle also has measure $\pi/4 + 2\pi = 9\pi/4$, however, and the polar coordinates of P also could be given as $(2, 9\pi/4)$.

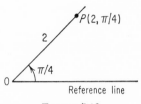

FIGURE 7.12

Either coordinate r or θ could be negative. The interpretation of negative values of θ is the same as that previously given; that is, θ is negative if the angle having the reference line as its initial side and the line OP as its terminal side has the negative sense. The coordinate r is positive if it is measured from O to P along the terminal side of the angle having measure θ. It is negative if it is measured from O to P along the terminal side of the angle having measure $\pi + \theta$. Can you verify that the coordinates $(2, \pi/4)$ and $(-2, 5\pi/4)$ represent the same point?

Special polar-coordinate graph paper is available for plotting points given by polar coordinates. This paper contains an origin O, a reference half-line drawn from O horizontally and to the right, a set of equally-spaced concentric circles centered at O, and a set of rays emanating from O. To locate the point (r, θ), we select the ray making the angle θ with the reference line, and proceed along this ray to its intersection with the circle having radius r. If polar-coordinate paper is not available, ordinary graph paper may be used, together with a protractor. In the following example, polar-coordinate graph paper is used.

Example 7.9. Plot the points having polar coordinates

$$(4, \pi/3), \quad (2, -3\pi/2), \quad (-3, 2\pi/3), \quad \text{and} \quad (-1, -\pi/4)$$

Solution: These points are plotted on polar-coordinate graph paper in Figure 7.13.

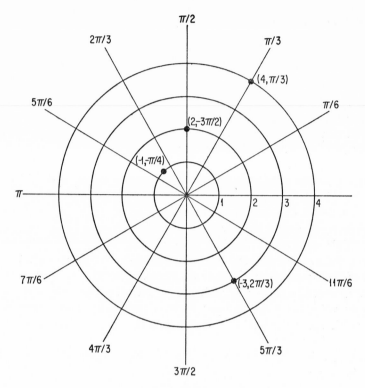

FIGURE 7.13

The rectangular coordinates of a point whose polar coordinates are given may be found with the aid of trigonometric functions. In Figure 7.14 is shown a point P with rectangular coordinates (x, y). A circle is drawn with its center at the origin of the rectangular coordinate system and passing through the point P. The polar coordinates of P are $r =$ the radius of the circle, and $\theta =$ the measure of the angle between the X-axis and the radius OP. From the figure, $\sin \theta = y/r$ and $\cos \theta = x/r$. Thus, the equations

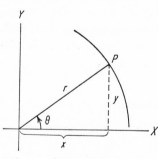

FIGURE 7.14

$$(7.3) \qquad \begin{aligned} x &= r \cos \theta \\ y &= r \sin \theta \end{aligned}$$

give the rectangular coordinates (x, y) of P when its polar coordinates (r, θ) are known.

It is possible also to find polar coordinates of P when the rectangular coordinates are given.   From Equations 7.3 we have

$$x^2 + y^2 = r^2 \cos^2 \theta + r^2 \sin^2 \theta = r^2$$

and

$$\frac{y}{x} = \frac{\sin \theta}{\cos \theta} = \tan \theta$$

Thus, we can find r and θ from the equations

(7.4)
$$r^2 = x^2 + y^2$$

$$\tan \theta = \frac{y}{x} \quad (x \neq 0)$$

Note that Equations 7.4 do not specify the sign of r, nor do they determine θ uniquely.   In any problem where the rectangular coordinates of P are given, it is helpful to plot the point P, determining θ so that it lies between 0 and 2π, and the proper sign of r by inspection.

The use of formulas 7.3 and 7.4 to change from polar to rectangular coordinates, and vice versa, is illustrated in the following examples.

Example 7.10. Find the rectangular coordinates of the point having polar coordinates $(2, \pi/6)$.

Solution: Using Equations 7.3 and the fact that

$$\sin \frac{\pi}{6} = 1/2 \text{ and } \cos \frac{\pi}{6} = \frac{\sqrt{3}}{2}$$

we have

$$x = 2 \cos \frac{\pi}{6} = \sqrt{3}$$

$$y = 2 \sin \frac{\pi}{6} = 1$$

Example 7.11. Find a set of polar coordinates for the point having rectangular coordinates $(-1, 1)$.

Solution: From Equations 7.4 we have

$$r^2 = (-1)^2 + (1)^2 = 2$$

$$\tan \theta = \frac{1}{(-1)} = -1$$

Plotting the point $(-1, 1)$, we have $\theta = 3\pi/4$ with $r = \sqrt{2}$.   Can you verify that the polar coordinates $(-\sqrt{2}, -\pi/4)$ also represent this point?

PROBLEMS A

1. Plot the points whose polar coordinates are given, using polar-coordinate graph paper or rectangular graph paper and a protractor.

(a) $(1, \pi/6)$ (b) $(3, \pi/3)$ (c) $(2, 2\pi/3)$
(d) $(4, 7\pi/4)$ (e) $(1, -\pi/2)$ (f) $(3, -\pi/3)$
(g) $(\frac{1}{2}, \pi)$ (h) $(\frac{1}{4}, -2\pi/3)$ (i) $(1, 6\pi)$
(j) $(-1, \pi/4)$ (k) $(-2, \pi/2)$ (l) $(-1, -\pi)$

2. Find the rectangular coordinates of the points whose polar coordinates are given in Problem 1.

3. Find a pair of polar coordinates representing the points whose rectangular coordinates are given.

(a) $(1, 0)$ (b) $(0, -1)$
(c) $(1, 1)$ (d) $(-1, 1)$
(e) $(\sqrt{3}, 1)$ (f) $(3, 3\sqrt{3})$
(g) $(-\sqrt{2}, -\sqrt{2})$ (h) $(2, -\sqrt{12})$
(i) $(0, 0)$ (j) $(3, -4)$

PROBLEMS B

1. Sometimes a function can be defined more satisfactorily with an equation involving its polar coordinates. Plot the graph of the function defined by $r = \sin \theta$ on the domain $0 \le \theta \le \pi$.

2. Without resorting to actual plotting, describe the graph of the function defined by $r = r_0$, where r_0 is a constant.

3. Without resorting to actual plotting, describe the graph of the function defined by $\theta = \theta_0$, where θ_0 is a constant.

4. Find the polar-coordinate equation corresponding to the following rectangular-coordinate equation.

$$(x^2 + y^2)^2 - 2a^2xy = 0$$

5. Find the rectangular-coordinate equation corresponding to the following polar-coordinate equation.

$$r = 5 \sec \theta$$

7.6 The Trigonometric Form of a Complex Number

If we represent the complex number $z = x + yi$ as a point on the complex plane, we note that the ordered pair (x, y) gives the rectangular coordinates of this point. Thus, in terms of polar coordinates, we have $(r \cos \theta, r \sin \theta)$, and we can write the complex number z in the form

(7.5) $$z = r(\cos \theta + i \sin \theta)$$

When written in this form, the complex number z is said to be in **polar** or **trigonometric form**. In this representation, the real number r is always chosen to be nonnegative, and is called the **absolute value** or **modulus** of z. The real number θ is called the **amplitude** or **argument** of z. Can you prove that r is, in fact, the absolute value of z; that is, can you prove that

$$|r(\cos \theta + i \sin \theta)| = r$$

Conversion of complex numbers from the form $x + yi$ to the trigonometric form is accomplished in exactly the same way that we converted from rectangular to polar coordinates. The following examples illustrate this process, and the process of conversion from the trigonometric form to the form $x + yi$.

Example 7.12. Express the complex number $z = 3 - \sqrt{3}\,i$ in trigonometric form.

Solution: Using Equations 7.4 with $x = 3$ and $y = -\sqrt{3}$, we have

$$r^2 = 3^2 + (\sqrt{3})^2 = 12$$

$$\tan \theta = -\frac{\sqrt{3}}{3}$$

Plotting the point $(3, -\sqrt{3})$, we have $\theta = 11\pi/6$ with $r = \sqrt{12}$. Thus,

$$z = \sqrt{12}\left(\cos \frac{11\pi}{6} + i \sin \frac{11\pi}{6}\right)$$

Example 7.13. Express the complex number

$$z = \cos (\pi/4) + i \sin (\pi/4) \text{ in the form } x + yi.$$

Solution: Using Equations 7.3 with $r = 1$ and $\theta = \pi/4$, we have

$$x = 1 \cdot \cos \frac{\pi}{4} = \frac{\sqrt{2}}{2}$$

$$y = 1 \cdot \sin \frac{\pi}{4} = \frac{\sqrt{2}}{2}$$

$$z = \frac{\sqrt{2}}{2} + \frac{\sqrt{2}}{2}\,i$$

The usefulness of the trigonometric form of a complex number becomes apparent when we examine the product $z_1 z_2$ of two complex numbers. If we have

$$z_1 = r_1(\cos \theta_1 + i \sin \theta_1)$$

$$z_2 = r_2(\cos \theta_2 + i \sin \theta_2)$$

the product z_1z_2 can be written in the form

$$z_1z_2 = r_1(\cos\theta_1 + i\sin\theta_1) \cdot r_2(\cos\theta_2 + i\sin\theta_2)$$
$$= r_1r_2[(\cos\theta_1\cos\theta_2 - \sin\theta_1\sin\theta_2) + i(\sin\theta_1\cos\theta_2 + \cos\theta_1\sin\theta_2)]$$

Using Theorem 7.3, we have

(7.6) $$z_1z_2 = r_1r_2[\cos(\theta_1 + \theta_2) + i\sin(\theta_1 + \theta_2)]$$

Thus, *the modulus of the product of two complex numbers is the product of their moduli, and the argument of their product is the sum of their arguments.*

Now we consider the quotient $w = z_1/z_2$. Writing w in the trigonometric form with modulus r and argument θ, and z_1 and z_2 as before, we have

$$z_1 = wz_2 = rr_2[\cos(\theta + \theta_2) + i\sin(\theta + \theta_2)]$$

Since the complex numbers z_1 and wz_2 are equal, we can equate their moduli and arguments, obtaining $r_1 = rr_2$ and $\theta_1 = \theta + \theta_2$, or

$$r = \frac{r_1}{r_2} \quad \text{and} \quad \theta = \theta_1 - \theta_2$$

Thus, *the modulus of the quotient of two complex numbers is the quotient of their moduli, and the argument of their quotient is the difference of their arguments.*

These results can be used to establish an important theorem concerning the positive integer powers of a complex number. This theorem, known as *De Moivre's theorem*, can be stated as follows.

Theorem 7.7. *If* n *is a positive integer and*

$$z = r(\cos\theta + i\sin\theta)$$

then

$$z^n = r^n(\cos n\theta + i\sin n\theta)$$

A formal proof of this theorem requires the Axiom of Induction, and it is postponed until Chapter 15. However, it is easy to verify that the theorem is true for specific values of n. For example, if $n = 2$, we may use Equation 7.6 with $r_1 = r_2 = r$ and $\theta_1 = \theta_2 = \theta$, to obtain

$$z^2 = r \cdot r[\cos(\theta + \theta) + i\sin(\theta + \theta)]$$
$$= r^2(\cos 2\theta + i\sin 2\theta)$$

If $n = 3$, we let $r_1 = r$, $r_2 = r^2$, $\theta_1 = 0$, and $\theta_2 = 2\theta$ to obtain

$$z^3 = z \cdot z^2 = r \cdot r^2[\cos(\theta + 2\theta) + \sin(\theta + 2\theta)]$$
$$= r^3(\cos 3\theta + i\sin 3\theta)$$

Proceeding in this way, we can establish De Moivre's theorem for any given positive integer n. The application of this theorem is illustrated in the following example.

Example 7.14. Express $(1 + i)^5$ in the form $x + yi$.

Solution: First we write $z = 1 + i$ in the trigonometric form, obtaining

$$z = \sqrt{2}\left(\cos\frac{\pi}{4} + i\sin\frac{\pi}{4}\right)$$

Applying De Moivre's theorem, we have

$$z^5 = (\sqrt{2})^5\left(\cos\frac{5\pi}{4} + i\sin\frac{5\pi}{4}\right)$$

$$= 2^{5/2}\left(-\frac{\sqrt{2}}{2} - i\frac{\sqrt{2}}{2}\right) = -4 - 4i$$

In Section 2.4 we discussed the number of real qth roots possessed by a real number, where q is a positive integer. De Moivre's theorem can be used to show that every complex number has exactly q qth roots. Since every real number can be regarded as a special complex number, we conclude also that every real number has exactly q qth roots, although all are not necessarily real.

To find the qth roots of a complex number, let z be a qth root of w, that is, let $z^q = w$. If the trigonometric forms of z and w are

$$z = r(\cos\theta + i\sin\theta) \quad \text{and} \quad w = R(\cos\phi + i\sin\phi)$$

respectively, we have

$$R(\cos\phi + i\sin\phi) = [r(\cos\theta + i\sin\theta)]^q$$

$$= r^q(\cos q\theta + i\sin q\theta)$$

after applying De Moivre's theorem. Thus,

$$R = r^q, \quad \cos\phi = \cos q\theta, \quad \text{and} \quad \sin\phi = \sin q\theta$$

Since the modulus of any complex number is nonnegative, r is the principle qth root of R, or $r = \sqrt[q]{R}$. To find θ, note that

$$\cos(\phi + 2k\pi) = \cos\phi \quad \text{and} \quad \sin(\phi + 2k\pi) = \sin\phi$$

where k is any integer. Thus, there are many values of θ, each satisfying the equation $\phi + 2k\pi = q\theta$, or

$$\theta = \frac{\phi + 2k\pi}{q}$$

Note that, if $k = q, \theta = \dfrac{\phi}{q} + 2\pi$.   Since

$$\cos\left(\frac{\phi}{q} + 2\pi\right) = \cos\frac{\phi}{q} \quad \text{and} \quad \sin\left(\frac{\phi}{q} + 2\pi\right) = \sin\frac{\phi}{q}$$

after taking any q successive integer values of k the arguments of z repeat. We may conclude from this discussion that *the q qth roots of the complex number with modulus* R *and argument* ϕ *have the modulus* $\sqrt[q]{R}$ *and arguments given by* $\dfrac{\phi + 2k\pi}{q}$, *with* k = 0, 1, 2, ..., q − 1.   This result is applied in the following examples.

Example 7.15. Find the fourth roots of $w = -2 + 2i$.

Solution: In trigonometric form

$$w = \sqrt{8}\left(\cos\frac{3\pi}{4} + i\sin\frac{3\pi}{4}\right)$$

Thus, $R = \sqrt{8}$ and $\phi = 3\pi/4$.   We compute

$$r = (\sqrt{8})^{1/4} = 2^{3/8}, \quad \text{and} \quad \theta = \frac{3\pi/4 + 2k\pi}{4} \quad (k = 0, 1, 2, 3)$$

The fourth roots are

$$z_1 = 2^{3/8}\left(\cos\frac{3\pi}{16} + i\sin\frac{3\pi}{16}\right)$$

$$z_2 = 2^{3/8}\left(\cos\frac{11\pi}{16} + i\sin\frac{11\pi}{16}\right)$$

$$z_3 = 2^{3/8}\left(\cos\frac{19\pi}{16} + i\sin\frac{19\pi}{16}\right)$$

$$z_4 = 2^{3/8}\left(\cos\frac{27\pi}{16} + i\sin\frac{27\pi}{16}\right)$$

Example 7.16. Find the three cube roots of 1.

Solution: In trigonometric form

$$1 = \cos 0 + i\sin 0$$

Thus, $R = 1$ and $\phi = 0$.   We compute

$$r = 1^{1/3} = 1 \quad \text{and} \quad \theta = \frac{0 + 2k\pi}{3} \quad (k = 0, 1, 2)$$

The cube roots of 1 are

$$z_1 = \cos 0 + i \sin 0 = 1$$

$$z_2 = \cos \frac{2\pi}{3} + i \sin \frac{2\pi}{3} = -\frac{1}{2} + \frac{\sqrt{3}\,i}{2}$$

$$z_3 = \cos \frac{4\pi}{3} + i \sin \frac{4\pi}{3} = -\frac{1}{2} - \frac{\sqrt{3}\,i}{2}$$

If we plot the three cube roots of 1 on the complex plane, as shown in Figure 7.15, we note that the three points determine an equilateral triangle inscribed in the unit circle.   If we plot the fourth roots of 1 (they are 1, i, -1, and $-i$) we find that they determine another equilateral polygon; namely, a square inscribed in the unit circle.   In general, the q qth roots of 1 determine a regular polygon of q sides, inscribed in the unit circle.

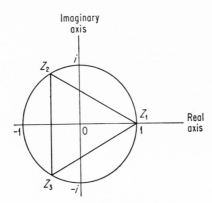

FIGURE 7.15

PROBLEMS A

1. Express the following numbers in trigonometric form.

(a) $5 - 5i$ (b) $-3 + 3i$
(c) $\sqrt{3} + i$ (d) $i - \sqrt{3}$
(e) $2i$ (f) $-i$
(g) 6 (h) -4
(i) $3 + 4i$ (j) $12 - 5i$

2. Evaluate the following products, quotients, and powers.   Put your answer in the form $x + yi$.

(a) $2\left(\cos \dfrac{\pi}{12} + i \sin \dfrac{\pi}{12} \right) \cdot 6\left(\cos \dfrac{\pi}{4} + i \sin \dfrac{\pi}{4} \right)$

(b) $-3(\cos 15° + i \sin 15°) \cdot 5(\cos 25° + i \sin 25°)$

(c) $4(\cos 80° + i \sin 80°)/(-2)(\cos 30° + i \sin 30°)$

(d) $-9\left(\cos \dfrac{\pi}{6} + i \sin \dfrac{\pi}{6}\right)\Big/\left(-36\right)\left(\cos \dfrac{\pi}{3} + i \sin \dfrac{\pi}{3}\right)$

(e) $(1 - i)/(1 + i)$ (f) $(-\sqrt{3} - i)/(1 - \sqrt{3}\,i)$

(g) $(2 - 2i)^4$ (h) $(1 + \sqrt{3}\,i)^6$

(i) $(\sqrt{3} - i)^5$ (j) $(-7 - 7i)^3$

3. Use De Moivre's theorem to find the following roots.

(a) cube roots of $125\left(\cos \dfrac{\pi}{3} + i \sin \dfrac{\pi}{3}\right)$.

(b) fifth roots of $32\left(\cos \dfrac{7\pi}{6} + i \sin \dfrac{7\pi}{6}\right)$,

(c) fourth roots of $8\sqrt{2} - 8\sqrt{2}\,i$.   (d) square roots of $7 - 24i$.

(e) fourth roots of -1.   (f) square roots of i.

(g) cube roots of $-i$.   (h) sixth roots of 1.

(i) cube roots of $1 + i$.   (j) square roots of i^3.

4. If $z = r(\cos \theta + i \sin \theta)$, prove that $|z| = r$.

5. If $z = r(\cos \theta + i \sin \theta)$, prove that $\bar{z}$ has the modulus r and the argument $-\theta$.

6. Establish De Moivre's theorem for $n = 4$.

7. Use the results of Problem 3h to verify that the sixth roots of 1 determine a regular hexagon inscribed in the unit circle.

PROBLEMS B

1. Find all the solutions of $z^{4/3} = 1 + i$.

2. Assuming the validity of De Moivre's theorem for positive integers n, establish this theorem for negative integers $-n$.

3. Let ω be the qth root of 1 corresponding to $k = 1$. Prove that the qth roots of 1 can be written as $1, \omega, \omega^2, \ldots, \omega^{q-1}$.

8

Inverse Functions

8.1 Introduction

In Section 5.2 we defined the logarithmic function by interchanging the range and the domain of the exponential function, but preserving the correspondence. It was possible to define the logarithmic function in this way because the exponential function establishes a *one-to-one correspondence* between the elements of its range and its domain. On page 69 we pointed out that **f** establishes a one-to-one correspondence if to every element x in its domain there corresponds exactly one element $f(x)$ in its range, *and* to every element $f(x)$ there corresponds exactly one element x.

Interchanging the domain and the range of a function defines a new function if and only if the correspondence of the original function is one-to-one. If we attempt to define a new function by interchanging the domain and the range of a function establishing a many-to-one correspondence, the resulting correspondence will be one-to-many and, according to Definition 4.1, it cannot define a function. For example, the quadratic function having the equation $f(x) = x^2$, defined on the domain of all real numbers, assigns the same element $f(x)$ in its range to the two elements x and $-x$ in its domain. Thus, if we attempt to define a new function by "solving" the equation $y = x^2$ for x, we obtain $x = \pm\sqrt{y}$. The equation $x = g(y) = \pm\sqrt{y}$ does not define a function **g** on the domain of nonnegative real numbers.

It is easy to determine whether or not a function establishes a one-to-one correspondence by looking at its graph. If the correspondence is

151

one-to-one, every line drawn parallel to the X-axis will intersect the graph in *at most one point*. If such a line intersects the graph in more than one point, there is some value of $f(x)$ corresponding to more than one value of x. The quadratic function **f**, where $f(x) = x^2$ on the domain of all real numbers, is graphed in Figure 8.1, and you can see that every horizontal line above the X-axis intersects this graph in two points. Note that it is possible to define a new function using the correspondence $f(x) = x^2$ such that every horizontal line intersects its graph in, at most, one point. Such a function is defined by suitably restricting the domain of the original function; for example, if we restrict the domain of the function graphed in Figure 8.1 to non-negative values of x, its correspondence is one-to-one, as shown in Figure 8.2.

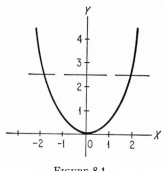

FIGURE 8.1

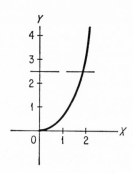

FIGURE 8.2

If a function establishes a one-to-one correspondence, a new but closely-related function may be defined as follows.

Definition 8.1. *If* **f** *is a function having as its domain the set* X, *as its range the set* Y, *and a one-to-one correspondence between the elements of* X *and* Y, *then there exists an* **inverse function f⁻¹**, *having the domain* Y, *the range* X, *and the same correspondence between elements of* X *and* Y.

If a function is defined by a table of values, and its inverse exists, then the same table of values serves to define the inverse function. Moreover, if **f** is defined by the equation $y = f(x)$ on the domain X, and **f** has the range Y, then **f⁻¹** is defined by the same equation on the domain Y, and **f⁻¹** has the range X. Sometimes the equation $y = f(x)$ can be "solved for x," that is, it can be written in the form $x = f^{-1}(y)$ (read "f-inverse of y"). For example, if $y = 2x$, then $x = y/2$; if a function **f** is defined by the equation $y = 2x$ on the domain $0 \le x \le 1$, then its inverse can be defined by the equation $x = y/2$ on the domain $0 \le y \le 2$.

It is not necessary to be able to "solve" the equation $y = f(x)$ for x in order for $\mathbf{f}^{-1}$ to be defined. For example, if

$$y = f(x) = x + 2^x \quad (0 \leq x \leq 2)$$

it is not possible to "solve for x" and obtain an expression of the form $x = f^{-1}(y)$. Nonetheless, it is evident from the graph of $\mathbf{f}$ in Figure 8.3 that to every real number x with $0 \leq x \leq 2$ there corresponds exactly one real number y with $1 \leq y \leq 6$, and vice versa. Thus, the inverse function $\mathbf{f}^{-1}$ is defined, even though it is not possible to express its correspondence by means of an equation of the form $x = f^{-1}(y)$. Given the graph of $\mathbf{f}$, however, it is possible to find the graph of $\mathbf{f}^{-1}$ by reflecting the given graph about the line making an angle of 45° with the horizontal axis. (Even though we use the symbol y temporarily to stand for an element of the domain, the y-value is located on the horizontal axis in the graph of $\mathbf{f}^{-1}$.) Figure 8.4 is the graph of the inverse of the function graphed in Figure 8.3.

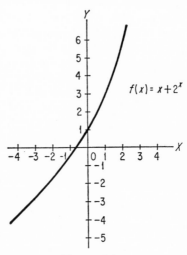

FIGURE 8.3

So far, we have spoken of a function $\mathbf{f}$ and its inverse $\mathbf{f}^{-1}$. It is evident from Definition 8.1 that, if a given function has an inverse, then the

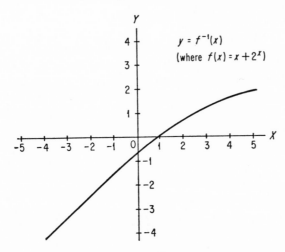

FIGURE 8.4

inverse of the inverse of that function exists and is the function itself; that is, $(\mathbf{f}^{-1})^{-1} = \mathbf{f}$. Thus, we can speak of $\mathbf{f}$ and $\mathbf{f}^{-1}$ as inverse pairs. For example, the exponential function also can be thought of as the inverse of the logarithmic function, and the exponential and logarithmic functions are inverse pairs.

PROBLEMS A

1. Graph the inverses of the functions defined. Whenever possible, write the equation giving the correspondence of the inverse function.

(a) $f(x) = 2x + 1$, $(-2 \le x \le 1)$ (b) $f(x) = x$, $(-1 \le x \le 1)$
(c) $f(u) = 1/u$, $(u > 0)$ (d) $f(x) = 4x^2$, $(x \ge 0)$
(e) $f(x) = 2^x$, (all real x)   (f) $f(z) = \log (z + 1)$, $(z > -1)$
(g) $f(x) = |x|$, $(x \le 0)$ (h) $f(u) = u - u^2$, $(u < \frac{1}{2})$
(i) $f(x) = x \log x$, $(x > 0)$ (j) $f(v) = v \cdot 2^v$, $(v \le 0)$

2. Prove that the inverse of any linear function is also a linear function.

PROBLEMS B

1. What can be said about the graph of a function that is its own inverse? Give some examples of such functions.

2. Prove that the graph of $\mathbf{f}^{-1}$ is the reflection of the graph of $\mathbf{f}$ about the 45-degree line described in the text. *Hint:* If (x, y) is a point on the graph of $\mathbf{f}$, what can you say about the corresponding point on the graph of $\mathbf{f}^{-1}$?

8.2   The Inverse Trigonometric Functions

It is evident from the graph of the sine function (Figure 7.3) that this function does not establish a one-to-one correspondence. Thus, we cannot speak of the inverse of the sine function. As we pointed out on page 152, however, it is possible to define a function using the correspondence $f(x) = \sin x$ such that its inverse exists. If we graph the sine function (Figure 8.5) we note that the longest segment on the X-axis for which no horizontal line intersects the curve more than once is of length π. For convenience, we select the segment from $x = -\pi/2$ to $x = \pi/2$, and define a new function using the correspondence $f(x) = \sin x$, but on the restricted domain $-\pi/2 \le x \le \pi/2$, as follows.

$$\text{Sin } x = \sin x \quad \left(-\frac{\pi}{2} \le x \le \frac{\pi}{2} \right)$$

Note that Sin x is *not defined* outside the interval given.

The Sine function so defined establishes a one-to-one correspondence between the real numbers x in the interval $-\pi/2 \leq x \leq \pi/2$ and the real numbers y in the interval $-1 \leq y \leq 1$.   Thus, the inverse of the Sine function is defined on the domain $-1 \leq x \leq 1$.   An element of its range is denoted by the symbol Arc sin x.   *The equation* y = *Arc sin* x *means* x = *Sin* y, *that is,* y *is the number such that Sin* y = x.

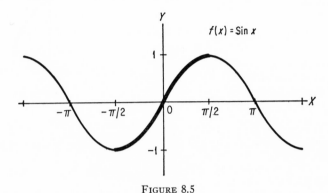

FIGURE 8.5

In a similar way, we may restrict the domains of the cosine and tangent functions so that the resulting functions will have inverses.   We define

$$\text{Cos } x = \cos x \quad (0 \leq x \leq \pi)$$

$$\text{Tan } x = \tan x \quad (-\pi/2 < x < \pi/2)$$

Elements in the range of the inverse Cosine and Tangent functions are denoted by Arc cos x and Arc tan x, respectively.   *The equations* y = *Arc cos* x *and* y = *Arc tan* x *mean that* x = *Cos* y *and* x = *Tan* y, *respectively.*

To summarize the definitions of the inverse trigonometric functions described in this section, it is helpful to have the following table.

Function	Correspondence	Domain	Range
Arc sine	$x = \text{Sin } y$	$-1 \leq x \leq 1$	$-\frac{\pi}{2} \leq y \leq \frac{\pi}{2}$
Arc cosine	$x = \text{Cos } y$	$-1 \leq x \leq 1$	$0 \leq y \leq \pi$
Arc tangent	$x = \text{Tan } y$	All real numbers	$-\frac{\pi}{2} < y < \frac{\pi}{2}$

The graphs of these functions may be obtained by reflecting the graphs of the Sine, Cosine, and Tangent functions about the line making a 45° angle with the X-axis.   These graphs are shown in Figures 8.6, 8.7, and 8.8.

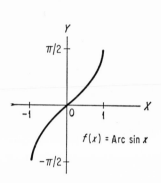

FIGURE 8.6

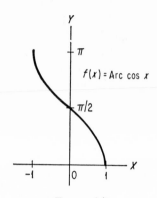

FIGURE 8.7

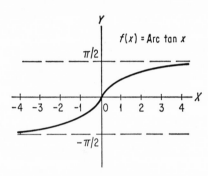

FIGURE 8.8

In the following examples we make use of known values of the trigonometric functions to find values of the inverse trigonometric functions.

Example 8.1. Evaluate Arc tan 1.

Solution:

$$y = \text{Arc tan } 1 \quad \text{means} \quad 1 = \text{Tan } y$$

The only number y between $-\pi/2$ and $\pi/2$ such that $\tan y = 1$ is $y = \pi/4$.
Thus,

$$\text{Arc tan } 1 = \pi/4$$

Example 8.2. Evaluate $\sin\left[\text{Arc cos}\left(-\dfrac{\sqrt{3}}{2}\right)\right]$.

Solution:

$$y = \text{Arc cos}\left(-\frac{\sqrt{3}}{2}\right) \quad \text{means} \quad -\frac{\sqrt{3}}{2} = \text{Cos } y$$

The only number y between 0 and π such that $\cos y = -\sqrt{3}/2$ is $5\pi/6$. Thus,

$$\text{Arc} \cos\left(-\frac{\sqrt{3}}{2}\right) = \frac{5\pi}{6} \quad \text{and} \quad \sin\left[\text{Arc} \cos\left(-\frac{\sqrt{3}}{2}\right)\right] = \sin\frac{5\pi}{6} = \frac{1}{2}$$

PROBLEMS A

1. Evaluate the following.

(a) Arc sin 1

(b) Arc cos 0

(c) Arc tan $\sqrt{3}$

(d) Arc cos $\dfrac{\sqrt{2}}{2}$

(e) Arc sin $\left(-\dfrac{\sqrt{2}}{2}\right)$

(f) Arc cos $(-\tfrac{1}{2})$

(g) Arc tan (-1)

(h) Arc sin .4147

(i) Arc cos .6626

(j) Arc tan 4.275

2. Evaluate the following.

(a) cos (Arc tan 1)

(b) tan (Arc sin 0)

(c) cot $\left[\text{Arc} \cos\left(-\dfrac{\sqrt{2}}{2}\right)\right]$

(d) sec (Arc cos 1)

(e) Arc tan $\left(\cot \dfrac{\pi}{2}\right)$

(f) Arc cos $\left(2 \sin \dfrac{\pi}{6}\right)$

(g) Arc tan $[2 \sin (\text{Arc} \cos \tfrac{1}{2})]$

(h) Arc sin $\{\cos [\text{Arc} \tan (-1)]\}$

3. Which of the following are identities?

(a) Arc sin $(-x) = -$Arc sin x

(b) $u + v = $ Arc sin $(\sin u \cos v + \cos u \sin v)$

(c) $t = $ Arc cos $\left[\sin\left(\dfrac{\pi}{2} + t\right)\right]$

PROBLEMS B

1. Define the Cosecant function so that on its domain its correspondence is the same as that of the cosecant function but it establishes a one-to-one correspondence. Sketch the graph of the inverse of this function.

2. Repeat Problem 1 for the Secant function.

3. Repeat Problem 1 for the Cotangent function.

PART 3

Equations and
Inequalities

In your study of mathematics to date, you have met many kinds of mathematical relations.   In this book, we have used the equality relation and the inequality relations, and in your study of plane geometry you have used the similarity and congruence relations.   Relations play an important role in mathematics, as well as in logic, language, and so forth. Examples of nonmathematical relations are "brother of," "co-worker of," etc.

Relations have many interesting properties.   For example, the equality relation, denoted by the symbol $=$, has the property that for any quantity a, we can write $a = a$; that is, any quantity equals itself.   Other properties of the equality relation are "if $a = b$, then $b = a$" and "if $a = b$ and $b = c$, then $a = c$."   The relation "brother of" has only the third of these three properties; for example, if a is the brother of b, b may be the sister of a.   The relation "co-worker of" has the second of these properties, but neither the first nor the third.

The inequality relations "less than" and "greater than" share the third property of the equality relation, but not the first two.   For example, if $a < b$ and $b < c$, then $a < c$, but we cannot say that $a < a$.   It is our purpose in Part III to study properties of the equality and inequality relations and to apply these properties to the solution of several important and classical problems of mathematics.

9

Equations

9.1 Identical and Conditional Equations

So far, we have used the equal sign without paying explicit attention to its properties. It has been assumed, for example, that it is understood by the statement $a = b$ that a and b are two symbols standing for the same quantity. We now list three fundamental properties of the equality relation, where a, b, and c are numbers.

Property 1. Reflexive Law: $a = a$.

Property 2. Symmetric Law: *If* $a = b$, *then* $b = a$.

Property 3. Transitive Law: *If* $a = b$ *and* $b = c$, *then* $a = c$.

The reflexive law gives us the right to equate any quantity to itself. The symmetric law states that the left-hand and right-hand sides of an equality may be interchanged. The transitive law allows us to establish a "chain" of equalities, and, as we shall see, it plays a fundamental role in the solution of equations.

Although these properties form the foundation for operations with the equal sign, we require two additional properties that tell us how the operations of addition and multiplication affect the relation of equality.

Property 4. *If* $a = b$ *and* $c = d$, *then* $a + c = b + d$.

Property 5. *If* $a = b$ *and* $c = d$, *then* $a \cdot c = b \cdot d$.

These properties tell us that we may add or multiply equal quantities by equal quantities without destroying the relation of equality. For example, if $x = 3$ and $y = 4$, then

$$x + y = 3 + 4 = 7, \quad \text{and} \quad x \cdot y = 3 \cdot 4 = 12$$

Given some function **f**, an equality that can be put in the form $f(x) = 0$ is called an **equation** in the variable x. For example,

$$x^2 - 1 = 0 \quad \text{and} \quad \tan x + \sin x = 0$$

are equations in x. Note that, if we make use of Property 4 of the equality relation, we can put an expression such as $x^2 - 5 = 2x$ in the form $x^2 - 2x - 5 = 0$. More generally, an expression of the form $f(x) = g(x)$ can be put in the form $f(x) - g(x) = 0$, and it is an equation in x. Furthermore, $x^2 + y^2 = 4$ can be written in the form $f(x, y) = 0$, where $f(x, y) = x^2 + y^2 - 4$, and it is an equation in the *two variables* x and y.

An equation need not be a true statement. For example, the expression $\sin x = 2$ is an equation, even though there is no number x such that $\sin x = 2$. If we are given the equation $f(x) = 0$, these numbers x for which the equation is a true statement are called the **solutions** of the equation. For example, the equation $\sin x = 2$ has no solutions, the equation $x + 1 = 0$ has the solution $x = -1$, and the equation $x^2 - 1 = 0$ has the two solutions $x = 1$ and $x = -1$. The set of numbers X, consisting of all the solutions of a given equation, is called the **solution set** of that equation.

In each of the examples given, there are values of x for which the equation is not satisfied, that is, for which the equality is not a true statement. In contrast, the equation

$$(x - 2)^2 = x^2 - 4x + 4$$

is satisfied for every value of x.

If there is at least one value of the variable x for which an equation in x is not satisfied, it is called a **conditional equation.** If the equation $f(x) = g(x)$ is satisfied for every value of x, *for which both* **f** *and* **g** *are defined*, it is called an **identical equation,** or an **identity.** To determine whether an equation of the form $f(x) = g(x)$ is an identity, we take advantage of the transitive law, and use valid algebraic operations and, perhaps, other known identities, to change the form of one side of the equation so that it is identical to the other side. If we suspect that an equation is not an identity, we verify this suspicion if we find a value of x for which the equation is not satisfied. These procedures are illustrated in the following examples.

Example 9.1. Show that the equation

$$\frac{1}{x-1} = \frac{2}{x^2-1} + \frac{1}{x+1}$$

where $x \neq 1$ and $x \neq -1$, is an identity.

Solution: Working with the right-hand side, we have

$$\frac{2}{x^2-1} + \frac{1}{x+1} = \frac{2}{(x+1)(x-1)} + \frac{1}{x+1}$$

$$= \frac{2 + (x-1)}{(x+1)(x-1)}$$

$$= \frac{x+1}{(x+1)(x-1)}$$

$$= \frac{1}{x-1}$$

By successive use of the transitive law, we have

$$\frac{2}{x^2-1} + \frac{1}{x+1} = \frac{1}{x-1}$$

and we can conclude that the equation is an identity.

Note that the equation in Example 9.1 is not satisfied for $x = 1$ and $x = -1$. It is still an identity, however, because $\dfrac{1}{x-1}$ is *not defined* for $x = 1$ and $\dfrac{2}{x^2-1} + \dfrac{1}{x+1}$ is *not defined* for $x = 1$ or $x = -1$.

Example 9.2. Establish whether the equation

$$\sqrt{\frac{3}{x}} - \sqrt{\frac{2}{x}} = \sqrt{\frac{1}{x}}$$

is an identity.

Solution: If we substitute $x = 1$ in the above equation, the left-hand side equals $\sqrt{3} - \sqrt{2}$ and the right-hand side equals $\sqrt{1} = 1$. Since $\sqrt{3} - \sqrt{2} \neq 1$, this is a conditional equation.

A classical problem of mathematics is that of "solving" an equation, that is, finding the solution set of a given conditional equation. The procedure consists of using the properties of equality to find other equations having the same solution set, called **equivalent equations.** For example, in solving the equation

$$3x + 2 = 5 - x$$

we use Property 4 to add x to each side, obtaining the equivalent equation $4x + 2 = 5$.   Then, we add -2 to each side to obtain $4x = 3$.   Finally, we use Property 5 to multiply each side by $\frac{1}{4}$, obtaining $x = \frac{3}{4}$.   This last equation obviously has the single solution $x = \frac{3}{4}$ and, from the chain of equivalent equations, we can conclude that the original equation $3x + 2 = 5 - x$ also has the single solution $x = \frac{3}{4}$.   In the following example, this procedure is applied to solve a more elaborate equation.

Example 9.3. Solve the equation $x^2 = x + 2$.

Solution: Adding $-x - 2$ to each side, we obtain

$$x^2 - x - 2 = 0$$

Factoring, we have

$$(x + 1)(x - 2) = 0$$

The equation is satisfied if

$$x + 1 = 0 \quad or \text{ if} \quad x - 2 = 0$$

Thus, the solutions are $x = -1$ and $x = 2$, that is, the solution set consists of the two numbers -1 and 2.

When solving certain equations, it may be convenient to multiply both sides of the original equation by an expression involving the variable x. For example, to solve the equation

$$\frac{1}{x} + \frac{1}{x + 1} = 0$$

we can multiply by the LCD $x(x + 1)$ of the two fractions to obtain the equation

$$(x + 1) + x = 0, \quad \text{or} \quad 2x + 1 = 0, \quad \text{or} \quad x = -\tfrac{1}{2}.$$

In general, this process may not always lead to an equivalent equation. Given the equation $f(x) = 0$, if we multiply by $g(x)$, we obtain the equation $f(x) \cdot g(x) = 0$.   Although this equation is satisfied by every value of x for which $f(x) = 0$, it is also satisfied by every value of x for which $g(x) = 0$.   Thus, the solution set of the equation $f(x) \cdot g(x) = 0$ includes all the elements of the solution set of $g(x) = 0$ *in addition* to those of $f(x) = 0$.   If we are not lucky, there will be solutions of $g(x) = 0$ that are not also solutions of $f(x) = 0$; such solutions are called **extraneous solutions.**   Thus, if in solving an equation, you multiply both sides by an expression involving x, it is necessary to check all solutions so obtained by substituting into the original equation.   The extraneous solutions will not satisfy the original equation.

Example 9.4. Solve the equation $\sqrt{x+4} = x - 2$.

Solution: Using Property 5 with $a = c = \sqrt{x+4}$ and $b = d = x - 2$, we have

$$ac = bd$$

$$x + 4 = (x - 2)^2$$

(In other words, we may square each side of an equation.) Expanding $(x - 2)^2$, we have

$$x + 4 = x^2 - 4x + 4$$

or

$$0 = x^2 - 5x$$

Factoring,

$$0 = x(x - 5)$$

Thus, the solutions are $x = 0$ and $x = 5$. If we substitute these solutions into the original equation, we find that $x = 5$ is a solution, but $x = 0$ is not, because $\sqrt{4} = 2$, not -2.

Similar reasoning shows that we can lose one or more solutions of an equation if we divide both sides by an expression involving x, as shown in the following example.

Example 9.5. Solve the equation $x^3 - x^2 = 2x$.

Solution: Adding $-2x$ to each side and factoring, we obtain

$$x(x + 1)(x - 2) = 0$$

Thus, the solutions are $x = 0$, $x = -1$, and $x = 2$.
If we had divided the original equation by x, to obtain the equation $x^2 - x = 2$, we would have gotten the solutions $x = -1$ and $x = 2$, but we would have lost the solution $x = 0$.

PROBLEMS A

1. Which of the five properties of the equality relation is illustrated?

(a) If $0 = x^2$, then $x^2 = 0$. (b) If $x = y$ and $y = 1$, then $x = 1$.
(c) $x - x = 0$. (d) $2^2 = 4$.
(e) If $x + 1 = 2$, then $x = 1$. (f) If $3x = 6$, then $x = 2$.

2. Determine whether the given number is a solution of the given equation.

(a) $x + 2 = 0 \ (-2)$ (b) $3x + 1 = 0 \ (\frac{1}{3})$

(c) $x^2 + x - 2 = 0 \ (-2)$ (d) $x^3 - 1 = 0 \left(-\dfrac{1}{2} + \dfrac{\sqrt{3}}{2} i\right)$

(e) $\sqrt{x+1} = -2 \ (3)$ (f) $\dfrac{1}{x} - \dfrac{2}{x} = 1 \ (-1)$

(g) $\sin x - \cos x = 0 \ (0)$ (h) $\tan^2 x = \frac{1}{2} \ (-\pi/4)$

3. Which of the following equations are identities?

(a) $2x = x + 3x - 2x$

(b) $(x + 3)^2 = x^2 + 9 + 6x$

(c) $(x + 1)^2 - (x - 1)^2 = 4x$

(d) $\dfrac{1}{x + 1} + \dfrac{1}{x + 2} = \dfrac{1}{x + 3}$

(e) $\sqrt{4x^2} = -2x$

(f) $\sqrt{1 - x} = -\sqrt{x - 1}$

(g) $\cos x \tan x = \sin x$

(h) $\cos^2 x = 2 - 2 \sin x - (1 - \sin x)^2$

4. Find the solution sets of the following equations.

(a) $3x = 15$

(b) $x + 2 = -7x + 26$

(c) $2(3 - 4x) = 3(5 - 6x)$

(d) $6 + 3(2x - 5) = 5(x - 4) + 6 - 4x$

(e) $\dfrac{1}{x + 2} + \dfrac{1}{3} = \dfrac{1}{2}$

(f) $\dfrac{2}{4x - 3} + \dfrac{3}{5x - 1} = 0$

(g) $x^2 + 5x + 6 = 0$

(h) $2x^2 + x - 1 = 0$

(i) $\sqrt{x + 7} = x + 5$

(j) $x - 2 = \sqrt{3x + 4}$

(k) $x^2 = x$

(l) $3x^3 - 4x^2 + x + 7 = x + 7$

5. Each equation involves expressions in several variables. Solve for the variable indicated.

(a) $v + gt = 0 \ (t)$

(b) $vt + \dfrac{g}{2}t^2 = 0 \ (t)$

(c) $F = \left(\dfrac{a + b}{2}\right)x \ (x)$

(d) $xy - xz = y^2 - z^2 \ (x)$

(e) $xy - x = 0 \ (y)$

(f) $x^2y - y^2x = 0 \ (y)$

PROBLEMS B

1. Find *all* the solutions of the equation $x^p = 2$.

2. Find an equation having the solutions $x = 1, 2,$ and 3.

3. Under what conditions is the solution set of the equation $f(x) = 0$ identical to that of the equation $f(x) \cdot g(x) = 0$.

4. Given the solution set of the equation $f(x) = 0$ and the solution set of the equation $g(x) = 0$, what can be said about the solution sets of the following equations?

(a) $f(x) + g(x) = 0$

(b) $f(x) - g(x) = 0$

9.2 Linear Equations

Let us find the solutions of equations that can be put in the form

$$ax + b = 0$$

where a and b are real constants and $a \neq 0$. Such an equation is called a **linear equation** because, in the form $f(x) = 0$, **f** is a linear function. To solve this equation, we subtract b from each side, obtaining the equivalent equation $ax = -b$; then we multiply each side by $1/a$ to obtain the single solution $x = -b/a$.

A solution of an appropriate equation may satisfy the conditions of a stated problem. For example, if we are asked to find the number which is increased by 3 when it is doubled, we may express the conditions of the problem in the form of an equation. If we let x represent the unknown number, the conditions of this problem are equivalent to the equation

$$2x = x + 3$$

The solution to this equation, $x = 3$, is the required number. Many such problems lead to linear equations, as illustrated in the following examples.

Example 9.6. A father is now three times as old as his son. Twelve years ago he was six times as old as his son. Find the present age of each.

Solution: Let x represent the present age of the son. Then $3x$ represents the present age of his father. Twelve years ago, the son's age was $x - 12$, and his father's age was $3x - 12$. Thus,

$$6(x - 12) = 3x - 12$$

The solution to this equation is $x = 20$. Thus, the son is now 20 and his father is 60.

Example 9.7. The cooling system of an automobile contains 24 quarts of a coolant consisting of 4 quarts of antifreeze and 20 quarts of water. How much of this mixture must be drained and replaced by pure antifreeze so that the cooling system will contain 8 quarts of antifreeze?

Solution: Let x represent the number of quarts of mixture to be drained. Then $\frac{4}{24}x = x/6$ quarts of antifreeze will be drained, and $4 - x/6$ quarts of antifreeze will be left in the cooling system. Since x quarts of pure antifreeze are to be added, the final mixture consists of $\left(4 - \dfrac{x}{6}\right) + x$ quarts of antifreeze. Thus, we have the equation

$$4 - \frac{x}{6} + x = 8$$

with the solution $x = \frac{24}{5}$; or 4.8 quarts of coolant are to be drained.

PROBLEMS A

1. Find two consecutive integers whose sum is 27.

2. Three times a number, diminished by 10, is the number itself. Find the number.

3. A mother and daughter share an apartment. If the monthly rent is $60 and the daughter pays twice as much toward the rent as the mother, how much does the mother pay?

4. John's father is thirty years older than John. In ten years he will be twice as old as John will be. Find the present age of each.

5. A grocer has 60 pounds of hazel nuts costing 40 cents per pound, and 80 pounds of peanuts costing 25 cents per pound. How many pounds of peanuts should he mix with the hazel nuts to obtain a mixture costing 35 cents per pound?

6. A dairy has 40 gallons of milk containing 3 per cent butterfat, and 15 gallons of cream containing 21 per cent butterfat. How many gallons of milk should be mixed with cream to obtain 30 gallons of half-and-half, containing 12 per cent butterfat?

7. An amount of money was divided among three brothers so that the first brother received $\frac{1}{3}$ of the amount, the second brother received $\frac{1}{3}$ of what was left, and the third brother received $\frac{1}{3}$ of what the second brother left. The remaining amount of money was $16. What was the original amount?

8. A worker can dig a ditch in 8 days, but another worker requires 12 days to dig the same ditch. How long would it take to dig the ditch if both men worked together?

9. A passenger train travelling at the speed of 75 miles per hour leaves Phoenix at 8 A.M. for Los Angeles. A freight train with a speed of 45 miles per hour leaves Phoenix bound for Los Angeles 2 hours earlier. How far from Phoenix will the passenger train overtake the freight train?

10. A boat makes a trip of 36 miles downstream in 6 hours. If the speed of the current is 2 miles per hour, what is the speed of the boat?

PROBLEMS B

1. What time is it when the two hands of a clock coincide between 8 and 9 o'clock?

2. If doubling the number of sides of a regular polygon increases the angle between adjacent sides by 10°, what is the original number of sides?

3. Two fill pipes fill a tank containing 120 gallons of liquid while a drain pipe is emptying the tank. The first fill pipe could fill the tank (if there were no drainage) in 15 minutes. The second fill pipe delivers 7 more gallons per minute than the first fill pipe. The drain pipe drains at the rate of 2 gallons per minute faster than the first fill pipe. How long does it require to fill the tank to capacity?

9.3   Trigonometric Identities

In Section 6.4 we derived the six elementary relations among the trigonometric functions. These relations are true for every element t in the domains of the corresponding trigonometric functions, and might properly be called the *six elementary trigonometric identities*. It was illustrated in Example 6.10 that we can use these identities to prove other trigonometric identities. In this section, we shall further illustrate the techniques of proving trigonometric identities.

We noted on page 162 that an identity is proved by changing the form of one side of an equation so that it is identical with that of the other side. In working with trigonometric identities, it is often helpful to use one or more of the six fundamental trigonometric identities to write all expressions in terms of sines and cosines only. This process is illustrated in the following examples.

Example 9.8. Prove the identity $\sin t - \tan t \cos t = 0$.

Solution: Using the identity

$$\tan t = \frac{\sin t}{\cos t}$$

we can write the left-hand side of the equation in the form

$$\sin t - \tan t \cos t = \sin t - \frac{\sin t}{\cos t} \cos t$$
$$= \sin t - \sin t$$
$$= 0$$

Example 9.9. Prove the identity $\dfrac{1 - \cos t}{1 + \cos t} = (\csc t - \cot t)^2$, $\cos t \neq -1$.

Solution: By Theorem 6.1,

$$\csc t = \frac{1}{\sin t} \quad \text{and} \quad \cot t = \frac{\cos t}{\sin t}$$

and the right-hand side becomes

$$(\csc t - \cot t)^2 = \left(\frac{1}{\sin t} - \frac{\cos t}{\sin t} \right)^2$$
$$= \frac{(1 - \cos t)^2}{\sin^2 t}$$

Using the identity $\sin^2 t = 1 - \cos^2 t$ and factoring, we have

$$(\csc t - \cot t)^2 = \frac{(1 - \cos t)^2}{(1 - \cos t)(1 + \cos t)}$$
$$= \frac{1 - \cos t}{1 + \cos t}$$

Sometimes, use of the addition formulas or the formulas for the values of the functions at $2t$ and $\frac{1}{2}t$ will help prove an identity, as illustrated in the following examples.

Example 9.10. Prove the identity

$$\frac{1 - \tan^2 \frac{t}{2}}{\cos t} = \frac{2}{1 + \cos t} \quad (\cos t \neq 0, -1)$$

Solution: The left-hand side can be written

$$\frac{1 - \tan^2 \frac{t}{2}}{\cos t} = \frac{1 - \dfrac{1 - \cos t}{1 + \cos t}}{\cos t}$$

$$= \frac{1 + \cos t - (1 - \cos t)}{(1 + \cos t)\cos t}$$

$$= \frac{2 \cos t}{(1 + \cos t)\cos t}$$

$$= \frac{2}{1 + \cos t}$$

Example 9.11. Prove the identity $\sin 2t = (1 + \cos 2t)\tan t$.

Solution: The left-hand side can be written

$$\sin 2t = 2 \sin t \cos t$$

The right-hand side can be written

$$(1 + \cos 2t)\tan t = (1 + 2\cos^2 t - 1)\frac{\sin t}{\cos t}$$

$$= 2\cos^2 t \frac{\sin t}{\cos t}$$

$$= 2 \cos t \sin t$$

Note in Example 9.11 that we proved the identity by changing *both sides* of the original equation to forms that are identical. Also note that the choice of the identity

$$\cos 2t = 2 \cos^2 t - 1$$

makes the work simpler than if we had chosen the identity

$$\cos 2t = \cos^2 t - \sin^2 t$$

or the identity

$$\cos 2t = 1 - 2 \sin^2 t$$

PROBLEMS A

1. Prove the following identities.

(a) $\csc t = \cot t \cos t + \sin t$

(b) $\sin t(\csc t + \cot t) = 1 + \cos t$

(c) $\dfrac{\sin t}{\cos t \tan t} = 1$

(d) $(1 - \cos^2 t)(1 + \tan^2 t) = \tan^2 t$

(e) $\dfrac{1}{\tan t + \cot t} - \sin t \cos t = 0$

(f) $\sec t - \tan t = \dfrac{\cos t}{1 + \sin t}$

(g) $\left(\dfrac{\csc t}{\cot t}\right)^2 = 1 + \tan^2 t$

(h) $\tan^2 t - \sin^2 t = \tan^2 t \sin^2 t$

(i) $\dfrac{2}{\cos t + 1} - \dfrac{2}{\cos t - 1} = 4 \csc^2 t$

(j) $\dfrac{1 - \sin t}{1 + \sin t} = (\sec t - \tan t)^2$

(k) $\sin \dfrac{t}{2} \cos \dfrac{t}{2} = \dfrac{\sin t}{2}$

(l) $\cot t - \tan t = 2 \cot 2t$

(m) $\cos 4t = 1 - 8 \cos^2 t + 8 \cos^4 t$

(n) $\sin 6t = 2 \sin t \cos t(3 - 16 \cos^2 t + 16 \cos^4 t)$

(o) $\sec t = \dfrac{\tan (t/2) + \cot (t/2)}{\cot (t/2) - \tan (t/2)}$

(p) $1 + \dfrac{\cos t - \cos^2 (t/2)}{\sin^2 (t/2)} = 0$

(q) $\sin\left(t - \dfrac{\pi}{4}\right) + \sin\left(t + \dfrac{\pi}{4}\right) = \sqrt{2} \sin t$

(r) $\tan\left(t - \dfrac{3\pi}{4}\right) + \tan\left(t + \dfrac{3\pi}{4}\right) = 2 \tan 2t$

2. Find identities having the given expression on the left-hand side and *only* the given trigonometric functions on the right-hand side.

(a) $\dfrac{\tan t \sin t}{\tan t - \sin t}$ $(\sin t, \cos t)$

(b) $\dfrac{\cos t}{1 + \sin t} + \tan t$ $(\sec t)$

(c) $\sin^2 t + \dfrac{1 - \tan^2 t}{\sec^2 t}$ $(\cos t)$

(d) $\dfrac{1 + \sec t}{\csc t}$ $(\sin t, \csc t)$

(e) $\tan \left(\dfrac{3\pi}{4} + \dfrac{t}{2} \right)$ $(\tan t, \sec t)$

(f) $\cot \left(\dfrac{t}{2} - \dfrac{3\pi}{4} \right)$ $(\tan t, \sec t)$

(g) $\dfrac{2 \sin t - \sin 2t}{2 \sin t + \sin 2t}$ $\left(\tan \dfrac{t}{2} \right)$

(h) $\dfrac{\cos t}{\sec 4t} + \dfrac{\sin t}{\csc 4t}$ $(\cos 3t)$

PROBLEMS B

1. If $r + s + t = \pi$, show that

$$\cos t + \cos r \cos s - \sin r \sin s = 0$$

2. Prove that

$$|\sin t + \cos t| = \sqrt{1 + 2 \sin t \cos t}$$

3. Prove that

$$\cos (\text{Arc} \sin x + \text{Arc} \cos y) = y\sqrt{1 - x^2} - x\sqrt{1 - y^2}$$

9.4 Trigonometric Equations

If we wish to solve the equation $\sin t = 0$, we note that every number in the set $\ldots -2\pi, -\pi, 0, \pi, 2\pi, \ldots$, or every number of the form $t = k\pi$, where k is an integer, satisfies $\sin t = 0$. From the periodicity of the trigonometric functions, we reason that a trigonometric equation can have an unlimited number of solutions.

As a further example, consider the equation

$$\tan 2t = 1$$

We know that $\tan (\pi/4) = 1$ and that the tangent function has the period π. Thus, the tangent of every number of the form $\pi/4 + k\pi$ equals 1, where k is an integer. We can conclude that

$$2t = \frac{\pi}{4} + k\pi, \quad \text{or} \quad t = \frac{\pi}{8} + k\frac{\pi}{2}$$

that is, the solution set of the equation $\tan 2t = 1$ is

$$\ldots \frac{-7\pi}{8}, \frac{-3\pi}{8}, \frac{\pi}{8}, \frac{5\pi}{8}, \frac{9\pi}{8}, \ldots$$

Trigonometric equations often involve more than one trigonometric function. They may be solved by using algebraic operations and trigonometric identities in one of two ways: (1) Write the equation in terms of one trigonometric function only. (2) Write the equation in the form $f(t) = 0$ and factor $f(t)$ so that each factor involves only one trigonometric function. The solution set of the given equation is obtained from a knowledge of values of the trigonometric functions and their periods. These methods are illustrated in the following examples.

Example 9.12. Solve the equation $2 \cos^2 t + 3 \sin t = 0$.

Solution: Using the identity $\cos^2 t + \sin^2 t = 1$, we have

$$2(1 - \sin^2 t) + 3 \sin t = 0$$

or

$$2 \sin^2 t - 3 \sin t - 2 = 0$$

Factoring, we have

$$(2 \sin t + 1)(\sin t - 2) = 0$$

Thus, the solutions of the original equation satisfy the equations $\sin t = -\frac{1}{2}$ or $\sin t = 2$. Since $\sin (\pi/6) = \frac{1}{2}$, we may make use of the relations $\sin (-t) = -\sin t$ and $\sin (\pi + t) = -\sin t$ to conclude that $-\pi/6$ and $7\pi/6$ are solutions. Furthermore, the sine function has the period 2π; thus, the solutions corresponding to $\sin t = -\frac{1}{2}$ are of the form $-\pi/6 + 2k\pi$ and $7\pi/6 + 2k\pi$, where k is an integer. There are no further solutions of the original equation because the equation $\sin t = 2$ has no solutions.

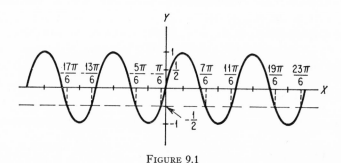

FIGURE 9.1

To find all the solutions of a trigonometric equation, it is helpful to sketch a graph like that shown in Figure 9.1. Those values of t for which the graph of the sine function intersects the horizontal line $\frac{1}{2}$ unit below the X-axis shown in the figure correspond to the solutions of the equation $\sin t = -\frac{1}{2}$. With the aid of such a graph, you can observe the periodicity of the solutions of a trigonometric equation, and check to see that none have been duplicated or omitted.

Example 9.13. Solve the equation $\sin t = \tan t$.

Solution: Using the identity

$$\tan t = \frac{\sin t}{\cos t}$$

we have $$\sin t = \frac{\sin t}{\cos t}$$

or $$\sin t - \frac{\sin t}{\cos t} = 0$$

Factoring, we obtain

$$\sin t \left(1 - \frac{1}{\cos t}\right) = 0$$

Thus, the solutions of the original equation satisfy the equations

$$\sin t = 0 \quad \text{or} \quad 1 - \frac{1}{\cos t} = 0$$

The solutions of $\sin t = 0$ have already been found to be $t = k\pi$. The equation $1 - (1/\cos t) = 0$ can be written in the form $\cos t = 1$. Can you verify that the solutions of the equation $\cos t = 1$ are $t = 2k\pi$? Thus, the solution set arising from this equation is already contained in the solution set arising from the equation $\sin t = 0$, and the required solutions are given by

$$t = k\pi, \quad \text{or} \quad t = \ldots -2\pi, -\pi, 0, \pi, 2\pi, \ldots$$

Note that we would have lost many of the solutions of the equation in the last example if we had carelessly "cancelled" $\sin t$ in the equation $\sin t = \sin t/\cos t$ to obtain the equation $1 = 1/\cos t$. Which solutions would we have lost?

PROBLEMS A

1. Solve the following equations.

(a) $\sin t = 1$

(b) $\cos t = \frac{\sqrt{2}}{2}$

(c) $\sec\left(t - \frac{\pi}{2}\right) = 2$

(d) $\tan(t + \pi) = 1$

(e) $\cos 2t = -\frac{1}{2}$

(f) $\sin(3t + \pi) = -\frac{\sqrt{3}}{2}$

(g) $\sin^2 t + 2\sin t + 1 = 0$

(h) $\cos^2 t - \cos t = 0$

(i) $\tan t \csc t + \sqrt{2} = 0$

(j) $\cot t = 1 - \csc t$

(k) $3\tan\frac{t}{2} = \cot\frac{t}{2}$

(l) $\sec^2 2t = 1 - \tan 2t$

(m) $\sin 2t + \cos t = 0$

(n) $\cos 2t + \sin^2 t = 0$

(o) $\cos^4 t - \sin^4 t = 1$

(p) $4\sin t \cos t = 1$

PROBLEMS B

1. Solve the equation $\sin t + \cos t = 1$.

(a) by squaring each side.

(b) by using the formula $A \sin (bt + c) = B \sin bt + C \cos bt$.

2. Solve the equation $\text{Cos } x = \text{Sin } x$.

3. Solve the equation $\text{Arc sin } x = \text{Arc cos } x$.

4. Solve the equation $\tan (\text{Arc tan } x - \text{Arc cot } x) = 0$.

5. Solve the equation $\text{Arc cos } 2x = \dfrac{\pi}{3} - \text{Arc cos } x$.

9.5   Other Transcendental Equations

In Section 9.4 we studied methods for solving certain transcendental equations, that is, equations that could be put in the form $f(x) = 0$, where **f** is not an algebraic function. There are many transcendental equations, however, that can be solved only graphically, or by methods of advanced mathematics.

If an equation is in the form $f(x) = 0$, we may graph the function **f**, and read from the graph the value or values of x at which the graph crosses the X-axis. Such values of x correspond to zero-values of $f(x)$, and are solutions of the equation $f(x) = 0$. In contrast, if an equation is more conveniently put in the form $f(x) = g(x)$, we graph both functions **f** and **g** on the same set of axes. Those values of x for which the two graphs intersect are the solutions of the equation $f(x) = g(x)$. Such graphical procedures as we have described are only approximate, and there is always the possibility that you may miss one or more solutions. A carefully constructed graph will add precision to the results, and a thorough knowledge of the properties of the functions graphed will help avoid missing solutions.

Example 9.14. Solve the equation $x^2 + \log x = 0$ by graphical methods.

Solution:

(a) In Figure 9.2 is the graph of **f**, where $f(x) = x^2 + \log x$. The curve crosses the axis at $x = .53$, approximately. Note that when $x > 0$ both x^2 and $\log x$ increase with x; thus, their sum increases with increasing x. Consequently, the curve cannot "turn around" and cross the X-axis again; that is, there is at most one solution of $x^2 + \log x = 0$.

(b) As an alternate method of solution, we can write the equation $x^2 + \log x = 0$ in the form $\log x = -x^2$. In Figure 9.3 are shown the graphs of f, where $f(x) = \log x$, and g, where $g(x) = -x^2$. The x-coordinate of their point of intersection is $x = .53$, approximately.

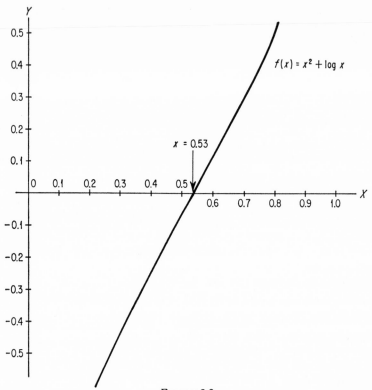

FIGURE 9.2

Sometimes transcendental equations can be solved by rewriting them in a form that makes their solution evident, as shown in the following example.

Example 9.15. Solve the equation

$$3 \cdot 3^x + 2 \cdot 3^{x+1} + 3^{x+2} = 27 \cdot 2^x$$

Solution: The left-hand side of this equation can be rewritten in the form

$$3 \cdot 3^x + 2 \cdot 3^{x+1} + 3^{x+2} = (3 + 2 \cdot 3 + 3^2)3^x$$

Thus, we have

$$18 \cdot 3^x = 27 \cdot 2^x$$

or

$$\left(\tfrac{3}{2}\right)^x = \tfrac{27}{18} = \tfrac{3}{2}$$

Since $\left(\tfrac{3}{2}\right)^x = \left(\tfrac{3}{2}\right)^1$, we have $x = 1$.

The solution of some transcendental equations is simplified by taking the logarithm of each side. Why does this procedure lead to an equivalent equation?

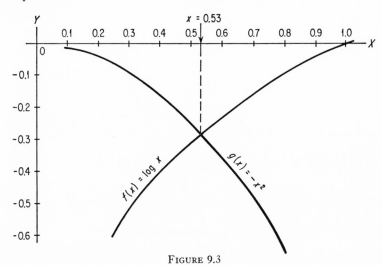

FIGURE 9.3

Example 9.16. Solve the equation $\sqrt{x^{\log x}} = 100$.

Solution: Squaring, we obtain

$$x^{\log x} = (100)^2 = 10^4$$

Taking logarithms

$$(\log x)(\log x) = \log 10^4 = 4$$

Therefore $\log x = \pm 2$ and the solutions are $x = 10^2 = 100$, and $x = 10^{-2} = .01$.

PROBLEMS A

1. Solve graphically.

(a) $\dfrac{x}{2} = \sin x$
            (b) $\tan x = 2x \quad \left(-\dfrac{\pi}{2} < x < \dfrac{\pi}{2}\right)$

(c) $x \log x = 1$
            (d) $2x^2 - 4x + 1 = 0$

(e) $3^x = x^3$
            (f) $x + \sin x = \cos x - x^2$

2. Solve exactly.

(a) $2^x + 2^{x+1} + 2^{x+2} = 112$
            (b) $\sqrt{3^x} - \sqrt{9^x} = 0$

(c) $4^{x+1} + 16^{x+1} = 6$
            (d) $\log (\sin x) = 0$

PROBLEMS B

1. Is there a real number x for which $x^x = 0$?

2. Solve exactly: $\log 49 + \log (2 + 7^x) = x \log 7 + \log 51$.

Polynomial Equations

10.1 Quadratic Equations

In this chapter, we shall be concerned with solving equations of the form $f(x) = 0$, where $f(x)$ is a polynomial in x.   (Polynomials were defined in Section 2.5.)   To begin, let us restrict $f(x)$ to be a polynomial of degree 2; that is, let us study the equation

(10.1) $$ax^2 + bx + c = 0$$

where $a \neq 0$.   Any equation that can be put in the form 10.1 is called a **quadratic equation.**

If it is convenient to factor the quadratic polynomial $ax^2 + bx + c$ into the product of two first-degree polynomials, the solutions of Equation 10.1 can be obtained by solving two linear equations.   In Example 9.3, page 164, we solved the equation $x^2 = x + 2$ by factoring the polynomial $x^2 - x - 2$ into the product $(x + 1)(x - 2)$, and found the solutions to be $x = -1$ and $x = 2$.

If it is not convenient to factor $ax^2 + bx + c$, we may use the process of "completing the square," described on page 81.   This process is applied to the solution of a quadratic equation in the following example.

Example 10.1. Solve the equation $x^2 - 6x + 7 = 0$.

Solution: First, we write the equation in the form

$$x^2 - 6x = -7$$

Next, we add the square of half the coefficient of x to each side of the equation, obtaining

$$x^2 - 6x + 9 = 2$$

The left-hand side of this equation is now a perfect square, and we have

$$(x - 3)^2 = 2$$

Thus, either

$$x - 3 = \sqrt{2} \quad \text{or} \quad x - 3 = -\sqrt{2}$$

and the solutions are

$$x = 3 + \sqrt{2} \quad \text{and} \quad x = 3 - \sqrt{2}$$

If the coefficient of x^2 does not equal 1 in a given quadratic equation, the process of completing the square is facilitated by dividing both sides of the equation by this coefficient.

Example 10.2. Solve the equation $2x^2 + 4x - 9 = 0$.

Solution: Dividing by 2 and adding 9/2 to each side, we have

$$x^2 + 2x = \tfrac{9}{2}$$

Completing the square, we obtain

$$x^2 + 2x + 1 = \tfrac{11}{2}$$
$$(x + 1)^2 = \tfrac{11}{2}$$

Thus, either

$$x + 1 = \sqrt{\frac{11}{2}} = \frac{\sqrt{22}}{2}, \quad \text{or} \quad x + 1 = -\frac{\sqrt{22}}{2}$$

and the solutions are

$$x = -1 + \frac{\sqrt{22}}{2} \quad \text{and} \quad x = -1 - \frac{\sqrt{22}}{2}$$

Since the process of completing the square was carried out for the general coefficients a, b, and c on page 81, we may use that result to find a formula giving the solutions of any quadratic equation. Using Equation 4.3, we have

$$ax^2 + bx + c = a\left(x + \frac{b}{2a}\right)^2 + \left(c - \frac{b^2}{4a}\right)$$

and we can write the equation $ax^2 + bx + c = 0$ in the form

$$a\left(x + \frac{b}{2a}\right)^2 + \left(c - \frac{b^2}{4a}\right) = 0$$

Adding $-\left(c - \dfrac{b^2}{4a}\right)$ to each side, we have

$$a\left(x + \frac{b}{2a}\right)^2 = -\left(c - \frac{b^2}{4a}\right) = \frac{b^2}{4a} - c$$

Since $a \neq 0$, we may divide by a to obtain

$$\left(x + \frac{b}{2a}\right)^2 = \frac{b^2}{4a^2} - \frac{c}{a}$$

$$= \frac{b^2 - 4ac}{4a^2}$$

Thus, either

$$x + \frac{b}{2a} = \sqrt{\frac{b^2 - 4ac}{4a^2}} = \frac{\sqrt{b^2 - 4ac}}{2a}$$

or

$$x + \frac{b}{2a} = \frac{-\sqrt{b^2 - 4ac}}{2a}$$

If we add $-b/2a$ to each side in each of the last two equations and combine fractions, we obtain the solutions

(10.2)

$$r_1 = \frac{-b + \sqrt{b^2 - 4ac}}{2a}$$

$$r_2 = \frac{-b - \sqrt{b^2 - 4ac}}{2a}$$

Equations 10.2 give the solutions of Equation 10.1 in terms of the coefficients a, b, and c. These equations are called the **quadratic formulas** and they completely solve the problem of finding the solutions of any quadratic equation.

In using the quadratic formulas, the reader should remember to write the given equation in the form of Equation 10.1. In this form, the coefficients a, b, and c are readily identified.

Example 10.3. Solve the equation $3x - 5 = 4x^2$.

Solution: Writing this equation in the form

$$4x^2 - 3x + 5 = 0$$

we identify the coefficients to be $a = 4$, $b = -3$, and $c = 5$. Applying the quadratic formulas, we obtain the solutions

$$r_1 = \frac{3 + \sqrt{9 - 80}}{8} \qquad r_2 = \frac{3 - \sqrt{9 - 80}}{8}$$

or

$$r_1 = \frac{3}{8} + \frac{\sqrt{71}\,i}{8} \qquad r_2 = \frac{3}{8} - \frac{\sqrt{71}\,i}{8}$$

Sometimes the solution to a stated problem is a solution of a certain quadratic equation. In choosing the appropriate solution, or deciding whether both solutions are appropriate, you should determine which solutions satisfy the conditions of the stated problem as well as the quadratic equation.

Example 10.4. The length of a rectangle is 7 inches more than its width. Its area is 228 square inches. What are its dimensions?

Solution: Let x represent the width of the rectangle. Then its length is $x + 7$, and its area is $x(x + 7)$. Thus

$$x(x + 7) = 228$$

or

$$x^2 + 7x - 228 = 0$$

By means of the quadratic formula the solutions are found to be

$$r_1 = \frac{-7 + \sqrt{49 + 4 \cdot 228}}{2} \quad \text{and} \quad r_2 = \frac{-7 - \sqrt{49 + 4 \cdot 228}}{2}$$

or

$$r_1 = 12 \quad \text{and} \quad r_2 = -19$$

Since the width of a rectangle is a positive number, we choose the solution $r_1 = 12$ inches. The length of the rectangle is $12 + 7 = 19$ inches.

PROBLEMS A

1. Solve the following quadratic equations by factoring.

(a) $x^2 - x = 0$ (b) $x^2 - 3x + 2 = 0$
(c) $x^2 - 2x + 1 = 0$ (d) $4x^2 + 4x + 1 = 0$
(e) $2x^2 = -6x$ (f) $x^2 - 2 = x$
(g) $3x^2 - 4x - 4 = 0$ (h) $2x^2 + 5x - 3 = 0$
(i) $12x^2 - 25x - 7 = 0$ (j) $-14x^2 + 31x - 15 = 0$
(k) $x^2 + \frac{5}{6}x - \frac{1}{6} = 0$ (l) $x^2 + \frac{1}{4}x - \frac{3}{8} = 0$

2. Solve the following quadratic equations by completing the square.

(a) $x^2 - 2x - 3 = 0$ (b) $x^2 + 4x - 2 = 0$
(c) $x^2 = 2x + 1$ (d) $x^2 - 14x + 44 = 0$
(e) $x^2 + 3x + 4 = 0$ (f) $x - 1 = x^2$
(g) $3x^2 = 5x - 2$ (h) $4x^2 - 5x + 1 = 0$
(i) $-2x^2 + 6x + 5 = 0$ (j) $16x^2 - 24x + 9 = 0$
(k) $\frac{1}{3}x^2 - \frac{2}{3}x + 1 = 0$ (l) $\frac{3}{5}x^2 = 20 + \frac{1}{5}x$

3. Solve the quadratic equations in Problem 2 by using the quadratic formulas.

4. Solve the following quadratic equations for the variable indicated.

(a) $x^2 + y^2 + 2xy = 0$, x (b) $2x^2 + 3y^2 + 4x - y = 0$, y
(c) $Ax^2 + Bxy + Cx + D = 0$, x (d) $(x - y)^2 + (x - y) + 1 = 0$, x
(e) $S = v_0t + \frac{1}{2}gt^2$, t (f) $u\sqrt{v} = u^2v + v^2$, u

5. The area of a rectangular lot is 432 square feet.   Find its dimensions if its width is six feet greater than its length.

6. The difference between a real number and its reciprocal is $\frac{5}{6}$.   Find the number.

7. A fraction is derived from a certain number so that the numerator is the number less three, and the denominator is the number less two.   The fraction equals one eighth of the number.   Find the number.

8. A cattle man bought a number of cows for $6000.   He kept twenty cows and sold the others for $6000.   Of those he sold, he made a profit of $150 per head.   How many cows did he buy?

9. The sum of the squares of two consecutive natural numbers is 113.   Find the two numbers.

10. The hypothenuse of a right triangle is three inches longer than the longer leg.   The shorter leg is three inches smaller than the longer leg.   Find the length of the hypothenuse.

11. A realtor has two adjacent rectangular lots having a total area of 208 square feet.   The length of the first lot is three feet longer than its width, and the length of the second lot is five feet less than the width of the first lot. The width of the second lot is eight feet less than the width of the first lot. Find the width of the first lot.

12. A group of students takes a trip of 84 miles in 14 hours.   They walk the first 14 miles and go by bicycle the rest of the trip.   If their speed is 8 miles per hour more by bicycle than by walking, how fast do they travel by bicycle?

PROBLEMS B

1. Solve the following quadratic equation:

$$x^2 + (1 - i)x - 2(1 + i) = 0$$

2. Prove that the quadratic polynomial $ax^2 + bx + c$ is a perfect square if and only if $b^2 - 4ac = 0$.

3. Prove that the quadratic polynomial $ax^2 + bx + c$, with rational coefficients, factors into the product of two linear polynomials with rational coefficients if and only if $b^2 - 4ac$ is a perfect square.

10.2   Solutions of a Quadratic Equation with Real Coefficients

In Example 10.3 we observed that the quadratic equation

$$4x^2 - 3x + 5 = 0$$

has real coefficients, but its solutions are not real numbers.   From the quadratic formulas, we observe that the solutions of a quadratic equation with real coefficients are distinct complex conjugates whenever $b^2 - 4ac$ is a negative real number. Thus, if we wish to conclude that any quadratic equation with real coefficients has at least one solution, we must allow its solution set to consist of elements from the field of complex numbers.

The value of the expression $b^2 - 4ac$ sheds further light on the character of the solutions of the quadratic equation $ax^2 + bx + c = 0$ when a, b, and c are *real numbers*. From the quadratic formulas, we observe that this equation has two real and equal solutions when $b^2 - 4ac = 0$. The common value $-b/2a$ of these equal solutions is called a **double solution.** We have already observed that there are two distinct complex-conjugate solutions when $b^2 - 4ac < 0$. Furthermore, if $b^2 - 4ac > 0$, there are two distinct real solutions.

The expression $b^2 - 4ac$ is called the **discriminant** of the quadratic polynomial $ax^2 + bx + c$, and it is abbreviated by the letter D. We have observed that the solutions of the equation $ax^2 + bx + c = 0$ are characterized by the sign of the discriminant. Our conclusions are summarized in the following table.

Value of D	Character of the Solutions
$D = 0$	Two real and equal solutions
$D > 0$	Two distinct real solutions
$D < 0$	Two distinct complex-conjugate solutions

In Section 9.5 we saw that real solutions of the equation $f(x) = 0$ correspond to the values of x where the graph of the function **f** crosses the X-axis. A graph of the quadratic function **f** gives geometric meaning to the character of the solutions of the quadratic equation $f(x) = 0$, when $f(x)$ has real coefficients. If $D = 0$, there are two real and equal solutions, and the graph touches the X-axis only once, at $x = -b/2a$. On page 81, we showed that the maximum or minimum value of $f(x)$ occurs at $x = -b/2a$, and we can conclude that the graph is *tangent* to the X-axis at this point if $D = 0$. If $D > 0$, there are two distinct real solutions, and the graph crosses the X-axis at two distinct points. If $D < 0$, there are two nonreal solutions. Since the X-axis is an axis of real numbers, the graph cannot cross the X-axis if $D < 0$. These conclusions are illustrated in the following example.

Example 10.5. Determine the character of the solutions of the following equations, and graph the corresponding quadratic functions:

(a) $x^2 - 2x + 1 = 0$

(b) $x^2 - 1 = 0$

(c) $x^2 + 1 = 0$

Solution:

(a) $$a = 1, \quad b = -2, \quad c = 1$$

thus

$$D = (-2)^2 - 4 = 0$$

There is the double solution, $r_1 = r_2 = 1$.

(b) $$a = 1, \quad b = 0, \quad c = -1$$

thus

$$D = (0)^2 + 4 = 4$$

There are two real solutions, $r_1 = 1$, and $r_2 = -1$.

(c) $$a = 1, \quad b = 0, \quad c = 1$$

thus

$$D = (0)^2 - 4 = -4$$

The solutions are the complex conjugates $r_1 = i$, and $r_2 = -i$. The graphs are shown in Figure 10.1.

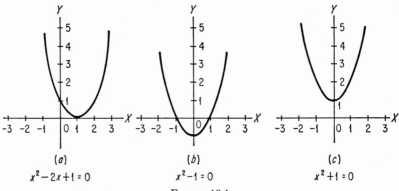

(a)
$$x^2 - 2x + 1 = 0$$

(b)
$$x^2 - 1 = 0$$

(c)
$$x^2 + 1 = 0$$

FIGURE 10.1

If we add the two solutions given by the quadratic formulas, we obtain

$$r_1 + r_2 = \frac{-b + \sqrt{b^2 - 4ac}}{2a} + \frac{-b - \sqrt{b^2 - 4ac}}{2a}$$

$$= -\frac{b}{a}$$

If we multiply these solutions, we obtain

$$r_1 \cdot r_2 = \left(\frac{-b + \sqrt{b^2 - 4ac}}{2a} \right) \cdot \left(\frac{-b - \sqrt{b^2 - 4ac}}{2a} \right)$$

$$= \frac{1}{4a^2} \cdot [b^2 - (b^2 - 4ac)]$$

$$= \frac{c}{a}$$

Thus, *the sum and product of the solutions of the quadratic equation* $ax^2 + bx + c = 0$ *equal* $-b/a$ *and* c/a, *respectively*. Note that, if a, b, and c are real numbers, then $r_1 + r_2$ and $r_1 \cdot r_2$ are real numbers even when the solutions r_1 and r_2 are complex numbers.

We can use these results to obtain a quadratic equation having two given solutions. From the equation $r_1 + r_2 = -b/a$, we have $b = -a(r_1 + r_2)$, and from the equation $r_1 \cdot r_2 = c/a$, we have $c = ar_1r_2$. Thus,

$$ax^2 + bx + c = ax^2 - a(r_1 + r_2)x + ar_1r_2$$
$$= a[x^2 - (r_1 + r_2)x + r_1r_2]$$
$$= a(x - r_1)(x - r_2)$$

Thus, the equation $(x - r_1)(x - r_2) = 0$ is equivalent to the equation $ax^2 + bx + c = 0$. Given the solutions r_1 and r_2 of a quadratic equation, we can obtain the equation, *except for a multiplicative constant*, by forming the product of the factors $x - r_1$ and $x - r_2$.

Example 10.6. Find a quadratic equation having the solutions $r_1 = 1 + i$, and $r_2 = 1 - i$.

Solution: The equation

$$[x - (1 + i)][x - (1 - i)] = 0$$

or

$$x^2 - 2x + 2 = 0$$

has the required solutions. (Why does the equation $-3x^2 + 6x - 6 = 0$ also have the same solutions?)

PROBLEMS A

1. Determine the character of the solutions of the following quadratic equations and graph the corresponding quadratic functions.

(a) $x^2 - 7x + 12 = 0$ (b) $x^2 - x - 48 = 0$
(c) $x^2 - 5x + 9 = 0$ (d) $4x^2 + 4x + 1 = 0$
(e) $2x^2 - 6x - 1 = 0$ (f) $x^2 = 4x + 3$
(g) $x^2 + 8x = -16$ (h) $3x^2 + 22 = 35x$
(i) $\frac{1}{2}x^2 - \frac{3}{4}x + \frac{1}{3} = 0$ (j) $\frac{7}{4}x^2 + \sqrt{3}\,x = \frac{1}{2}$

2. Find a quadratic equation having the given solutions.

(a) $3, -1$ (b) $-7, -5$
(c) $\frac{1}{5}, \frac{2}{3}$ (d) $\frac{1}{4}, -7$
(e) $2 + \sqrt{3}, 2 - \sqrt{3}$ (f) $\dfrac{3 + \sqrt{5}}{2}, \dfrac{3 - \sqrt{5}}{2}$
(g) $2 + 3i, 2 - 3i$ (h) $-4 - i, -4 + i$
(i) $a + bi, a - bi$ (j) $a + b\sqrt{c}, a - b\sqrt{c}$

3. Determine the real values of k so the solutions have the given character.
(a) $x^2 + kx + 1 = 0$, one real solution.
(b) $2x^2 - x + k = 0$, two real solutions.
(c) $kx^2 + 3x + k = 0$, complex-conjugate solutions.
(d) $kx^2 = 2k - (k + 1)x$, one real solution.

4. Prove that $r_1 + r_2$ and $r_1 \cdot r_2$ are real numbers when $r_1 = a + bi$ and $r_2 = a - bi$.

PROBLEMS B

1. Factor the following quadratic polynomials in x into a product of linear polynomials in x.
(a) $x^2 + 1$ (b) $ix^2 + (2 - i)x - i + 1$
(c) $kx^2 + (k^2 - k - 1)x - k + 1$ (d) $3x^2y^2 + 6xy^2z - 5x - 10z$

2. Find k if $x^2 - 6x + k = 0$ and the quotient of the solutions of this equation is 2.

10.3   Equations in Quadratic Form

An equation such as $x^4 - x^2 - 2 = 0$ can be regarded as a quadratic equation in the variable x^2. This equation is readily solved for x^2 by factoring, as follows.

$$x^4 - x^2 - 2 = 0$$

or

$$(x^2 - 2)(x^2 + 1) = 0$$

Thus, the required solutions for x^2 are 2 and -1. We can solve the equations $x^2 = 2$ and $x^2 = -1$ for x, obtaining the four solutions

$$x = \sqrt{2}, \quad x = -\sqrt{2}, \quad x = i, \quad \text{and} \quad x = -i$$

With respect to this example, we note that the equation $x^4 - x^2 - 2 = 0$ has *two solutions when it is regarded as a quadratic equation in* x^2. However, the same equation has *four solutions when it is regarded as an equation in* x.

In general, any equation of the form $f(y) = 0$ is said to be in **quadratic form in** x if $y = g(x)$ and **f** is a quadratic function. Additional examples of equations in quadratic form are

$$x^6 + 2x^3 - 1 = 0$$

$$2 \sin^2 t - 3 \sin t + 1 = 0$$

$$x + 1 = 1 - \sqrt{x + 1}$$

If we let $y = x^3$ in the first equation, it becomes the following quadratic equation in y:

$$y^2 + 2y - 1 = 0$$

Letting $y = \sin t$ and $y = \sqrt{x+1}$ in the second and third equations, respectively, we get the equations

$$2y^2 - 3y + 1 = 0 \quad \text{and} \quad y^2 = 1 - y$$

In Example 9.12 on page 173, we solved the equation

$$2 \sin^2 t - 3 \sin t - 2 = 0$$

which we can now consider to be a quadratic equation in $\sin t$. The following is a further example of the solution of trigonometric equations in quadratic form.

Example 10.7. Solve the equation $\cos^2 t - \sin^2 t = 2 \sin t$.

Solution: Using the identity $\cos^2 t + \sin^2 t = 1$, we have

$$1 - 2 \sin^2 t = 2 \sin t$$

or

$$2 \sin^2 t + 2 \sin t - 1 = 0$$

This is a quadratic equation in $\sin t$ with $a = 2$, $b = 2$, and $c = -1$. The solutions are found by the quadratic formulas to be

$$\sin t = -\frac{1}{2} + \frac{\sqrt{3}}{2} \quad \text{and} \quad \sin t = -\frac{1}{2} - \frac{\sqrt{3}}{2}$$

Since $|\sin t| \leq 1$, there are no values of t satisfying $\sin t = -\frac{1}{2} - \frac{\sqrt{3}}{2}$.

Thus, we need only find values of t such that

$$\sin t = -\frac{1}{2} + \frac{\sqrt{3}}{2} = .366$$

From Table 2, we find that $\sin .375 = .366$, approximately. Thus, the solutions are

$$t = .375 + 2k\pi \quad \text{and} \quad t = \pi - .375 + 2k\pi = 2.78 + 2k\pi$$

where k is any integer.

Many equations involving radicals, such as

$$\sqrt{3x + 4} - \sqrt{x + 1} = 3$$

can be put in quadratic form. If we let $y = \sqrt{3x + 4}$ in the above equation, then

$$y^2 = 3x + 4, \quad \text{or} \quad x = \frac{y^2 - 4}{3}$$

(We could have chosen to let $y = \sqrt{x + 1}$.) The equation can be written

$$y - \sqrt{\frac{y^2 - 4}{3} + 1} = 3$$

or

$$y - 3 = \sqrt{\frac{y^2 - 1}{3}}$$

Squaring, we have

$$(y - 3)^2 = \frac{y^2 - 1}{3}$$

or

$$y^2 - 9y + 14 = 0$$

or

$$(y - 7)(y - 2) = 0$$

Thus, the solutions of this equation are $y = 7$ and $y = 2$. Since

$$x = \frac{y^2 - 4}{3}$$

we have $x = 15$ and $x = 0$. By squaring, we introduced the possibility of extraneous solutions. Successive substitution of $x = 15$ and $x = 0$ in the original equation shows that $x = 15$ is a solution, but $x = 0$ is not a solution.

The following example further illustrates the solution of equations in quadratic form that involve radicals.

Example 10.8. Solve the equation

$$\sqrt{\frac{x + 1}{x - 1}} + \sqrt{\frac{x - 1}{x + 1}} = \frac{4\sqrt{3}}{3}$$

Solution: Let $y = \sqrt{x + 1}$. Then

$$y^2 = x + 1 \quad \text{and} \quad x = y^2 - 1$$

Substituting into the original equation, we have

$$\frac{y}{\sqrt{y^2 - 2}} + \frac{\sqrt{y^2 - 2}}{y} = \frac{4\sqrt{3}}{3}$$

Squaring, we obtain

$$\frac{y^2}{y^2 - 2} + \frac{y^2 - 2}{y^2} + 2 = \frac{16}{3}$$

or

$$y^4 - 2y^2 - 3 = 0$$

Factoring, we obtain

$$(y^2 - 3)(y^2 + 1) = 0$$

Thus, $y^2 = 3$ or $y^2 = -1$. Since $x = y^2 - 1$, we have the solutions $x = 2$ and $x = -2$. Substitution into the original equation verifies both solutions.

PROBLEMS A

1. Solve the following equations.

(a) $x^4 - 3x^2 - 4 = 0$

(b) $y^6 - 7y^3 - 8 = 0$

(c) $Z^{-2} + Z^{-1} = 6$

(d) $\left(\dfrac{1}{x + 1}\right)^2 - \dfrac{2}{x + 1} + 5 = 0$

(e) $x - 33x^{1/2} + 32 = 0$

(f) $y^{4/3} - 8y^{2/3} = 9$

(g) $3\sqrt{2u - 1} + \sqrt[4]{2u - 1} = 10$

(h) $x^2 + (x^2 - 5x)^2 = 5x + 12$

(i) $3 \sin^2 t - 4 \sin t + 5 = 0$

(j) $\sin^2 t = \sin t + \cos^2 t$

(k) $\sin t + \cos 2t = 0$

(l) $(\log x)^2 - \log x - \log 100 = 0$

2. Find the real solutions of the following equations.

(a) $\sqrt{2x - 3} - 5 = 0$

(b) $2z + 3\sqrt{2z} = 4$

(c) $\sqrt{x + 2} + \sqrt{x - 1} = 2$

(d) $\sqrt{3y - 5} - \sqrt{y - 2} = 1$

(e) $\sqrt{4w + 9} - \sqrt{3w - 3} = \sqrt{7w - 24}$

(f) $4\sqrt{2x + 3} + \sqrt{2x - 21} = 3\sqrt{2x + 27}$

(g) $3\sqrt{x^2 + 2x + 4} = x^2 + 2x$

(h) $3y^2 - 12y - 64 = 8\sqrt{y^2 - 4y - 16}$

PROBLEMS B

1. Solve the following equation for x.

$$(\log \sin x^2)^2 - \log \tan x^2 = \log \cos x^2$$

10.4　Factoring Polynomials of Degree *n*

The problem of finding the solutions of the polynomial equation $f(x) = 0$ is closely related to the problem of factoring the polynomial $f(x)$.　If $f(x)$ factors into a product of nonconstant polynomials, the equation $f(x) = 0$ is satisfied for every value of x that makes at least one of the factors equal to zero. Since each factor has degree less than that of $f(x)$, the problem of solving an nth degree polynomial equation is reduced to that of solving a polynomial equation of lower degree. In this section, we derive some results that bear on the problem of factoring a polynomial.

If the polynomial $f(x)$ factors into the product of polynomials $d(x)q(x)$, then the remainder is zero when $f(x)$ is divided by $d(x)$. Otherwise, we obtain a remainder polynomial $r(x)$ of a lower degree than $d(x)$, as we observed in Section 2.7. Expressing this statement as an identity, we have

$$\frac{f(x)}{d(x)} = q(x) + \frac{r(x)}{d(x)} \quad (d(x) \neq 0)$$

or

(10.3) $$f(x) = d(x) \cdot q(x) + r(x)$$

We now prove the following theorem about the remainder when a polynomial is divided by $x - a$.

Theorem 10.1. *If a nonconstant polynomial* f(x) *is divided by the linear polynomial* x $-$ a, *then the remainder equals* f(a).

Proof: Let $d(x) = x - a$ in Equation 10.3. Since the remainder $r(x)$ is of degree less than $d(x)$, it is of degree zero, that is, $r(x)$ is a constant r. From Equation 10.3, we have

$$f(x) = (x - a)q(x) + r$$

Since this is an identity, it is true in particular for $x = a$, that is

$$f(a) = (a - a)q(a) + r$$
$$= r$$

and the theorem is proved.

Theorem 10.1 is called the **remainder theorem,** and an application is illustrated in the following example.

Example 10.9. If $f(x) = x^4 - 7x^2 + 29x - 13$, find the remainder when $f(x)$ is divided by $x + 4$.

Solution: Using $a = -4$ in Theorem 10.1, we have

$$f(-4) = (-4)^4 - 7(-4)^2 + 29(-4) - 13$$
$$= 15$$

Note that we have already performed the division of Example 10.9 in Example 2.17 on page 49. Using synthetic division, we obtained the remainder 15 without having to evaluate $(-4)^4 - 7(-4)^2 + 29(-4) - 13$. This suggests the application of the remainder theorem illustrated in the following example.

Example 10.10. If $f(x) = 2x^5 - 13x^4 - 53x^2 + 21x + 61$, find $f(7)$.

Solution: Using synthetic division to divide $f(x)$ by $x - 7$, we have

$$
\begin{array}{r|rrrrrr}
7 & 2 & -13 & 0 & -53 & 21 & 61 \\
  &   & 14 & 7 & 49 & -28 & -49 \\
\hline
  & 2 & 1 & 7 & -4 & -7 & 12
\end{array}
$$

Thus, the remainder when $f(x)$ is divided by $x - 7$ is 12. By the remainder theorem, we have $f(7) = 12$.

Using Theorem 10.1, we now deduce the **factor theorem.**

Theorem 10.2. *A nonconstant polynomial* $f(x)$ *has the factor* $x - r$ *if and only if* r *is a solution of the equation* $f(x) = 0$.

Proof: The phrase "if and only if" means that the implication goes both ways. Thus, we must prove (1) if r is a solution of $f(x) = 0$, then $f(x)$ has the factor $x - r$, and (2) if $f(x)$ has the factor $x - r$, then r is a solution of $f(x) = 0$.
(1) If r is a solution of $f(x) = 0$, we have $f(r) = 0$. Thus, by the remainder theorem, the remainder is zero when $f(x)$ is divided by $x - r$. From Equation 10.3 we have

$$f(x) = (x - r)q(x) + 0$$

which establishes that $x - r$ is a factor of $f(x)$.
(2) If $x - r$ is a factor of $f(x)$, we have

$$f(x) = (x - r)q(x)$$

Thus, the equations $f(x) = 0$ and $(x - r)q(x) = 0$ are equivalent. Since r is a solution of $(x - r)q(x) = 0$, it is also a solution of $f(x) = 0$.

Theorem 10.2 is of fundamental importance in algebra. It tells us that any polynomial $f(x)$, for which $f(r) = 0$, has the linear factor $x - r$. This theorem is applied to factoring a given polynomial in the following example.

Example 10.11. If the equation

$$x^4 + 2x^3 - 31x^2 - 32x + 60 = 0$$

has the solutions $r_1 = 1$ and $r_2 = -2$, write the polynomial

$$x^4 + 2x^3 - 31x^2 - 32x + 60$$

as a product of first-degree factors.

Solution: By the factor theorem, two factors are $(x - 1)$ and $(x + 2)$. Using synthetic division to divide the fourth-degree polynomial by $x - 1$, we have

$$
\begin{array}{r|rrrrr}
1 & 1 & 2 & -31 & -32 & 60 \\
  &   & 1 & 3 & -28 & -60 \\
\hline
  & 1 & 3 & -28 & -60 & 0
\end{array}
$$

Thus, the quotient is $x^3 + 3x^2 - 28x - 60$. (Why is the remainder equal to zero?) Dividing this polynomial by $x + 2$, we have

$$
\begin{array}{r|rrrr}
-2 & 1 & 3 & -28 & -60 \\
   &   & -2 & -2 & 60 \\
\hline
   & 1 & 1 & -30 & 0
\end{array}
$$

Thus, the quotient is $x^2 + x - 30$, and it factors into the product

$$(x - 5) \cdot (x + 6)$$

Summarizing, we found that the factors of

$$x^4 + 2x^3 - 31x^2 - 32x + 60$$

are

$$(x - 1), \quad (x + 2), \quad (x - 5), \quad \text{and} \quad (x + 6)$$

PROBLEMS A

1. If $f(x) = 3x^4 - 4x^3 + 5x^2 - 6x + 7$, find

(a) $f(1)$ (b) $f(8)$
(c) $f(-4)$ (d) $f(-6)$

2. If $f(x) = x^5 - 7x^2 + 9$, find

(a) $f(5)$ (b) $f(-9)$
(c) $f(2i)$ (d) $f(-\sqrt{3})$

3. Determine the values of k for which

(a) $3x^3 + 4x^2 + x - k$ has the factor $x - 1$.
(b) $2x^3 - x^2 + kx + 2$ has the factor $x + 2$.
(c) $x^4 + 5x^3 - kx^2 + x + k$ has the factor $x + 5$.
(d) $kx^3 + 2x^2 + 3kx + 1$ has the factor $x - i$.

PROBLEMS B

1. Under what conditions on the integer n is $x + a$ a factor of $x^n - a^n$?

2. If the polynomial $f(x)$, of degree two or higher, is divided by $(x - r)(x - s)$, prove that the remainder is given by

$$\frac{f(r) - f(s)}{r - s} x + \frac{rf(s) - sf(r)}{r - s}$$

10.5   Polynomial Equations of Degree n

We now consider equations of the form

$$a_0 + a_1x + a_2x^2 + \ldots + a_nx^n = 0$$

where n is a positive integer. Before seeking methods for determining solutions of such equations, it is helpful to have some assurance that such solutions exist. In this connection, we are supported by the following theorem, called the "fundamental theorem of algebra."

Theorem 10.3. *The equation*

$$a_0 + a_1x + a_2x^2 + \ldots + a_nx^n = 0$$

where n *is a positive integer, has at least one solution.*

Our background in mathematics does not permit us to prove this theorem. Theorem 10.3 is true for polynomials having real or complex coefficients, and the solution set of the equation given in this theorem may contain real or complex numbers.

Using this theorem, together with the factor theorem, we can answer the question of just how many solutions are possessed by the equation

$$a_0 + a_1x + \ldots + a_nx^n = 0$$

Theorem 10.4. *If* f(x) *is a polynomial in* x *of degree* n, *the equation* f(x) $= 0$ *has at most* n *solutions.*

Proof: By the fundamental theorem of algebra, the equation $f(x) = 0$ has at least one solution. If we call this solution r_1, we can use the factor theorem to write

$$f(x) = (x - r_1)f_1(x)$$

By Definition 2.5 on page 45, $f_1(x)$ is a polynomial of degree $n - 1$. Again using the fundamental theorem of algebra, we conclude that the equation $f_1(x) = 0$ has at least one solution. If we call this solution r_2, we have $f_1(x) = (x - r_2)f_2(x)$, or

$$f(x) = (x - r_1)(x - r_2)f_2(x)$$

where $f_2(x)$ is a polynomial of degree $n - 2$. Successive application of the preceding steps a total of n times shows that we can write

$$f(x) = (x - r_1)(x - r_2) \cdot \ldots \cdot (x - r_n) \cdot f_n(x)$$

However, $f(x)$ has degree n; thus, $f_n(x)$ must have degree zero; that is, $f_n(x)$ is a constant. Thus, the equation $f(x) = 0$ has the solutions $r_1, r_2, \ldots, r_n$.

If $r_1, \ldots, r_n$ are all distinct numbers, we can conclude from the proof of Theorem 10.4 that the equation $f(x) = 0$, where $f(x)$ is a polynomial of degree n, has *exactly* n solutions.   However, if at least two of the numbers $r_1, \ldots, r_n$ are equal, $f(x) = 0$ has *fewer than* n solutions.   If k of the numbers $r_1, \ldots, r_n$ are equal, we call their common value a **solution of multiplicity k.**   Counting solutions of multiplicity k as k solutions, we can conclude from Theorem 10.4 that every polynomial equation of degree n has exactly n solutions.   Furthermore, we can conclude that the polynomial $f(x)$ has exactly n linear factors.   Corresponding to each solution r of the equation $f(x) = 0$, there is a factor $x - r$ of the polynomial $f(x)$.

Theorems 10.3 and 10.4 can be used together with synthetic division to reduce a polynomial equation of degree n to one of degree less than n if one or more solutions are known.   If the resulting equation, called the **depressed equation,** is a quadratic equation or a linear equation, it can be solved by methods previously discussed.

Example 10.12. If $r_1 = 1$ is a solution of the equation

$$x^3 - 3x^2 + 4x - 2 = 0$$

find the remaining two solutions.

Solution: Using synthetic division to divide the cubic polynomial by $x - 1$, we have

$$
\begin{array}{r|rrrr}
1 & 1 & -3 & 4 & -2 \\
  &   & 1 & -2 & 2 \\
\hline
  & 1 & -2 & 2 & 0
\end{array}
$$

Thus, the depressed equation is $x^2 - 2x + 2 = 0$.   (Why is the remainder equal to zero?)   Using the quadratic formulas, we find the remaining solutions to be

$$r_2 = 1 + i \quad \text{and} \quad r_3 = 1 - i$$

Synthetic division is useful in finding any integer solutions of a given polynomial equation by trial and error.   With a little practice, you can become quite proficient at finding any solutions that are small integers.

Example 10.13. Solve the equation

$$x^4 + 4x^3 + 6x^2 - x - 10 = 0$$

Solution: Noting that the coefficients sum to zero, we conclude that $r_1 = 1$ is a solution.   Why?   Dividing by $x - 1$, we have

$$
\begin{array}{r|rrrrr}
1 & 1 & 4 & 6 & -1 & -10 \\
  &   & 1 & 5 & 11 & 10 \\
\hline
  & 1 & 5 & 11 & 10 & 0
\end{array}
$$

Evidently neither -1 nor 1 is a solution of the depressed cubic equation

$$x^3 + 5x^2 + 11x + 10 = 0$$

Having tried 2 unsuccessfully, we next try $r_2 = -2$, and we have

$$
\begin{array}{r|rrrr}
-2 & 1 & 5 & 11 & 10 \\
   &   & -2 & -6 & -10 \\
\hline
   & 1 & 3 & 5 & 0
\end{array}
$$

The remainder is zero, therefore $r_2 = -2$ is a solution. The depressed quadratic equation $x^2 + 3x + 5 = 0$ can be solved by the quadratic formulas to obtain the solutions

$$r_3 = -\frac{3}{2} + \frac{\sqrt{11}}{2}i \quad \text{and} \quad r_4 = -\frac{3}{2} - \frac{\sqrt{11}}{2}i$$

PROBLEMS A

1. Find the remaining solutions of the following equations.
(a) $x^3 + x^2 - x - 1 = 0,\ r_1 = 1$
(b) $2x^3 + 7x^2 + x - 10 = 0,\ r_1 = -2$
(c) $x^3 + x^2 + x + 1 = 0,\ r_1 = i$
(d) $2x^4 - 7x^3 + 15x^2 - 17x + 7 = 0,\ r_1 = r_2 = 1$

2. Solve the following equations.
(a) $x^3 - x^2 + x - 1 = 0$
(b) $x^5 + 2x^3 + x = 0$
(c) $x^4 - 4x^3 + 6x^2 - 4x + 1 = 0$
(d) $x^3 - 3x^2 + 4 = 0$

PROBLEMS B

1. Prove that the solutions of the equation

$$a_0k^n + a_1k^{n-1}y + a_2k^{n-2}y^2 + \ldots + a_ny^n = 0$$

are k times the solutions of the equation

$$a_0 + a_1x + a_2x^2 + \ldots + a_nx^n = 0$$

2. In the equation

$$a_0 + a_1x + a_2x^2 + a_3x^3 = 0$$

having solutions r_1, r_2, and r_3, prove that
(a) $a_2/a_3 = -(r_1 + r_2 + r_3)$
(b) $a_1/a_3 = r_1r_2 + r_1r_3 + r_2r_3$
(c) $a_0/a_3 = -r_1r_2r_3$

10.6   Solutions of a Polynomial Equation with Real Coefficients

In Section 10.5 we learned that a polynomial equation of degree n has exactly n solutions. When we are given the solutions $r_1, \ldots, r_n$ the original polynomial can be written as a constant times the product

$$(x - r_1)(x - r_2) \cdot \ldots \cdot (x - r_n)$$

If the polynomial

$$a_0 + a_1 x + a_2 x^2 + \ldots + a_n x^n$$

has *real coefficients*, some of the solutions may not be real. Evidently, we must impose certain conditions on any complex solutions in order that the product $(x - r_1)(x - r_2) \cdot \ldots \cdot (x - r_n)$ be a polynomial with real coefficients.

In the following theorem we prove that any polynomial equation with real coefficients that has the solution $a + bi$ also has the solution $a - bi$. To prove this theorem, we make use of the properties of the complex conjugate,

$$\overline{z_1 + z_2} = \overline{z_1} + \overline{z_2} \quad \text{and} \quad \overline{z_1 z_2} = \overline{z_1} \cdot \overline{z_2},$$

given in Theorems 3.1 and 3.2 on page 61. These properties can be extended readily to include more than two complex numbers; that is, it can be proved that

$$\overline{z_1 + z_2 + \ldots + z_n} = \overline{z_1} + \overline{z_2} + \ldots + \overline{z_n}$$

and

$$\overline{z_1 \cdot z_2 \cdot \ldots \cdot z_n} = \overline{z_1} \cdot \overline{z_2} \cdot \ldots \cdot \overline{z_n}$$

Theorem 10.5. *If* $f(x)$ *is a polynomial in* x *with real coefficients, and the complex number* r *is a solution of the equation* $f(x) = 0$, *then* $\bar{r}$, *the conjugate of* r, *is also a solution of the equation* $f(x) = 0$.

Proof: If r is a solution of the equation $f(x) = 0$, then $f(r) = 0$, or

$$a_0 + a_1 r + a_2 r^2 + \ldots + a_n r^n = 0$$

Thus, we can state also that the conjugate of the number

$$a_0 + a_1 r + a_2 r^2 + \ldots + a_n r^n$$

equals the conjugate of zero. Since $\overline{0} = 0$, we have

$$\overline{a_0 + a_1 r + a_2 r^2 + \ldots + a_n r^n} = 0$$

Thus

$$\overline{a_0} + \overline{a_1 r} + \overline{a_2 r^2} + \ldots + \overline{a_n r^n} = 0$$

and

$$\overline{a_0} + \overline{a_1} \cdot \bar{r} + \overline{a_2} \cdot \bar{r}^2 + \ldots + \overline{a_n} \cdot \bar{r}^n = 0$$

However, $a_0, a_1, a_2, \ldots, a_n$ are real coefficients, and the conjugate of a real number is the number itself. Thus

$$a_0 + a_1\bar{r} + a_2\bar{r}^2 + \ldots + a_n\bar{r}^n = 0$$

The last equation states that $f(\bar{r}) = 0$; that is, $\bar{r}$ is a solution of the equation $f(x) = 0$.

According to Theorem 10.5, if $a + bi$ is a solution of a polynomial equation with real coefficients, then $a - bi$ is also a solution. Thus, the polynomial

$$[x - (a + bi)] \cdot [x - (a - bi)]$$

is a factor of the original polynomial. Multiplying, we have

$$[x - (a + bi)] \cdot [x - (a - bi)]$$
$$= x^2 - (a + bi)x - (a - bi)x + (a + bi)(a - bi)$$
$$= x^2 - 2ax + (a^2 + b^2)$$

Thus, the quadratic polynomial $x^2 - 2ax + (a^2 + b^2)$, *with real coefficients*, is a factor of $f(x)$. We can conclude that a polynomial with real coefficients can be factored into a product of polynomials having real coefficients and the degree at most two.

Example 10.14. If the equation $f(x) = 0$ has the solutions 1, $2 + 3i$, and $2 - 3i$, find factors of $f(x)$ having real coefficients.

Solution: The required factors are

$$(x - 1) \quad \text{and} \quad [x - (2 + 3i)] \cdot [x - (2 - 3i)]$$

or

$$(x - 1) \quad \text{and} \quad (x^2 - 4x + 13)$$

Example 10.15. If $1 + i$ is a solution of the equation

$$x^4 - 2x^3 + 3x^2 - 2x + 2 = 0$$

find the other three solutions.

Solution: Since $1 + i$ is a solution, $1 - i$ is also a solution, and the fourth-degree polynomial has the factor

$$[x - (1 + i)] \cdot [x - (1 - i)] = x^2 - 2x + 2$$

Using long division, we find that the quotient is $x^2 + 1$ when the fourth-degree polynomial is divided by $x^2 - 2x + 2$. The quadratic equation $x^2 + 1 = 0$ has the solutions $x = i$ and $x = -i$.

We could also have obtained the depressed equation $x^2 + 1 = 0$ with the use of synthetic division, as follows,

$$
\begin{array}{r|rrrrr}
1 + i & 1 & -2 & 3 & -2 & 2 \\
& & i+1 & -2 & i+1 & -2 \\
\hline
1 - i & 1 & i-1 & 1 & i-1 & \mid \ 0 \\
& & -i+1 & 0 & -i+1 & \\
\hline
& 1 & 0 & 1 & \mid \ 0 &
\end{array}
$$

If the polynomial equation $f(x) = 0$ has *rational coefficients*, and one of its solutions is of the form $a + b\sqrt{c}$, where a, b, and c are rational numbers, it is possible to prove that $a - b\sqrt{c}$ is also a solution. Note that the factor

$$[x - (a + b\sqrt{c})] \cdot [x - (a - b\sqrt{c})] = x^2 - 2ax + a^2 - b^2c$$

is a quadratic polynomial with *rational* coefficients.

Any polynomial equation with rational coefficients has an equivalent polynomial equation with *integer coefficients*. For example, the equations

$$\tfrac{3}{2}x^3 - \tfrac{1}{3}x^2 + \tfrac{1}{4}x - \tfrac{5}{6} = 0$$

and

$$18x^3 - 4x^2 + 3x - 10 = 0$$

are equivalent. The second equation was obtained from the first by multiplying by 12, the LCD of the coefficients of the first equation. We now prove the following theorem about the *rational solutions* of a polynomial equation with *integer coefficients*.

Theorem 10.6. *If* $a_0 + \ldots + a_nx^n$ *is a polynomial in* x *with integer coefficients, and the rational number* b/c, *expressed in lowest terms, is a solution of the equation* $a_0 + \ldots + a_nx^n = 0$, *then* b *is a factor of* a_0 *and* c *is a factor of* a_n.

Proof: If b/c is a solution of $a_0 + \ldots + a_nx^n = 0$, then

$$a_0 + a_1\left(\frac{b}{c}\right) + a_2\left(\frac{b}{c}\right)^2 + \ldots + a_n\left(\frac{b}{c}\right)^n = 0$$

Multiplying by c^n, we have,

$$a_0c^n + a_1bc^{n-1} + a_2b^2c^{n-2} + \ldots + a_nb^n = 0$$

or

$$b(a_1c^{n-1} + a_2bc^{n-2} + \ldots + a_nb^{n-1}) = -a_0c^n$$

However, the coefficients $a_1, \ldots, a_n$ are integers; thus, the left-hand side of the above equation is an integer having the factor b. Therefore, $-a_0c^n$ is an integer having the factor b. Since b/c is in lowest terms,

b and c are relatively prime integers; that is, b and c have no common factors. It can be proved that b and c^n have no common factors, and we can only conclude that b is a factor of a_0. Writing

$$a_0 c^n + a_1 b c^{n-1} + \ldots + a_n b^n = 0$$

in the form

$$c(a_0 c^{n-1} + a_1 b c^{n-2} + \ldots + a_{n-1} b^{n-1}) = -a_n b^n$$

and using a similar argument, we can conclude that c is a factor of a_n.

We can use Theorem 10.6 to find any rational solutions of a polynomial equation with rational coefficients. First, we rewrite the equation so that its coefficients are integers, then we list all the factors of a_0 and a_n forming all possible fractions in lowest terms from these factors. Using synthetic division, we check each of these fractions to determine which, if any, are solutions. If we find a solution by this method, we reapply the method to the reduced equation.

Example 10.16. Solve the equation

$$\tfrac{3}{2}x^4 + \tfrac{1}{4}x^3 - \tfrac{1}{2}x^2 + \tfrac{1}{2}x - \tfrac{1}{4} = 0$$

Solution: Multiplying by 4, we obtain

$$6x^4 + x^3 - 2x^2 + 2x - 1 = 0$$

If there is a rational solution, its numerator is a factor of 1 and its denominator is a factor of 6 when it is put in lowest terms. Such numbers are ± 1, $\pm \tfrac{1}{2}$, $\pm \tfrac{1}{3}$, and $\pm \tfrac{1}{6}$. Using synthetic division, we try 1, obtaining a remainder of 6; thus, 1 is not a solution. When we try -1, we obtain

$$
\begin{array}{r|rrrrr}
-1 & 6 & 1 & -2 & 2 & -1 \\
   &   & -6 & 5 & -3 & 1 \\
\hline
   & 6 & -5 & 3 & -1 & 0
\end{array}
$$

Thus, $r_1 = -1$ is a solution, and the reduced equation is

$$6x^3 - 5x^2 + 3x - 1 = 0$$

Its possible rational solutions are also ± 1, $\pm \tfrac{1}{2}$, $\pm \tfrac{1}{3}$, and $\pm \tfrac{1}{6}$. (Except that we already know that 1 is not a solution.) When we try $\tfrac{1}{2}$, we obtain

$$
\begin{array}{r|rrrr}
\tfrac{1}{2} & 6 & -5 & 3 & -1 \\
             &   & 3 & -1 & 1 \\
\hline
             & 6 & -2 & 2 & 0
\end{array}
$$

Thus, $r_2 = \tfrac{1}{2}$ is a solution, and the reduced equation is

$$6x^2 - 2x + 2 = 0, \quad \text{or} \quad 3x^2 - x + 1 = 0$$

Solving this equation by means of the quadratic formulas, we obtain the solutions

$$r_3 = \frac{1}{6} + \frac{\sqrt{11}}{6}i \quad \text{and} \quad r_4 = \frac{1}{6} - \frac{\sqrt{11}}{6}i;$$

In the following example, the work is displayed in a short form.

Example 10.17. Solve the equation

$$x^4 - 11x^2 - 12x + 4 = 0$$

Solution: The only possible rational solutions are ± 1, ± 2, and ± 4. If we try them successively, we obtain finally

$$
\begin{array}{r|rrrrr}
r_1 = -2 & 1 & 0 & -11 & -12 & 4 \\
         &   & -2 & 4 & 14 & -4 \\
\hline
r_2 = -2 & 1 & -2 & -7 & 2 & 0 \\
         &   & -2 & 8 & -2 & \\
\hline
         & 1 & -4 & 1 & 0 &
\end{array}
$$

Using the quadratic formulas to solve the depressed equation $x^2 - 4x + 1 = 0$, we obtain

$$r_3 = 2 + \sqrt{3}$$
$$r_4 = 2 - \sqrt{3}$$

Note that the depressed cubic equation $x^3 - 2x^2 - 7x + 2 = 0$ could have had only the rational solutions ± 1 and ± 2.

PROBLEMS A

1. Given the following solutions of $f(x) = 0$, with real coefficients, find the factors of $f(x)$ having real coefficients.

(a) $2, -3, 4$　　　　　　　　　　(b) $3, -1, 2, -5$
(c) $-2, 1 - 2i, 1 + 2i$　　　　　(d) $3, -1 - i, -1 + i$
(e) $4, -2, 3 + 7i, 3 - 7i$　　　(f) $1, -3, 5, 7 + i, 7 - i$
(g) $-9, \sqrt{3} + \sqrt{2}\,i, \sqrt{3} - \sqrt{2}\,i$
(h) $4, -1, 1 - \sqrt{3}\,i, 1 + \sqrt{3}\,i$
(i) $1 + i, 1 - i, -2 - 3i, -2 + 3i$
(j) $-1, -1 + i, -1 - i, -1 + 2i, -1 - 2i$

2. Find the remaining solutions of the following equations.

(a) $x^3 - 2x^2 + x - 2 = 0, r_1 = i$
(b) $x^2 - 6x + 13 = 0, r_1 = 3 + 2i$
(c) $x^4 - 3x^3 + 3x^2 - 2 = 0, r_1 = 1 + i$
(d) $x^4 + x^3 - 2x^2 - 6x - 4 = 0, r_1 = -1 - i$
(e) $x^4 + 4x^3 + 14x^2 + 20x + 25 = 0, r_1 = -1 + 2i$
(f) $x^6 - x^5 - 3x^4 + 4x^3 - 4x + 4 = 0, r_1 = r_2 = \sqrt{2}$

3. What can be said about the coefficients in the equation $a_0 + a_1x + a_2x^2 + a_3x^3 + a_4x^4 = 0$ if

(a) $1 + i$, $1 - i$, 2 and 3 are solutions.
(b) $1 + 2\sqrt{3}$, $1 - 2\sqrt{3}$, i and $-i$ are solutions.
(c) 1, 2, 3 and 4 are solutions.
(d) $1 + i$, $1 - i$, $2 + \sqrt{3}$, and -4 are solutions.
(e) $1 + i$ is a solution, but $1 - i$ is not a solution.
(f) i and $2 + 3\sqrt{5}$ are solutions.

4. Solve the following polynomial equations with rational coefficients.

(a) $x^3 - 2x^2 - x + 2 = 0$ (b) $x^3 - 8x^2 + 17x - 6 = 0$
(c) $2x^3 + 3x^2 + 2x + 3 = 0$ (d) $3x^3 + x^2 + x - 2 = 0$
(e) $x^4 - 8x^2 + 16 = 0$ (f) $x^4 + 4x^3 + 2x^2 - x + 6 = 0$
(g) $2x^4 - 7x^3 + x^2 + 10x = 0$ (h) $48x^4 - 52x^3 + 13x - 3 = 0$
(i) $4x^4 + 5x^3 - 10x^2 - 5x + 6 = 0$
(j) $x^5 + 3x^4 + 6x^3 + 10x^2 + 9x + 3 = 0$

PROBLEMS B

1. If $f(x)$ and $g(x)$ are two polynomials in x of degree n, and they are equal for more than n values of x, prove that $f(x)$ and $g(x)$ are identically equal polynomials. *Hint:* Consider the equation

$$(a_0 - b_0) + (a_1 - b_1)x + \ldots + (a_n - b_n)x^n = 0$$

2. Use the results of Problem 1 to find the constants A and B in the identity

$$x - 5 = A(x + 1) + B(x - 3)$$

3. Prove that $\sqrt{2}$ is an irrational number. *Hint:* Consider the equation $x^2 - 2 = 0$.

11

Systems of Equations

11.1   Linear Equations in Two Variables

In Section 9.2 we discussed the solution of linear equations in one variable. In this section, we consider linear equations in two variables, that is, equations of the form

$$(11.1) \qquad\qquad ax + by = c$$

where a, b, and c are real numbers, and a and b are different from zero.

If we solve Equation 11.1 for y, we obtain

$$y = -\frac{a}{b}x + \frac{c}{b}$$

Note that this equation establishes a one-to-one correspondence which assigns a real value of y to each real value of x.   Thus, by Definition 4.1, this equation defines a function $\mathbf{f}$; furthermore, $\mathbf{f}$ is a *linear function.*

By the **graph of an equation**, we mean the set of all points for which the equation is satisfied.   (How this definition may differ from that of the graph of a function will be illustrated in Section 11.4, where we discuss quadratic equations in two variables.)   Since the equation $y = ax + b$ gives the correspondence of a linear function, the graph of this equation is a straight line.

If we have *two* linear equations in two variables

$$(11.2) \qquad\qquad \begin{aligned} a_1 x + b_1 y &= c_1 \\ a_2 x + b_2 y &= c_2 \end{aligned}$$

the graph of each equation is a straight line. If these lines are distinct and not parallel, they will intersect in exactly one point (x_0, y_0). The point (x_0, y_0) is a point on the line determined by the equation $a_1x + b_1y = c_1$, and it is also a point on the line determined by the equation $a_2x + b_2y = c_2$. Thus, the point (x_0, y_0) satisfies both equations *simultaneously*, and it is called the **unique solution** of the System of Equations 11.2.

If there is a unique solution of the System 11.2, it may be found approximately by graphing each equation and finding the coordinates of the point of intersection of the graphs. It may be found exactly by two closely-related methods — the method of **substitution** and the method of **elimination.**

The method of substitution consists of rewriting one of the equations and expressing one variable, say y, in terms of the other, x. Then, this expression in x is substituted for y in the remaining equation. The result is usually a linear equation in x, which can be solved by known methods. The method of substitution is illustrated in the following example.

Example 11.1. Solve the system:

$$3x + 2y = 11$$
$$-x + 5y = 2$$

Solution: It is convenient to solve the second equation for x, obtaining

$$x = 5y - 2$$

Substituting in the first equation, we have

$$3(5y - 2) + 2y = 11$$
$$17y = 17$$

Thus, $y = 1$. To obtain x, we substitute $y = 1$ in the equation $x = 5y - 2$, obtaining $x = 3$. The solution of the system of equations is the *ordered number pair* (3, 1).

The method of elimination is based on the principle of finding **equivalent systems** of equations. Analogous to the definition of equivalent equations, we say that two systems of equations are equivalent if they have the same solution set. We find equivalent systems of equations by using the properties of equalities given in Section 9.1. Given a system of two linear equations, if we can find an equivalent system of two linear equations such that the coefficients of one of the variables are identical, we can use a modified form of Property 4 of equalities to subtract corresponding sides of one equation from the other. In this way, one of the variables is eliminated, and the solution can be obtained as before.

Example 11.2. Solve the system:

$$3x + 2y = 4$$
$$-2x + 5y = -9$$

Solution: We can find an equivalent system with identical coefficients of x by multiplying both sides of the first equation by 2 and both sides of the second equation by -3, to obtain

$$6x + 4y = 8$$
$$6x - 15y = 27$$

Subtracting corresponding sides of the first equation from those of the second equation, we obtain

$$-19y = 19$$

or $y = -1$. We can obtain x by substituting $y = -1$ in either of the original equations. Using the first equation, we have

$$3x + 2(-1) = 4$$

or $x = 2$. The solution of the system is $(2, -1)$.

In solving the equations of Example 11.2, we obtained the equation $-19y = 19$. The system of equations

$$3x + 2y = 4$$
$$- 19y = 19$$

formed by taking the first equation of the original system together with the equation $-19y = 19$, is equivalent to the original system of equations. Such a system of two linear equations is said to be written in **triangular form.** A system of linear equations in triangular form is readily solved, as shown in Example 11.2.

The solution of certain stated problems employs the methods of solving systems of linear equations, as shown in the following example.

Example 11.3. The sum of the digits of a two-digit number is 8. If we reverse the order of the digits, then the new number is 10 more than twice the original number. Find the original number.

Solution: Let the "tens" digit of the original number be denoted by x, and the "units" digit be denoted by y. Then the sum of the digits is given by

$$x + y = 8$$

The number itself is given by $10x + y$, and the number with the digits reversed is given by $10y + x$. Thus,

$$10y + x = 2(10x + y) + 10$$

or

$$-19x + 8y = 10$$

Thus, we have the system

$$x + y = 8$$
$$-19x + 8y = 10$$

If we multiply each side of the first equation by 8 and subtract corresponding sides from those of the second equation, we obtain the following equivalent system in triangular form.

$$x + y = \quad 8$$
$$-27x \quad = -54$$

Hence, $x = 2$ and $y = 6$, and the original number is 26.

PROBLEMS A

1. Solve the following systems.

(a) $x + 2y = 16$
$\quad x - 3y = 11$

(b) $2x - 3y = 5$
$\quad x + 3y = 7$

(c) $4x + 5y = \ -6$
$\quad 3x - 2y = -16$

(d) $-7x + 4y = 12$
$\quad 3x + 6y = \ 1$

(e) $\sqrt{2}\,x + \sqrt{3}\,y = \sqrt{6}$
$\quad \sqrt{3}\,x - \sqrt{2}\,y = \ 3$

(f) $\quad 4x - \sqrt{5}\,y = 2$
$\quad \sqrt{5}\,x + \quad 4y = 1$

(g) $-\frac{1}{2}x + \frac{3}{2}y = \frac{1}{4}$
$\quad 4x + \ y = -\frac{1}{2}$

(h) $\frac{3}{5}x + \frac{2}{3}y = \frac{1}{10}$
$\quad -\frac{1}{3}x + \ y = \ 5$

(i) $(1 + \sqrt{2})x + y = 5$
$\quad (1 - \sqrt{2})x - y = 1$

(j) $\dfrac{\sqrt{3}}{2}(x + y) = \quad 2$

$\quad \dfrac{\sqrt{3}}{2}(x - y) = -\dfrac{1}{2}$

(k) $\dfrac{x + y}{x - 2y} = -7$

$\quad 3x + 6y = \ 27$

(l) $y = 2x + 4$

$\quad \dfrac{x - 3}{y} = 1$

2. Solve the following systems of equations in *linear form.*

(a) $\dfrac{1}{x} + \dfrac{1}{y} = 3$

$\quad \dfrac{1}{x} - \dfrac{1}{y} = 1$ $(x \neq 0, y \neq 0)$

(b) $\text{Sin } x + \text{Cos } y = 1$
$\quad \text{Sin } x - \text{Cos } y = 1$

(c) $\log x + 2 \log y = \log 2$ $(x \neq 0, y \neq 0)$
$\quad \log x + \quad \log y = \ -1$

(d) $\quad 2^z + \quad 4^u = 16$
$\quad 3 \cdot 2^z - 2 \cdot 2^{2u} = \ 8$

3. The sum of two numbers is 17. Their difference is 2. Find the two numbers.

4. The sum of the digits of a two-digit number is 8. If the digits of the number are reversed the number with the digits reversed is 18 more than the original number. Find the original number.

5. A man paid $3.70 for 6 pounds of apples and 10 pounds of pears. He sold 4 pounds of apples and made a profit of $0.10 per pound. He sold 5 pounds of pears and made a profit of $0.25 per pound. For the apples and pears that he sold he received $3.70. What did he pay per pound for the apples?

6. If we add 1 to the numerator of a certain fraction and subtract 1 from its denominator, we obtain $\frac{3}{2}$. If we subtract 1 from the numerator and add 1 to the denominator, we obtain $\frac{1}{4}$. Find the fraction.

PROBLEMS B

1. Find the values of a and b such that $(x + 1)$ and $(x - 2)$ are factors of the polynomial $ax^3 + 2x^2 - bx + 1$.

2. Obtain all the solutions to the system:

$$|x + y| = 2$$
$$|x - y| = 1$$

11.2 Inconsistent and Dependent Systems

So far, we have considered only systems of linear equations in two variables having a unique solution. We have seen that a unique solution exists if the graphs of the equations

$$a_1x + b_1y = c_1 \quad \text{and} \quad a_2x + b_2y = c_2$$

are distinct, nonparallel straight lines. If the lines determined by these equations are parallel, there is no point (x, y) at which these lines intersect; therefore, there is no number pair satisfying these equations simultaneously. However, if these lines are identical, then every point on the common line is a point of intersection, and every number pair satisfying one of these equations also satisfies the other equation. Accordingly, we state the following definition.

Definition 11.1. *A system of linear equations is* **consistent** *if it has at least one solution. A consistent system is* **dependent** *if it has more than one solution.*

This definition is illustrated in the following example.

Example 11.4. Determine which of the following systems is consistent and which is dependent:

(a) $3x + 2y = 11$ (b) $x - 2y = 5$ (c) $x - 2y = 5$

    $-x + 5y = 2$ $3x - 6y = 15$ $3x - 6y = 7$

Solution:

(a) This system was solved in Example 11.1. The solution was found to be (3, 1), and Figure 11.1(a) shows that we have a pair of intersecting straight lines. The system is *consistent and independent*.

(b) Graphs of these equations are shown in Figure 11.1(b). You can verify that the two lines are coincident. Thus, every point on the common line is a solution to the system, and the system is *consistent and dependent*.

(c) Graphs of these equations are shown in Figure 11.1(c). You can verify that the two lines are parallel. Thus, there is no solution, and the system is *inconsistent*.

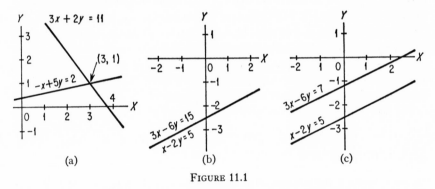

FIGURE 11.1

In order to determine conditions on the coefficients a_1, b_1, c_1, a_2, b_2, and c_2 such that a system of two linear equations in two variables has a unique solution, is dependent, or is inconsistent, we attempt to solve the system

$$a_1x + b_1y = c_1$$
$$a_2x + b_2y = c_2$$

First, we multiply both sides of the first equation by b_2 and both sides of the second equation by b_1, obtaining the equivalent system

$$a_1b_2x + b_1b_2y = c_1b_2$$
$$a_2b_1x + b_2b_1y = c_2b_1$$

Subtracting corresponding sides of the second equation from those of the first equation, we obtain

(11.3) $$(a_1b_2 - a_2b_1)x = c_1b_2 - c_2b_1$$

Next, we multiply both sides of the original equations by a_2 and a_1, respectively, and subtract corresponding sides of the first equation so obtained from those of the second equation, obtaining

(11.4) $(a_1b_2 - a_2b_1)y = a_1c_2 - a_2c_1$

Note that the coefficients of x and y in Equations 11.3 and 11.4 are the same. If this common coefficient $a_1b_2 - a_2b_1$ does not equal zero, we can divide both sides of each of these equations by this coefficient, to obtain the unique solution

$$x = \frac{c_1b_2 - c_2b_1}{a_1b_2 - a_2b_1}$$

(11.5) $(a_1b_2 - a_2b_1 \neq 0)$

$$y = \frac{a_1c_2 - a_2c_1}{a_1b_2 - a_2b_1}$$

If $a_1b_2 - a_2b_1 = 0$, however, there is no unique solution. To determine whether the system is dependent or inconsistent, we must examine the right-hand sides of Equations 11.3 and 11.4. If both right-hand sides are equal to zero, both equations are true for all x and all y; thus, the system is *dependent*. Conversely, if at least one of the right-hand sides does not equal zero, these equations are not both true statements; thus, the system has no solutions and it is *inconsistent*.

The foregoing may be restated as follows: The system is dependent if

$$a_1b_2 - a_2b_1 = c_1b_2 - c_2b_1 = 0$$

and it is inconsistent if

$$a_1b_2 - a_2b_1 = 0 \quad \text{and} \quad c_1b_2 - c_2b_1 \neq 0$$

Writing these equations in a different way, we can obtain the following conclusions: *A system of two linear equations in two variables is dependent if*

$$\frac{a_1}{a_2} = \frac{b_1}{b_2} = \frac{c_1}{c_2}$$

and it is inconsistent if

$$\frac{a_1}{a_2} = \frac{b_1}{b_2} \neq \frac{c_1}{c_2}$$

To illustrate, we observe in Example 11.4-b that

$$\frac{a_1}{a_2} = \frac{b_1}{b_2} = \frac{c_1}{c_2} = \frac{1}{3}$$

and in Example 11.4-c that

$$\frac{a_1}{a_2} = \frac{b_1}{b_2} = \frac{1}{3} \quad \text{but} \quad \frac{c_1}{c_2} = \frac{5}{7}$$

An important special case of consistent systems of equations is the system

$$a_1x + b_1y = 0$$
$$a_2x + b_2y = 0$$

called a **homogeneous system** of linear equations. In a homogeneous system $c_1 = c_2 = 0$, and we cannot talk about the ratio c_1/c_2. Referring to Equations 11.3 and 11.4, however, we note that a homogeneous system is equivalent to the system

$$(a_1b_2 - a_2b_1)x = 0$$
$$(a_1b_2 - a_2b_1)y = 0$$

If $a_1b_2 - a_2b_1 \neq 0$, we obtain the unique solution $(0, 0)$, called the **trivial solution**. If $a_1b_2 - a_2b_1 = 0$, then both equations of the homogeneous system are true statements *for all* x *and all* y, that is, the system has more than one solution and it is dependent.

PROBLEMS A

1. Graph each equation in the following systems, and determine which systems are consistent and which are inconsistent.

(a) $3x - 4y = 12$
　　$6x - 8y = 24$

(b) 　　$x + 2y = 5$
　　$-5x - 10y = 25$

(c) $-2x + 3y = 7$
　　$\frac{2}{3}x - y = -\frac{7}{3}$

(d) $\frac{2}{5}x - \frac{3}{4}y = 1$
　　$4x - \frac{15}{2}y = 10$

(e) $x - 5y = 6$
　　$2x - 5y = 6$

(f) $3y - 9 = 4x$
　　$3 + \frac{4}{3}x = y$

2. Determine which of the following systems are consistent and which are inconsistent without graphing.

(a) $3x - y = -3$
　　$6x - 2y = -6$

(b) $6x + 3y = 14$
　　$2x + y = 0$

(c) $x + 2y - 4 = 0$
　　$-4x - 8y + 16 = 0$

(d) $y = -\frac{1}{3}x + 2$
　　$3y + x = 6$

(e) $2x - 4y - \frac{17}{2} = 0$
　　$3x + 4y + 3 = 0$

(f) $\dfrac{x - 2}{3y} = -7$

　　$y = \dfrac{2 - x}{21}$

3. Find a value of k (if possible) such that the system is (i) consistent and independent, (ii) consistent and dependent, (iii) inconsistent.

(a) $kx + y = 2$
　　$2x - 3y = -6$

(b) $x - 5y = k$
　　$-2x + 10y = 7$

(c) $x + ky = 4$
　　$-x + y = 2$

(d) $k + x = y$
　　$1 + 2x = ky$

4. Prove that a system of two linear equations in two variables is dependent if one equation can be obtained from the other by multiplying both sides by the same constant.

PROBLEMS B

1. The sum of the digits of a two-digit number is 12. The number has the factor 3. Find an expression from which you can calculate any number satisfying these conditions and calculate at least one such number.

2. Given a system of three linear equations in the two variables x and y, find conditions such that the system (a) has a unique solution, (b) is dependent, (c) is inconsistent.

3. Prove the assertions made on page 208; that is, prove the following:

(a) If $a_1b_2 - a_2b_1 = c_1b_2 - c_2b_1 = 0$, then $a_1c_2 - a_2c_1 = 0$.

(b) If $a_1b_2 - a_2b_1 = c_1b_2 - c_2b_1 \neq 0$, then $a_1c_2 - a_2c_1 \neq 0$.

(c) If $a_1b_2 - a_2b_1 = c_1b_2 - c_2b_1 = 0$, then $a_1/a_2 = b_1/b_2 = c_1/c_2$.

(d) If $a_1b_2 - a_2b_1 = 0$ and $c_1b_2 - c_2b_1 \neq 0$, then $a_1/a_2 = b_1/b_2 \neq c_1/c_2$.

11.3   Linear Equations in More Than Two Variables

In this section, we extend our discussion of systems of linear equations to systems having more than two variables. We shall confine ourselves to solving equations in three variables, but the same method applies to the solution of systems of linear equations in more than three variables.

The linear equation

$$a_1x + b_1y + c_1z = d_1$$

in the three variables x, y, and z, has an unlimited number of solutions. Even the system of two linear equations in three variables

$$a_1x + b_1y + c_1z = d_1$$
$$a_2x + b_2y + c_2z = d_2$$

may have an unlimited number of solutions. To better understand this statement, consider the system

$$x - 4y + z = 6$$
$$2x + y - 3z = 1$$

If we rewrite these equations in the form

$$x - 4y = 6 - z$$
$$2x + y = 1 + 3z$$

they can be regarded as a pair of linear equations in the two variables x and y for any fixed value of z. In terms of z, the solution of these equations is

$$x = \frac{10 + 11z}{9}$$

$$y = \frac{-11 + 5z}{9}$$

Thus, to each number z there corresponds a unique pair of numbers (x, y) that satisfies this system of equations. For example, if $z = 1$, then $x = \frac{7}{3}$ and $y = -\frac{2}{3}$, and if $z = 2$, then $x = \frac{32}{9}$ and $y = -\frac{1}{9}$. Thus, two solutions of the original system of equations are $(\frac{7}{3}, -\frac{2}{3}, 1)$ and $(\frac{32}{9}, -\frac{1}{9}, 2)$.

The system of three linear equations in three variables

$$a_1x + b_1y + c_1z = d_1$$
$$a_2x + b_2y + c_2z = d_2$$
$$a_3x + b_3y + c_3z = d_3$$

can have a unique solution, it can have more than one solution, or it can have no solutions. Analogous to Definition 11.1, we say that this system is **consistent** if it has at least one solution, and it is **dependent** if it has more than one solution. The conditions on the coefficients $a_1, b_1, \ldots, c_3$ such that the system falls into each of these categories will be discussed in Chapter 12.

The methods for solving a system of n linear equations in n variables are similar to those used when $n = 2$. If $n = 3$, for example, the method of substitution requires that one of the equations be solved for, say, z in terms of x and y. Substituting the resulting expression for z in the remaining two equations, we obtain two linear equations in x and y, which can be solved by the methods of Section 11.1.

Example 11.5. Solve the system:

$$2x + y + 2z = 5$$
$$8x + y - z = 5$$
$$4x - y - 3z = 1$$

Solution: The second equation is most easily solved for z, and we obtain

$$z = 8x + y - 5$$

Substituting this expression for z in the remaining two equations, we obtain

$$2x + y + 2(8x + y - 5) = 5$$
$$4x - y - 3(8x + y - 5) = 1$$

or

$$18x + 3y = 15$$
$$-20x - 4y = -14$$

The solution of this system is $(\frac{3}{2}, -4)$. Substituting $x = \frac{3}{2}$ and $y = -4$ in the equation $z = 8x + y - 5$, we obtain $z = 3$. Thus, the solution of the original system is $(\frac{3}{2}, -4, 3)$. It is well to check your work by substituting this solution in each of the original equations.

An alternate method for solving systems of linear equations is more satisfactory when there are four or more equations. This method consists of finding an equivalent linear system in *triangular form*, if one exists. As we saw in Section 11.1, a system is in triangular form if one equation contains only one variable, a second equation contains only two variables, etc. The operations that enable us to find such an equivalent system have been illustrated in previous examples, but it would be well to review them here.

1. *Replacing any equation in the system with a new equation obtained by multiplying both sides of the original equation by the same number different from zero.*

2. *Replacing any equation with a new equation obtained by adding to its sides the corresponding sides of one or more other equations of the system.*

3. *Combining Operations 1 and 2 by replacing any equation in the system with a new equation whose sides are the sum of nonzero multiples of its sides and nonzero multiples of corresponding sides of any other equation or equations in the system.*

In the following example, we apply these operations to the solution of three simultaneous equations in three variables by finding an equivalent system in triangular form.

Example 11.6. Solve the system:

$$5x + 6y - 3z = 6$$
$$4x - 7y - 2z = -3$$
$$3x + y - 7z = 1$$

Solution: To eliminate z from the first equation, we multiply both sides of the first equation by 2, both sides of the second equation by -3, and add corresponding sides, obtaining $-2x + 33y = 21$. We replace the first equation by this new equation, obtaining the equivalent system

$$-2x + 33y \qquad\quad = 21$$
$$4x - 7y - 2z = -3$$
$$3x + y - 7z = 1$$

Now, to eliminate z from the second equation, we multiply both sides of the second equation by 7, both sides of the third equation by -2, and add corresponding sides, obtaining $22x - 51y = -23$. Replacing the second equation by this new equation, we obtain

$$-2x + 33y \qquad\quad = 21$$
$$22x - 51y \qquad\quad = -23$$
$$3x + y - 7z = 1$$

Finally, to eliminate x from the first equation, we multiply both sides of the first equation by 11 and add corresponding sides of the second equation, obtaining $312y = 208$, or $3y = 2$. Replacing the first equation by this one, and reordering the variables, we have the following equivalent system in triangular form.

$$3y \qquad\qquad\quad = 2$$
$$-51y + 22x \qquad = -23$$
$$y + 3x - 7z = 1$$

We solve this system by solving the equations successively, as follows.

$$y = \tfrac{2}{3}$$

Thus, $-51(\tfrac{2}{3}) + 22x = -23$, or

$$x = \tfrac{1}{2}$$

Thus, $(\tfrac{2}{3}) + 3(\tfrac{1}{2}) - 7z = 1$, or

$$z = \tfrac{1}{6}$$

The solution is $(\tfrac{1}{2}, \tfrac{2}{3}, \tfrac{1}{6})$. The best way to check this result is to substitute the solution in each of the *original* equations of the system.

Note from Example 11.6 that the strategy is to eliminate the same variable from each of two equations, then to use the resulting pair of equations in two variables to eliminate a second variable.

PROBLEMS A

1. Solve the following systems.

(a) $x + 2y - z = 1$
    $x - y \qquad = 2$
    $y + z = 3$

(b) $2x + y \qquad = 4$
    $x - 3y + 2z = 3$
    $-x + z = 3$

(c)
$$2x + 2y + z = 5$$
$$-3x + 4y - z = 1$$
$$-x + 8y + z = 5$$

(d)
$$2x + 3y + z = 3$$
$$7x - y - 3z = -2$$
$$5x - 4y - 2z = -3$$

(e)
$$x_1 - 3x_2 + 4x_3 + 5 = 0$$
$$x_1 + 2x_2 - 3x_3 + 1 = 0$$
$$-2x_1 - 6x_2 + 4x_3 - 3 = 0$$

(f)
$$\tfrac{1}{2}x + \tfrac{1}{8}y + \tfrac{1}{4}z + 1 = 0$$
$$\tfrac{5}{6}x + \tfrac{1}{4}y + \tfrac{3}{2}z - 3 = 0$$
$$\tfrac{2}{3}x - \tfrac{3}{4}y + \tfrac{1}{2}z + 8 = 0$$

(g)
$$\frac{5}{x} + \frac{6}{y} - \frac{3}{z} = 6$$
$$\frac{3}{x} + \frac{1}{y} - \frac{7}{z} = 1$$
$$\frac{1}{x} - \frac{2}{y} - \frac{7}{z} = -2$$

(h)
$$3 \log x - y + 5 \operatorname{Sin} z = 0$$
$$\log x - \qquad 4 \operatorname{Sin} z = 2$$
$$4 \log x - 2y - 3 \operatorname{Sin} z = -1$$

(i)
$$x + y - z = 1$$
$$x + y \qquad - w = -2$$
$$y - 2z + w = 4$$
$$x + 2y - 2z + w = -5$$

(j)
$$-2u + v + 3w - 4x - 11 = 0$$
$$3u - 2v - 2w + 2x + 3 = 0$$
$$-u + 3v + 2w + 4x + 8 = 0$$
$$2u + v + 2w - 2x - 9 = 0$$

2. Solve for x and y in terms of z and find at least two solutions to the system of equations.

(a)
$$x - 2y + z = 3$$
$$-2x + y - z = -1$$

(b)
$$2x - 5y + z = 4$$
$$x - y - 3z = 5$$

(c)
$$2x + 5y - 4z = -1$$
$$-3x + 7y + 5z = 2$$

(d)
$$x - y - 5z = \tfrac{1}{2}$$
$$\tfrac{3}{5}x - \tfrac{1}{2}y + \tfrac{3}{2}z = \tfrac{1}{3}$$

3. A pound of butter costs \$0.10 more than a dozen eggs and the same as three loaves of bread. Together, a pound of butter, a dozen eggs, and three loaves of bread cost \$2.60. Find the cost of a loaf of bread.

4. The sum of the digits of a three-digit number is 11. If we interchange the first and the last digits, the new number is greater than the original number by 594. If we interchange the last two digits of the new number, the resulting number is greater than the original number by 576. Find the original number.

PROBLEMS B

1. In a *Diophantine problem* we are asked to find any and all solutions to certain equations that are *natural numbers*.

(a) Solve the Diophantine equation

$$3x + y = 10$$

(b) Solve the Diophantine system

$$6x + 15y + 7z = 84$$
$$-3x + 5y - z = 3$$

2. The sum of the digits of a three-digit number is 4. If we replace the first digit by the second, the second by the third, and the third by the first, the new number is greater than the original number by 90. Find the original number.

11.4 Systems Involving Quadratic Equations

In this section, we shall study systems of two equations in which at least one equation is a quadratic equation in two variables. The most general quadratic equation in the two variables x and y can be written in the form

$$ax^2 + bxy + cy^2 + dx + ey + f = 0$$

The graph of this equation consists of the set of all points (x, y) for which the equation is a true statement. Such a graph does not always represent a function. For example, the graph of the equation

$$x^2 + y^2 - 1 = 0$$

is a circle having its center at the origin and its radius equal to 1. This graph does not represent a function because there are two values of y

$$y = \sqrt{1 - x^2} \quad \text{and} \quad y = -\sqrt{1 - x^2}$$

for every value of x with $-1 < x < 1$.

We consider first systems of two equations such that one of the equations is linear, and one is quadratic. Such systems are readily solved by using the linear equation to express, say y, in terms of x, substituting this expression for y in the quadratic equation, and solving the resulting quadratic equation. Generally speaking, there will be two solutions x_1 and x_2 of the quadratic equation; consequently, there will be a value of y corresponding to x_1 and a value of y corresponding to x_2. Care must be taken to associate the correct value of y with each solution x_1 and x_2.

Example 11.7. Solve the system:

$$2x - y = 4$$
$$x^2 - 3xy + y^2 + 2x = 1$$

Solution: Solving the linear equation for y, we obtain

$$y = 2x - 4$$

Substituting $2x - 4$ for y in the quadratic equation, we obtain

$$x^2 - 3x(2x - 4) + (2x - 4)^2 + 2x = 1$$

or

$$x^2 + 2x - 15 = 0$$

Factoring, we have

$$(x + 5)(x - 3) = 0$$

Thus, the solutions of the quadratic equation in x are $x = -5$ and $x = 3$. To find the corresponding values of y, we substitute -5 and 3, in turn, for x in the equation $y = 2x - 4$, obtaining the solutions $(-5, -14)$ and $(3, 2)$.

There are situations in which there is a double solution as a real solution, or there is no real solution of a system consisting of a linear equation and a quadratic equation in two variables. To understand why this is so, consider the following system of equations.

$$-x + y = c$$
$$x^2 + y^2 - 1 = 0$$

The graph of the equation $x^2 + y^2 - 1 = 0$ is the circle shown in Figure 11.2. If we take $c = 1$, the linear equation becomes

$$-x + y = 1$$

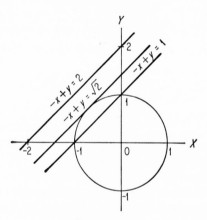

FIGURE 11.2

and the system has the two real solutions $(-1, 0)$ and $(0, 1)$ as shown in Figure 11.2. If we take $c = \sqrt{2}$, the linear equation becomes

$$-x + y = \sqrt{2}$$

and its graph is tangent to the circle of Figure 11.2 at the point $(-\sqrt{2}/2, \sqrt{2}/2)$. This number pair is a double solution of the system. Finally, if we take $c = 2$, the linear equation becomes

$$-x + y = 2$$

and its graph does not intersect the circle. There is no real solution of the resulting system of equations. (Can you find its nonreal solutions?)

Now we consider systems of two quadratic equations in two variables. Counting double solutions (points of tangency of the two graphs) as two solutions, such systems can have 0, 2, or 4 real solutions, as illustrated in Figure 11.3.

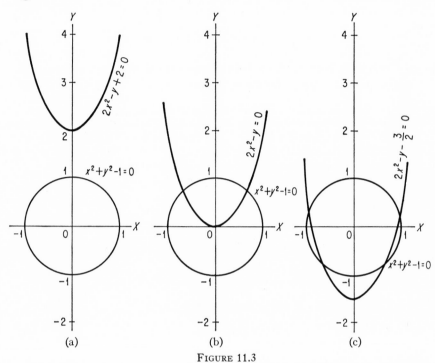

FIGURE 11.3

Approximate real solutions to such systems are readily obtained by graphing the two quadratic equations and noting the coordinates of the points of intersection of such graphs. Exact solutions are obtained algebraically, but the procedures can become somewhat tedious. We shall consider only two special cases in which the algebraic solutions are readily obtained.

If each equation of the system can be put in the form

$$ax^2 + cy^2 + f = 0$$

we can regard the system as being linear in x^2 and y^2. The solutions can be obtained by elimination, as illustrated in the following example.

Example 11.8. Solve the system:

$$x^2 + y^2 - 4 = 0$$
$$x^2 - 3y^2 - 1 = 0$$

Solution: Subtracting corresponding sides of the second equation from the first, we obtain

$$4y^2 - 3 = 0$$

The solutions of this quadratic equation in y are

$$y_1 = \frac{\sqrt{3}}{2} \quad \text{and} \quad y_2 = -\frac{\sqrt{3}}{2}$$

The corresponding values of x are obtained as follows.

$$y_1 = \frac{\sqrt{3}}{2}$$
$$x^2 + \left(\frac{\sqrt{3}}{2}\right)^2 - 4 = 0$$
$$x = \frac{\sqrt{13}}{2}, \quad x = -\frac{\sqrt{13}}{2}$$

$$y_2 = -\frac{\sqrt{3}}{2}$$
$$x^2 + \left(-\frac{\sqrt{3}}{2}\right)^2 - 4 = 0$$
$$x = \frac{\sqrt{13}}{2}, \quad x = -\frac{\sqrt{13}}{2}$$

The solutions are

$$\left(\frac{\sqrt{13}}{2}, \frac{\sqrt{3}}{2}\right), \quad \left(-\frac{\sqrt{13}}{2}, \frac{\sqrt{3}}{2}\right), \quad \left(\frac{\sqrt{13}}{2}, -\frac{\sqrt{3}}{2}\right), \quad \text{and} \quad \left(-\frac{\sqrt{13}}{2}, -\frac{\sqrt{3}}{2}\right)$$

If each equation of the system can be put in the form

$$ax^2 + bxy + cy^2 + f = 0$$

the solutions can be obtained by making the substitution $y = ux$. After this substitution has been made, each equation can be solved for x^2 in terms of u. If these expressions in u are equated, the result will be a quadratic equation in u. After solving this quadratic equation for u, you can find x and y. This procedure is illustrated in the following example.

Example 11.9. Solve the system:

$$xy - y^2 + 3 = 0$$
$$4x^2 - 3xy + 2 = 0$$

Solution: Letting $y = ux$ in each equation of the system, we obtain

$$ux^2 - u^2x^2 + 3 = 0$$
$$4x^2 - 3ux^2 + 2 = 0$$

Solving each of these equations for x^2, we obtain

$$x^2 = \frac{-3}{u - u^2} \quad \text{and} \quad x^2 = \frac{-2}{4 - 3u}$$

Equating the right-hand sides of these equations, we obtain

$$\frac{-3}{u - u^2} = \frac{-2}{4 - 3u}$$

or

$$2u^2 - 11u + 12 = 0$$

or

$$(2u - 3)(u - 4) = 0$$

Solving for u, finding the corresponding values of x, and using the equation $y = ux$ to obtain the corresponding values of y, we have

$u = \frac{3}{2}$		$u = 4$	
$x^2 = \dfrac{-2}{4 - 3(\frac{3}{2})} = 4$		$x^2 = \dfrac{-2}{4 - 3(4)} = \frac{1}{4}$	
$x = 2$	$x = -2$	$x = \frac{1}{2}$	$x = -\frac{1}{2}$
$y = 3$	$y = -3$	$y = 2$	$y = -2$

Thus, the solutions are $(2, 3)$, $(-2, -3)$, $(\frac{1}{2}, 2)$ and $(-\frac{1}{2}, -2)$.

PROBLEMS A

1. Graph each equation in the following systems and determine the number of real solutions.

(a) $3x - y = -4$
$x^2 + y^2 = 9$

(b) $y = 2x - 3$
$x^2 - 2x - y + 1 = 0$

(c) $x^2 + y^2 = 1$
$xy = 1$

(d) $25x^2 + 9y^2 = 225$
$x^2 + y^2 = 16$

(e) $x^2 - 2y = 5$
$2x^2 = 3y^2 - 1$

(f) $y^2 = 2x + 6$
$x^2 - y^2 = 9$

2. Solve the following systems.

(a) $-x + 2y = 3$
$x^2 - 3y = 0$

(b) $y + 2x = -3$
$x^2 + y^2 = 25$

(c) $5y - 3x - 13 = 0$
$x^2 - 4y = 0$

(d) $x + y - 1 = 0$
$x^2 + 2xy - y^2 + x = 0$

(e) $x^2 + y^2 = 16$
$x^2 - 2y^2 = 25$

(f) $x^2 - 2y^2 - 22 = 0$
$3x^2 - y^2 - 21 = 0$

(g) $xy = 1$
$x^2 + y^2 = 2$

(h) $x^2 - 4y^2 - 16 = 0$
$xy = 2$

(i) $3y^2 + x^2 - 28 = 0$
$4y^2 - xy + x^2 - 40 = 0$

(j) $-x^2 + 3y^2 = 1$
$x^2 + 2xy + y^2 = 0$

(k) $3xy - x^2 - y^2 - 4 = 0$
$2xy + x^2 - y^2 - 4 = 0$

(l) $16 - 2x^2 + 3xy - 2y^2 = 0$
$24 - 3x^2 + 5xy - 4y^2 = 0$

3. Two natural numbers are such that the sum of their squares is 193 and the difference of their squares is 95. Find the numbers.

4. Find the dimensions of a rectangle having a diagonal of 13 inches and a perimeter of 34 inches.

PROBLEMS B

1. Solve the following systems.

(a) $x^2 + y^2 - x - y = 2$ (b) $x^3 - y^3 = 26$

      $xy + 3x + 3y = 2$ $x - y = 2$

2. If you are given the formulas for the sum and the product of the solutions of a quadratic equation, could you derive the quadratic formulas?

12

Matrices

12.1 Introduction

In this chapter we introduce a new object, called a matrix, which can be applied to solve systems of linear equations, as well as to solve many other problems in mathematics and the sciences.   A matrix, like a number, can be defined as an abstract symbol that obeys certain laws, or postulates.   Before introducing matrices in this context, however, first we observe how the concept of a matrix arises from systems of linear equations.

Consider, for example, the system of equations

$$a_1 x + b_1 y = c_1$$
$$a_2 x + b_2 y = c_2$$

This system can be abbreviated by displaying only the constants a_1, b_1, . . . , c_2 in the following array.

$$\begin{bmatrix} a_1 & b_1 & c_1 \\ a_2 & b_2 & c_2 \end{bmatrix}$$

This array is characterized by having two *rows* and three *columns*; furthermore, the order of the elements in each row is important, because changing this order would change the system of equations for which the array stands.

Such rectangular arrays are profitably studied in their own right.   In the following definition, we abstract the ideas illustrated in the foregoing

221

paragraph, allowing the array to consist of elements of any kind (not necessarily numbers) but preserving the requirement that it be rectangular and that the order of the elements is important.

Definition 12.1. *A* **matrix** *is an ordered rectangular array of elements. A matrix of dimensions* m *by* n *has* m *rows and* n *columns.*

To display a matrix, we shall always enclose its elements within brackets, and to refer to given matrices, we shall use capital letters. For example

$$A = \begin{bmatrix} 1 & -2 & 3 \\ 4 & 2 & -5 \end{bmatrix} \quad \text{and} \quad B = \begin{bmatrix} 3 & 1 & -5 \\ -2 & 4 & 2 \end{bmatrix}$$

are matrices of dimensions 2 by 3. Although A and B have exactly the same elements, they are different matrices because their elements appear in different orders. Accordingly, we define the equality of two matrices as follows.

Definition 12.2. *If* A *and* B *are matrices having the same dimensions, and if the elements occupying corresponding positions are equal, then* A *and* B *are* **equal matrices,** *and we write* A = B.

Certain matrices, having special dimensions, are given special names. A matrix having one row only, like

$$[a_1 \quad a_2 \quad \dots \quad a_n]$$

is called a **row matrix.** A matrix having one column only, like

$$\begin{bmatrix} b_1 \\ b_2 \\ . \\ . \\ . \\ b_n \end{bmatrix}$$

is called a **column matrix.** A matrix having the same number of rows and columns, like

$$\begin{bmatrix} a_1 & b_1 & c_1 \\ a_2 & b_2 & c_2 \\ a_3 & b_3 & c_3 \end{bmatrix}$$

is called a **square matrix.**

In the remainder of this chapter, we shall be concerned only with matrices whose elements consist of real numbers. This restriction is made for simplicity only, and many of the properties of matrices to be discussed are true also for matrices having other kinds of elements, such as complex numbers, polynomials, and so forth.

PROBLEMS A

1. For the matrices having the given dimensions, state which is a row matrix, a column matrix, a square matrix, or none of these.

(a) 4 by 4   (b) 3 by 1
(c) 1 by 6   (d) 2 by 3
(e) 1 by 1   (f) 5 by 4
(g) a by 1   (h) 1 by b

2. If

$$\begin{bmatrix} x & y \\ y & x \end{bmatrix} = \begin{bmatrix} y & 1 \\ x & y \end{bmatrix}$$

find x and y.

3. If

$$\begin{bmatrix} x^2 + 1 & 2 \\ 3 & y^2 - 1 \end{bmatrix} = \begin{bmatrix} 0 & 2 \\ 3 & 1 \end{bmatrix}$$

find x and y.

4. Is it true that

$$\begin{bmatrix} 1 & 2 & 3 & 4 \end{bmatrix} = \begin{bmatrix} 1 \\ 2 \\ 3 \\ 4 \end{bmatrix}$$

Why?

PROBLEMS B

1. If A is any matrix, the **transpose of A**, denoted by A', is the matrix whose first row is the first column of A, whose second row is the second column of A, and so forth.

(a) Find A' if

$$A = \begin{bmatrix} 1 & 2 & 3 \\ 4 & 5 & 6 \\ 7 & 8 & 9 \end{bmatrix}$$

(b) If A is a 1-by-n row matrix, what can you say about A'?

2. A matrix may be **partitioned** by breaking it up into "blocks" or submatrices. For example, if

$$A = \begin{bmatrix} 1 & 2 & 3 & 4 \\ 5 & 6 & 7 & 8 \end{bmatrix} \quad A_1 = \begin{bmatrix} 1 & 2 \\ 5 & 6 \end{bmatrix} \quad \text{and} \quad A_2 = \begin{bmatrix} 3 & 4 \\ 7 & 8 \end{bmatrix}$$

we write

$$A = [A_1 \mid A_2]$$

Is it true that

$$\left[\begin{array}{c|c} A_1 & A_2 \\ \hline A_3 & A_4 \end{array} \right]' = \left[\begin{array}{c|c} A_1' & A_3' \\ \hline A_2' & A_4' \end{array} \right]$$

Hint: Check first with a numerical example. If it appears to be true, construct a general proof.

12.2   Addition and Multiplication of Matrices

To operate with matrices we need to define what is meant by matrix addition and matrix multiplication. Although we shall adopt the same symbols for addition and multiplication of matrices that we used for real numbers, these operations differ considerably from the like operations with real numbers. In fact, we shall discover that matrix addition and multiplication is not always defined, that matrix multiplication is, in general, not commutative, and that not every matrix has a multiplicative inverse.

First, we define the operation of matrix addition. We can add matrices only if they have the same dimensions; then their sum is given by the following definition.

Definition 12.3. *The* **sum of two matrices** *having the same dimensions is a matrix such that each element is the sum of the corresponding elements of the original matrices.*

As an example of Definition 12.3, we find the sum $A + B$, where

$$A = \begin{bmatrix} 2 & 1 & -6 \\ -3 & 0 & 4 \end{bmatrix} \quad \text{and} \quad B = \begin{bmatrix} -7 & 9 & 4 \\ 3 & 1 & -2 \end{bmatrix}$$

We have

$$A + B = \begin{bmatrix} 2 + (-7) & 1 + 9 & (-6) + 4 \\ (-3) + 3 & 0 + 1 & 4 + (-2) \end{bmatrix}$$

$$= \begin{bmatrix} -5 & 10 & -2 \\ 0 & 1 & 2 \end{bmatrix}$$

Using Definition 12.3, we can show that a matrix consisting entirely of zeros can be added to any other matrix A of the *same dimensions* without changing A. A matrix whose elements are all zero is called a **null matrix**, and it is denoted by the symbol **0**. There are many null matrices, one for each combination of dimensions. To prove that $A + \mathbf{0} = A$, we have only to note that each element of $A + \mathbf{0}$ is found by adding zero to the corresponding element of A, leaving the elements of A unchanged.

We define $-A$, the **negative** of the matrix A, to be a matrix of the same dimensions as A such that $A + (-A) = \mathbf{0}$. From Definition 12.3, it follows that $-A$ is a matrix whose elements are the negatives of the corresponding elements of A. For example, if

$$A = \begin{bmatrix} 1 & 3 \\ -2 & 0 \end{bmatrix} \quad \text{then} \quad -A = \begin{bmatrix} -1 & -3 \\ 2 & 0 \end{bmatrix}$$

Other additive properties of matrices whose elements are real numbers can be derived from Definition 12.3 and the additive properties of the system of real numbers. For example, if A, B, and C are matrices having the same dimensions, the following laws can be proved.

1. Commutative Law of Addition: $A + B = B + A$.

2. Associative Law of Addition: $(A + B) + C = A + (B + C)$.

Now, we define the operation of matrix multiplication. To introduce the process of multiplication, first we define the product of a row matrix, having dimensions 1 by n, and a column matrix, having dimensions n by 1. If

$$A = [a_1 \quad a_2 \quad \ldots \quad a_n] \quad \text{and} \quad B = \begin{bmatrix} b_1 \\ b_2 \\ \cdot \\ \cdot \\ \cdot \\ b_n \end{bmatrix}$$

then we define the product AB by the formula

(12.1) $$AB = [a_1 b_1 + a_2 b_2 + \ldots + a_n b_n]$$

Note that the product AB is defined only if A has as many columns as B has rows. Furthermore, this product is a matrix with only one row and one column. Its only element is the *number* $a_1 b_1 + a_2 b_2 + \ldots + a_n b_n$. Informally, we sometimes refer to this element as the product of the "row" $a_1, a_2, \ldots, a_n$ and the "column" $b_1, b_2, \ldots, b_n$.

This definition can be generalized to include the product of any two matrices A and B, *provided that* A *has as many columns as* B *has rows*.

Definition 12.4. *If* A *has dimensions* m *by* n, *and* B *has dimensions* n *by* p, *the* **product** AB *is a matrix having dimensions* m *by* p *such that each element in a given row and a given column of* AB *is the product of that* "*row*" *of* A *and that* "*column*" *of* B.

To illustrate Definition 12.4, let

$$A = \begin{bmatrix} 2 & -1 \\ 5 & 4 \end{bmatrix} \quad \text{and} \quad B = \begin{bmatrix} -3 & 5 & 1 \\ 2 & -4 & 3 \end{bmatrix}$$

The element in the *first row* and the *first column* of AB is the number obtained by multiplying the *first row* of A by the *first column* of B, analogous to Equation 12.1. We obtain

$$2(-3) + (-1)2 = -8$$

The element in the *first row* and the *second column* of AB is obtained by multiplying the *first row* of A by the *second column* of B, as follows.

$$2 \cdot 5 + (-1) \cdot (-4) = 14$$

Proceeding in this way, we can fill in the entire matrix AB to obtain

$$AB = \begin{bmatrix} -8 & 14 & -1 \\ -7 & 9 & 17 \end{bmatrix}$$

Note that the product BA is not defined in this example because B has three columns and A has only two rows. Thus, we see that the order of the factors in matrix multiplication is essential. Even when both AB and BA exist, they may not be equal. In the following example, we multiply two square matrices and show that AB does not necessarily equal BA.

Example 12.1. If

$$A = \begin{bmatrix} 1 & -2 \\ -3 & 5 \end{bmatrix} \quad \text{and} \quad B = \begin{bmatrix} -2 & 0 \\ 1 & 3 \end{bmatrix}$$

find AB and BA.

Solution:

$$AB = \begin{bmatrix} 1 & -2 \\ -3 & 5 \end{bmatrix} \cdot \begin{bmatrix} -2 & 0 \\ 1 & 3 \end{bmatrix}$$

$$= \begin{bmatrix} 1 \cdot (-2) + (-2) \cdot 1 & 1 \cdot 0 + (-2) \cdot 3 \\ (-3) \cdot (-2) + 5 \cdot 1 & (-3) \cdot 0 + 5 \cdot 3 \end{bmatrix}$$

$$= \begin{bmatrix} -4 & -6 \\ 11 & 15 \end{bmatrix}$$

Similarly, we find

$$BA = \begin{bmatrix} -2 & 0 \\ 1 & 3 \end{bmatrix} \cdot \begin{bmatrix} 1 & -2 \\ -3 & 5 \end{bmatrix}$$

$$= \begin{bmatrix} -2 & 4 \\ -8 & 13 \end{bmatrix}$$

We can conclude from Example 12.1 that *the commutative law does not hold for matrix multiplication.*

We have observed that, for every set of matrices of the same dimensions, there is an identity matrix under the operation of addition, called the null matrix. Now we shall discover that, for every set of *square matrices* of the same dimensions, there is an identity matrix under the operation of multiplication. The multiplicative identity matrix for a set of square matrices with n rows and n columns is a square matrix of the same dimensions, such that the elements on the diagonal from upper left to lower right equal 1, and all other elements equal 0. Such a square matrix is called more simply an **identity matrix**, and it is denoted by the symbol I. For example, the 3-by-3 identity matrix is

$$I = \begin{bmatrix} 1 & 0 & 0 \\ 0 & 1 & 0 \\ 0 & 0 & 1 \end{bmatrix}$$

To show, for example, that $IA = A$ for any matrix having 3 rows and 3 columns, we apply Definition 12.4 as follows.

$$IA = \begin{bmatrix} 1 & 0 & 0 \\ 0 & 1 & 0 \\ 0 & 0 & 1 \end{bmatrix} \begin{bmatrix} a_1 & b_1 & c_1 \\ a_2 & b_2 & c_2 \\ a_3 & b_3 & c_3 \end{bmatrix} =$$

$$\begin{bmatrix} 1 \cdot a_1 + 0 \cdot a_2 + 0 \cdot a_3 & 1 \cdot b_1 + 0 \cdot b_2 + 0 \cdot b_3 & 1 \cdot c_1 + 0 \cdot c_2 + 0 \cdot c_3 \\ 0 \cdot a_1 + 1 \cdot a_2 + 0 \cdot a_3 & 0 \cdot b_1 + 1 \cdot b_2 + 0 \cdot b_3 & 0 \cdot c_1 + 1 \cdot c_2 + 0 \cdot c_3 \\ 0 \cdot a_1 + 0 \cdot a_2 + 1 \cdot a_3 & 0 \cdot b_1 + 0 \cdot b_2 + 1 \cdot b_3 & 0 \cdot c_1 + 0 \cdot c_2 + 1 \cdot c_3 \end{bmatrix}$$

$$= \begin{bmatrix} a_1 & b_1 & c_1 \\ a_2 & b_2 & c_2 \\ a_3 & b_3 & c_3 \end{bmatrix} = A$$

If I and A are n-by-n matrices, it can be verified that $IA = AI$; that is, it can be shown that the order of multiplication is irrelevant when A is a square matrix and the other factor is I. If A is not a square matrix, but has n *columns*, it can be shown that $AI = A$, where I is the n-by-n identity matrix. In this case, however, we cannot conclude that

$AI = IA$ because IA is not defined.   Similarly, it can be shown that
$IA = A$ if A has n *rows* and I is the n-by-n identity matrix.

We have observed that, for every matrix A there is an additive inverse
matrix $-A$ having the property

$$A + (-A) = (-A) + A = \mathbf{0}.$$

However, it is not always possible to find a multiplicative inverse B for
the matrix A, having the property $AB = BA = I$.   Since AB can equal
BA only if both A and B are square matrices of the same dimensions, *we
define the multiplicative inverse of* A *only if* A *is a square matrix.*

Definition 12.5. *If* A *and* B *are square matrices having the same dimensions, and if* $AB = BA = I$, *then* B *is called the* **inverse** *of* A, *and we
write* $B = A^{-1}$.

If B is the inverse of A, we see from Definition 12.5 that A also is the
inverse of B.   Note, however, that Definition 12.5 does not guarantee
that every square matrix has an inverse; in fact, it can be shown that there
are many square matrices that have no inverse.   If A does not possess
an inverse, it is called a **singular matrix**.   If A is a **nonsingular matrix**,
that is, A has an inverse, it can be shown that it has only one inverse.
In Section 12.4 we shall discuss the problem of finding the inverse of a
nonsingular matrix.

PROBLEMS A

1. Find $A + B$.

(a) $A = \begin{bmatrix} 1 & -2 \\ 0 & 5 \end{bmatrix}$ $B = \begin{bmatrix} -2 & 4 \\ 1 & -5 \end{bmatrix}$

(b) $A = \begin{bmatrix} 1 & -4 & 3 \end{bmatrix}$ $B = \begin{bmatrix} -2 & 5 & 7 \end{bmatrix}$

(c) $A = \begin{bmatrix} a & -a & 4 \\ 0 & 5b & -3b \end{bmatrix}$ $B = \begin{bmatrix} -b & a & 1 \\ b & a & 3b \end{bmatrix}$

(d)

$A = \begin{bmatrix} 0 \\ 0 \\ 0 \\ 1 \end{bmatrix}$ $B = \begin{bmatrix} -1 \\ 0 \\ 0 \\ 0 \end{bmatrix}$

2. Find $A - B$, where $A - B$ is defined to equal $A + (-B)$.

(a)

$A = \begin{bmatrix} 3 \\ 1 \\ 2 \end{bmatrix}$ $B = \begin{bmatrix} 2 \\ -1 \\ 2 \end{bmatrix}$

(b) $A = -\begin{bmatrix} 1 & 2 \\ 3 & 4 \end{bmatrix}$ $B = \begin{bmatrix} 3 & 1 \\ 4 & 2 \end{bmatrix}$

(c) $A = [7 \quad 4 \quad 5 \quad 0]$ $\qquad B = [-4 \quad 0 \quad -5 \quad 1]$

(d)
$$A = \begin{bmatrix} x & y \\ 0 & 1 \\ y & 2 \end{bmatrix} \qquad B = \begin{bmatrix} -1 & y \\ x & 1 \\ 2x & -2 \end{bmatrix}$$

3. Prove the commutative law of addition, $A + B = B + A$, where A and B are matrices of the same dimensions having elements that are real numbers.

4. Prove the associative law of addition, $(A + B) + C = A + (B + C)$, where A, B, and C are matrices of the same dimensions having elements that are real numbers.

5. Find the following matrix products.

(a)
$$[1 \quad 2 \quad 4] \cdot \begin{bmatrix} 2 \\ -3 \\ 5 \end{bmatrix}$$

(b)
$$\begin{bmatrix} -3 & 2 \\ 1 & 5 \end{bmatrix} \cdot \begin{bmatrix} 2 & 1 \\ -7 & 3 \end{bmatrix}$$

(c)
$$\begin{bmatrix} 4 & \sqrt{2} \\ 1 & -3 \\ \sqrt{5} & 7 \end{bmatrix} \cdot \begin{bmatrix} -2 & 5 & \sqrt{20} \\ \sqrt{8} & -1 & 2 \end{bmatrix}$$

(d)
$$\begin{bmatrix} 0 & 0 & 3 \\ 0 & 4 & 2 \\ 1 & 3 & 5 \end{bmatrix} \cdot \begin{bmatrix} 1 & 3 & 0 \\ 2 & 0 & 0 \\ 0 & 0 & 0 \end{bmatrix}$$

(e)
$$\begin{bmatrix} 4 & -2 \\ -2 & 1 \end{bmatrix} \cdot \begin{bmatrix} 2 & -1 \\ 4 & -2 \end{bmatrix}$$

(f)
$$\begin{bmatrix} 1 & 2 \\ -3 & 5 \end{bmatrix} \cdot \begin{bmatrix} 1 & 2 \\ -3 & 5 \end{bmatrix}$$

(g)
$$\begin{bmatrix} 0 & 0 & 0 \\ 0 & 0 & 0 \\ 0 & 0 & 0 \end{bmatrix} \cdot \begin{bmatrix} 1 \\ 2 \\ 3 \end{bmatrix}$$

(h)
$$[1 \quad -2 \quad 4] \cdot \begin{bmatrix} -2 & 4 \\ 3 & 5 \\ -6 & -1 \end{bmatrix}$$

6. Prove the associative law of matrix multiplication, $(AB)C = A(BC)$ for the case

$$A = \begin{bmatrix} -3 & 4 \\ 5 & 2 \end{bmatrix} \qquad B = \begin{bmatrix} 3 \\ 5 \end{bmatrix} \qquad C = [-2 \quad 4 \quad 7]$$

7. Show that $IA = AI$, where

$$A = \begin{bmatrix} 3 & -4 & 2 \\ 1 & 5 & 9 \\ 2 & 6 & -7 \end{bmatrix}$$

8. Show that $AB = I$, where

$$A = \begin{bmatrix} 3 & 5 & 1 \\ -1 & 2 & 0 \end{bmatrix} \qquad \text{and} \qquad B = \begin{bmatrix} \frac{2}{11} & \frac{-5}{11} \\ \frac{1}{11} & \frac{3}{11} \\ 0 & 0 \end{bmatrix}$$

Why can't we say that $B = A^{-1}$?

PROBLEMS B

1. Prove that $A \cdot 0 = 0$ for any matrix A such that the product $A \cdot 0$ exists. Is there a like property for the *number* 0?

2. Find two nonnull 2-by-2 matrices A and B such that $AB = 0$. Is there a like property for the number 0?

3. Show that I is its own inverse; that is, prove that for any identity matrix I of given dimensions $I^{-1} = I$.

4. Prove that any square null matrix is a singular matrix.

12.3 Matrices and Simultaneous Equations

In Section 12.1 we learned that a system of equations, such as

(12.2)
$$3x + 5y = 13$$
$$-x + 2y = 3$$

can be represented by a matrix. The matrix

$$\begin{bmatrix} 3 & 5 & 13 \\ -1 & 2 & 3 \end{bmatrix}$$

is called the **augmented matrix** of System 12.2. The *square matrix* of coefficients of x and y in this system, namely

$$\begin{bmatrix} 3 & 5 \\ -1 & 2 \end{bmatrix}$$

is called the **coefficient matrix** of the system.

In Chapter 11 we learned that a system of equations like System 12.2 can be solved by finding an equivalent system of equations. The operations used to reduce a system to an equivalent system can be duplicated with parallel operations on the augmented matrix. We proceed as follows.

$$\begin{array}{ll} 3x + 5y = 13 & \begin{bmatrix} 3 & 5 & 13 \\ -1 & 2 & 3 \end{bmatrix} \\ -x + 2y = 3 & \end{array}$$

Multiplying both sides of the second equation by 3 and adding corresponding sides of the first equation, we obtain

$$\begin{array}{ll} 3x + 5y = 13 & \begin{bmatrix} 3 & 5 & 13 \\ 0 & 11 & 22 \end{bmatrix} \\ 11y = 22 & \end{array}$$

Dividing both sides of the second equation by 11, we obtain

$$3x + 5y = 13 \qquad \begin{bmatrix} 3 & 5 & 13 \\ 0 & 1 & 2 \end{bmatrix}$$
$$y = 2$$

Multiplying both sides of the second equation by -5 and adding to corresponding sides of the first equation, we obtain

$$3x = 3 \qquad \begin{bmatrix} 3 & 0 & 3 \\ 0 & 1 & 2 \end{bmatrix}$$
$$y = 2$$

Finally, dividing both sides of the first equation by 3, we obtain

$$x = 1 \qquad \begin{bmatrix} 1 & 0 & 1 \\ 0 & 1 & 2 \end{bmatrix}$$
$$y = 2$$

The preceding example shows that to each operation performed on the system of equations there is a corresponding operation that can be performed on the *rows* of the augmented matrix of the system. Such operations on the elements of matrices, derived from the analogous operations on systems of equations listed on page 212, are called the **elementary row operations**. These operations are summarized as follows.

1. *Replacing any row in the matrix with a new row obtained by multiplying each element of the original row by the same number different from zero.*

2. *Replacing any row with a new row obtained by adding to its elements the corresponding elements of one or more other rows of the matrix.*

3. *Combining Operations 1 and 2 by replacing any row in the matrix with a new row whose elements are the sum of nonzero multiples of its elements and nonzero multiples of corresponding elements of any other row or rows in the matrix.*

Consistent with the definition of equivalent systems of equations, we say that two matrices are **row-equivalent matrices** if one can be derived from the other by elementary row operations. Referring to the previous example, we note that the matrices

$$\begin{bmatrix} 3 & 5 & 13 \\ -1 & 2 & 3 \end{bmatrix} \quad \text{and} \quad \begin{bmatrix} 1 & 0 & 1 \\ 0 & 1 & 2 \end{bmatrix}$$

are row-equivalent matrices. Also, note that the system of equations having the augmented matrix

$$\begin{bmatrix} 1 & 0 & 1 \\ 0 & 1 & 2 \end{bmatrix}$$

has as its coefficient matrix the identity matrix. Any system of n linear equations in n variables whose coefficient matrix is the identity matrix can be solved by inspection; the solution is given by the elements of the last column of the augmented matrix of that system. In the following example, we solve a system of equations by transforming its coefficient matrix into an identity matrix by means of elementary row operations.

Example 12.2. Solve the system

$$x - 3y = -11$$
$$3x + y = -3$$

by using elementary row operations on its matrix.

Solution: The augmented matrix of the system is

$$\begin{bmatrix} 1 & -3 & -11 \\ 3 & 1 & -3 \end{bmatrix}$$

Multiplying each element of the first row by -3 and adding the results to corresponding elements of the second row, we obtain

$$\begin{bmatrix} 1 & -3 & -11 \\ 0 & 10 & 30 \end{bmatrix}$$

Multiplying each element of the second row by $\frac{1}{10}$, we obtain

$$\begin{bmatrix} 1 & -3 & -11 \\ 0 & 1 & 3 \end{bmatrix}$$

Multiplying each element of the second row by 3 and adding the results to corresponding elements of the first row, we obtain

$$\begin{bmatrix} 1 & 0 & -2 \\ 0 & 1 & 3 \end{bmatrix}$$

Thus, the solution of the system is $x = -2$, $y = 3$.

In the preceding example, the system had a unique solution, and it was possible to use elementary row operations to find an equivalent system whose coefficient matrix is the identity matrix. If the system does not have a unique solution, this is no longer possible. For example, consider the *dependent system*

$$3x - 2y = 4$$
$$-6x + 4y = -8$$

The augmented matrix of this system is

$$\begin{bmatrix} 3 & -2 & 4 \\ -6 & 4 & -8 \end{bmatrix}$$

and it can be transformed to the following row-equivalent matrix by multiplying each element of the second row by $\frac{1}{2}$ and adding to corresponding elements of the first row.

$$\begin{bmatrix} 0 & 0 & 0 \\ -6 & 4 & -8 \end{bmatrix}$$

This matrix hás a row consisting entirely of zeros, and it cannot be transformed by elementary row operations such that the transformed coefficient matrix is an identity matrix.

Similarly, if we have the *inconsistent system*

$$3x - 2y = 4$$
$$-6x + 4y = 5$$

its augmented matrix can be transformed into the following row-equivalent matrix having a row of zeros in the *coefficient matrix only*.

$$\begin{bmatrix} 0 & 0 & 13 \\ -6 & 4 & 5 \end{bmatrix}$$

In general, if we have a system of n linear equations in n variables, its augmented matrix has dimensions n by $n + 1$, and its coefficient matrix has dimensions n by n. Considering only matrices having at least as many columns as rows, we say that such a matrix has **rank n** if it cannot be transformed to a row-equivalent matrix having at least one row consisting entirely of zeros. If such a matrix can be transformed to a row-equivalent matrix having k rows, but not more than k rows, consisting entirely of zeros, then we say that it has **rank n − k.**

Using the concept of rank, it can be proved that a system of n linear equations in n variables is consistent if its augmented matrix and its coefficient matrix have the same rank, and it is inconsistent if its augmented matrix is of higher rank than its coefficient matrix. Furthermore, if a system is consistent and the rank of the coefficient matrix equals n, the system has a unique solution. Otherwise, a consistent system is dependent. These conclusions are illustrated in the following examples.

Example 12.3. Determine whether the following system has a unique solution, is dependent, or is inconsistent.

$$x - 3y + 4z = 11$$
$$3x + y - z = 4$$
$$7x - y + 2z = 19$$

Solution: The augmented matrix and the coefficient matrix of the system are

$$\begin{bmatrix} 1 & -3 & 4 & 11 \\ 3 & 1 & -1 & 4 \\ 7 & -1 & 2 & 19 \end{bmatrix} \quad \text{and} \quad \begin{bmatrix} 1 & -3 & 4 \\ 3 & 1 & -1 \\ 7 & -1 & 2 \end{bmatrix}$$

respectively. Multiplying the elements of the second row of each matrix by -2 and adding to corresponding elements of the third row, we obtain

$$\begin{bmatrix} 1 & -3 & 4 & 11 \\ 3 & 1 & -1 & 4 \\ 1 & -3 & 4 & 11 \end{bmatrix} \quad \text{and} \quad \begin{bmatrix} 1 & -3 & 4 \\ 3 & 1 & -1 \\ 1 & -3 & 4 \end{bmatrix}$$

Multiplying the elements of the first row by -1 and adding to corresponding elements of the third row, we obtain

$$\begin{bmatrix} 1 & -3 & 4 & 11 \\ 3 & 1 & -1 & 4 \\ 0 & 0 & 0 & 0 \end{bmatrix} \quad \text{and} \quad \begin{bmatrix} 1 & -3 & 4 \\ 3 & 1 & -1 \\ 0 & 0 & 0 \end{bmatrix}$$

To check whether it is possible to obtain another row of zeros in either matrix, we use elementary row operations to attempt to get an identity matrix in the upper left-hand corner, obtaining finally

$$\begin{bmatrix} 1 & 0 & \frac{1}{10} & \frac{23}{10} \\ 0 & 1 & \frac{-13}{10} & \frac{-29}{10} \\ 0 & 0 & 0 & 0 \end{bmatrix} \quad \text{and} \quad \begin{bmatrix} 1 & 0 & \frac{1}{10} \\ 0 & 1 & \frac{-13}{10} \\ 0 & 0 & 0 \end{bmatrix}$$

You can see that it is not possible to get another row of zeros in either matrix, and we conclude that both matrices have rank 2. The system is dependent, because the rank of the coefficient matrix is less than 3.

Example 12.4. Determine whether the following system has a unique solution, is dependent, or is inconsistent.

$$\begin{aligned} x - 3y + 4z &= 11 \\ 3x + y - z &= 4 \\ 7x - y + 2z &= 10 \end{aligned}$$

(This system is the same as that of Example 12.3, except that the constant in the third equation equals 10 instead of 19.)

Solution: The augmented matrix and the coefficient matrix of the system are

$$\begin{bmatrix} 1 & -3 & 4 & 11 \\ 3 & 1 & -1 & 4 \\ 7 & -1 & 2 & 10 \end{bmatrix} \quad \text{and} \quad \begin{bmatrix} 1 & -3 & 4 \\ 3 & 1 & -1 \\ 7 & -1 & 2 \end{bmatrix}$$

respectively.   Using the same operations shown in Example 12.3, we obtain the following row-equivalent matrices.

$$\begin{bmatrix} 1 & -3 & 4 & 11 \\ 3 & 1 & -1 & 4 \\ 0 & 0 & 0 & -9 \end{bmatrix} \quad \text{and} \quad \begin{bmatrix} 1 & -3 & 4 \\ 3 & 1 & -1 \\ 0 & 0 & 0 \end{bmatrix}$$

We can conclude that the rank of the augmented matrix is 3, but the rank of the coefficient matrix is 2; thus, the system is inconsistent.

PROBLEMS A

1. Solve the following systems by using elementary row operations on the augmented matrix.

(a) $x + y = 3$
    $x - y = 1$

(b) $2x - y = -5$
    $x + 3y = 8$

(c) $5x + 7y = 5$
    $15x + 14y = 12$

(d) $8x - 9y = -1$
    $-12x + 3y = 5$

(e) $\frac{3}{5}x - \frac{1}{2}y = \frac{1}{2}$
    $\frac{1}{3}x - y = -\frac{10}{3}$

(f) $x + 2y = 5$
    $-x + z = 2$
    $y - 2z = -4$

(g) $x + y - z = 1$
    $x - y + z = 1$
    $x + y = 2$

(h) $x - 2y = 5$
    $3y + z = -1$
    $5z - w = 9$
    $-2x + 3w = -3$

2. Use matrices to determine which of the following systems have a unique solution, are dependent, or are inconsistent.

(a) $x + 2y = 1$
    $2x - y = 2$

(b) $3x + 4y = 12$
    $6x + 8y = 5$

(c) $2x - 5y + z = -3$
    $x + y - 2z = 1$
    $4x - 3y - 5z = -1$

(d) $-x + 2y - 7z = 5$
    $7x - 8y + 11z = 7$
    $2x - y - 5z = 2$

(e) $x - 2y + 3z = 4$
    $2x + 3y - z = 7$
    $3x + y + z = 5$

(f) $3x - 3y + 9z = 12$
    $2x - 2y + 6z = 8$
    $x - y + 3z = 4$

PROBLEMS B

1. If we are given a coordinate system in terms of the coordinates (x, y), we can change to a new coordinate system (x', y') by means of the following equations.

$$x' = 3x + 2y$$
$$y' = 2x - 5y$$

(a) Find the coordinates of the point $(-2,1)$ in the new coordinate system.

(b) If we now transform from the coordinates (x', y') to the coordinates (x'', y'') by means of the equations

$$x'' = -x' + 2y'$$
$$y'' = 4x' - 3y'$$

find x'' and y'' in terms of x and y.

(c) The matrix of the transformation

$$x' = a_1 x + b_1 y$$
$$y' = a_2 x + b_2 y$$

is given by

$$\begin{bmatrix} a_1 & b_1 \\ a_2 & b_2 \end{bmatrix}$$

If C is the matrix of the transformation from (x, y) to (x'', y'') found in Part (b), B is the matrix of the transformation from (x', y') to (x'', y''), and A is the matrix of the transformation from (x, y) to (x', y'), show that

$$C = BA$$

This result motivates Definition 12.4, the definition of the product of two matrices.

12.4 The Inverse of a Matrix

In the preceding section, we observed how a system of linear equations can be solved by using elementary row operations to reduce its augmented matrix to a row-equivalent matrix. In this section, we shall discover how such a system can be solved by finding the inverse of its coefficient matrix.

First, we show that System 12.2 can be written as an equation involving matrices. Letting

$$A = \begin{bmatrix} 3 & 5 \\ -1 & 2 \end{bmatrix}$$

be the coefficient matrix of System 12.2,

$$X = \begin{bmatrix} x \\ y \end{bmatrix}$$

be the column matrix of the variables x and y, and

$$C = \begin{bmatrix} 13 \\ 3 \end{bmatrix}$$

be the column matrix of constants on the right-hand side of each equation, we form the matrix equation

$$AX = C$$

To show that this matrix equation leads to the original system of equations, we substitute for A, X, and C, to write

$$\begin{bmatrix} 3 & 5 \\ -1 & 2 \end{bmatrix} \cdot \begin{bmatrix} x \\ y \end{bmatrix} = \begin{bmatrix} 13 \\ 3 \end{bmatrix}$$

Multiplying the matrices on the left, we have

$$\begin{bmatrix} 3x + 5y \\ -x + 2y \end{bmatrix} = \begin{bmatrix} 13 \\ 3 \end{bmatrix}$$

Since these are equal matrices, corresponding elements are equal, and we can conclude that

$$3x + 5y = 13$$
$$-x + 2y = 3$$

which is the original system of equations.

Now, we solve this system of equations by working with the matrix equation $AX = C$. If A has an inverse, we can multiply each side of this equation on the left by A^{-1}, obtaining

$$A^{-1}AX = A^{-1}C$$

(Note that we could not have multiplied by A^{-1} on the right to obtain $AXA^{-1} = CA^{-1}$ because the product CA^{-1} does not exist. Why?) Since $A^{-1}A = I$, and $IX = X$, we can write this last equation in the form

$$X = A^{-1}C$$

Thus, if A is a nonsingular matrix, and if we can find A^{-1}, the solution to the system can be obtained by multiplying A^{-1} by the column matrix C.

Assuming for the moment that A^{-1} exists, we can find its elements by using elementary row operations in the same way that we used these operations to solve System 12.2 on page 230. Recall that in solving this system we transformed the coefficient matrix to an identity matrix. Thus, if we work backwards, we should be able to transform the identity matrix to the inverse of the coefficient matrix. This procedure is carried out by performing elementary row operations on A and the same operations on I. If we transform A to I by such operations, then the matrix resulting from using the same operations on I is A^{-1}. We transformed the matrix

$$A = \begin{bmatrix} 3 & 5 \\ -1 & 2 \end{bmatrix}$$

to I when we solved System 12.2. Thus, to find A^{-1} we have only to use the same operations on I, as follows.

<table>
<tr><td align="center">*Transformation of A*</td><td align="center">*Transformation of I*</td></tr>
</table>

$$A = \begin{bmatrix} 3 & 5 \\ -1 & 2 \end{bmatrix} \qquad I = \begin{bmatrix} 1 & 0 \\ 0 & 1 \end{bmatrix}$$

$$A_1 = \begin{bmatrix} 3 & 5 \\ 0 & 11 \end{bmatrix} \qquad I_1 = \begin{bmatrix} 1 & 0 \\ 1 & 3 \end{bmatrix}$$

$$A_2 = \begin{bmatrix} 3 & 5 \\ 0 & 1 \end{bmatrix} \qquad I_2 = \begin{bmatrix} 1 & 0 \\ \frac{1}{11} & \frac{3}{11} \end{bmatrix}$$

$$A_3 = \begin{bmatrix} 3 & 0 \\ 0 & 1 \end{bmatrix} \qquad I_3 = \begin{bmatrix} \frac{6}{11} & \frac{-15}{11} \\ \frac{1}{11} & \frac{3}{11} \end{bmatrix}$$

$$A_4 = \begin{bmatrix} 1 & 0 \\ 0 & 1 \end{bmatrix} \qquad I_4 = \begin{bmatrix} \frac{2}{11} & \frac{-5}{11} \\ \frac{1}{11} & \frac{3}{11} \end{bmatrix}$$

To obtain A_1 from A, recall that we multiplied each element of the second row of A by 3 and added the corresponding elements of the first row. Thus, to obtain I_1 from I, we multiply each element of the second row of I by 3 and add corresponding elements of the first row. We obtain I_2, I_3, and I_4 in a similar way.

To prove that $I_4 = A^{-1}$, we calculate I_4A as follows.

$$\begin{bmatrix} \frac{2}{11} & \frac{-5}{11} \\ \frac{1}{11} & \frac{3}{11} \end{bmatrix} \cdot \begin{bmatrix} 3 & 5 \\ -1 & 2 \end{bmatrix} = \begin{bmatrix} \frac{2}{11} \cdot 3 + (\frac{-5}{11})(-1) & \frac{2}{11} \cdot 5 + (\frac{-5}{11}) \cdot 2 \\ \frac{1}{11} \cdot 3 + \frac{3}{11} \cdot (-1) & \frac{1}{11} \cdot 5 + \frac{3}{11} \cdot 2 \end{bmatrix}$$

$$= \begin{bmatrix} 1 & 0 \\ 0 & 1 \end{bmatrix}$$

(Can you show also that $AI_4 = I$?)

Example 12.5. Find A^{-1} if $A = \begin{bmatrix} 1 & -3 \\ 3 & 1 \end{bmatrix}$

Solution: Using the same elementary row operations that we used in Example 12.2, we have

$$A = \begin{bmatrix} 1 & -3 \\ 3 & 1 \end{bmatrix} \qquad I = \begin{bmatrix} 1 & 0 \\ 0 & 1 \end{bmatrix}$$

$$A_1 = \begin{bmatrix} 1 & -3 \\ 0 & 10 \end{bmatrix} \qquad I_1 = \begin{bmatrix} 1 & 0 \\ -3 & 1 \end{bmatrix}$$

$$A_2 = \begin{bmatrix} 1 & -3 \\ 0 & 1 \end{bmatrix} \qquad I_2 = \begin{bmatrix} 1 & 0 \\ \frac{-3}{10} & \frac{1}{10} \end{bmatrix}$$

$$A_3 = \begin{bmatrix} 1 & 0 \\ 0 & 1 \end{bmatrix} \qquad I_3 = \begin{bmatrix} \frac{1}{10} & \frac{3}{10} \\ \frac{-3}{10} & \frac{1}{10} \end{bmatrix}$$

To check this result, we can multiply I_3 by A (or A by I_3) to obtain I.

We have seen that I can be transformed to A^{-1} if A can be transformed to I by means of elementary row operations. Thus, we can conclude that A^{-1} exists if A is row-equivalent to the identity matrix of the same dimensions as A. Conversely, if A cannot be transformed to I, then A^{-1} does not exist. We can conclude that the matrix equation

$$AX = C$$

representing a system of n linear equations in n variables, has a unique solution if and only if A^{-1} exists.

PROBLEMS A

1. Find the inverses of the following nonsingular matrices. Check your answers by using the equation $AA^{-1} = A^{-1}A = I$.

(a) $\begin{bmatrix} 1 & 3 \\ 0 & 2 \end{bmatrix}$

(b) $\begin{bmatrix} 3 & 5 \\ 1 & -1 \end{bmatrix}$

(c) $\begin{bmatrix} 1 & 2 \\ 2 & 1 \end{bmatrix}$

(d) $\begin{bmatrix} 0 & 1 \\ 1 & 0 \end{bmatrix}$

(e) $\begin{bmatrix} 0 & 1 \\ -1 & 1 \end{bmatrix}$

(f) $\begin{bmatrix} 1 & 1 & 0 \\ 0 & 1 & 1 \\ 1 & 0 & 1 \end{bmatrix}$

(g) $\begin{bmatrix} 1 & 2 & 3 \\ 0 & 4 & 5 \\ 0 & 0 & 6 \end{bmatrix}$

(h) $\begin{bmatrix} 2 & 1 & 1 \\ 3 & -1 & 1 \\ -2 & 2 & 1 \end{bmatrix}$

PROBLEMS B

1. If A and B are nonsingular matrices, solve the following matrix equation for X.

$$BXA = C$$

2. Referring to Problem B-1 at the end of Section 12.3, show that the matrix of the transformation from (x', y') to (x, y) is the inverse of the matrix of the transformation from (x, y) to (x', y').

3. Referring to Problem B-1 at the end of Section 12.1 for the definition of A', find $(A'A)^{-1}$ if

$$A = \begin{bmatrix} 1 & 3 \\ -2 & 0 \\ 2 & -1 \end{bmatrix}$$

12.5   The Determinant of a Matrix

In the preceding sections, we used matrices to solve certain systems of linear equations. In this section, we introduce the determinant of a square matrix, and show how such systems can be solved by determinants.

Given the 2-by-2 matrix

$$A = \begin{bmatrix} a_1 & b_1 \\ a_2 & b_2 \end{bmatrix}$$

we denote the determinant of A by $|A|$, and define it by the equation

(12.3)
$$\begin{vmatrix} a_1 & b_1 \\ a_2 & b_2 \end{vmatrix} = a_1b_2 - a_2b_1$$

If A is a 3-by-3 matrix, its determinant is defined by

(12.4)
$$\begin{vmatrix} a_1 & b_1 & c_1 \\ a_2 & b_2 & c_2 \\ a_3 & b_3 & c_3 \end{vmatrix} = a_1b_2c_3 + a_2b_3c_1 + a_3b_1c_2 - a_1b_3c_2 - a_2b_1c_3 - a_3b_2c_1$$

In general, if A is an n-by-n matrix, its determinant is said to have the **order** n, and it is defined by a rather complicated formula consisting of sums and differences of products. There are n factors in each product, each factor is an element of A, and each row and each column contributes exactly one factor to each product.

To remember the formulas for evaluating second- and third-order determinants, the following schemes are useful. To evaluate a second-order determinant, multiply the elements on the diagonal from upper left to lower right and subtract the product of the elements on the other diagonal, as shown in the following diagram.

$$\begin{vmatrix} a_1 & b_1 \\ a_2 & b_2 \end{vmatrix} = a_1b_2 - a_2b_1$$

To evaluate a third-order determinant, rewrite the first two columns following the third column, and use the following diagram.

$$\begin{vmatrix} a_1 & b_1 & c_1 \\ a_2 & b_2 & c_2 \\ a_3 & b_3 & c_3 \end{vmatrix} \begin{matrix} a_1 & b_1 \\ a_2 & b_2 \\ a_3 & b_3 \end{matrix}$$

The arrows pointing downward identify the three products having a positive sign, and the arrows pointing upward identify the three products

having a negative sign.   Comparison of the result of applying this scheme
with Equation 12.4 shows that the results are identical.

Example 12.6. Find the determinant of the matrix

$$A = \begin{bmatrix} 1 & -3 & 4 \\ 3 & 1 & -1 \\ 2 & -3 & 2 \end{bmatrix}$$

Solution: Using the scheme mentioned above, we have

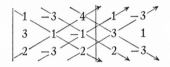

or

$$\begin{aligned} |A| &= 1 \cdot 1 \cdot 2 + (-3) \cdot (-1) \cdot 2 + 4 \cdot 3 \cdot (-3) \\ &\quad - 2 \cdot 1 \cdot 4 - (-3) \cdot (-1) \cdot 1 - 2 \cdot 3 \cdot (-3) \\ &= 2 + 6 - 36 - 8 - 3 + 18 \\ &= -21 \end{aligned}$$

The expansion of a determinant having order higher than three can be
facilitated by the use of minors, defined as follows.

Definition 12.6. *The* **minor** *of an element of a determinant of order* n *is
the* (n − 1)st *order determinant obtained by crossing out the row and
column in which the element appears.*

As an example of Definition 12.6, the minor of the element −3 in the
fourth-order determinant

$$\begin{vmatrix} 6 & 2 & 5 & -4 \\ -2 & 1 & -3 & 6 \\ 0 & 2 & -4 & 3 \\ 2 & 1 & 0 & 7 \end{vmatrix}$$

is obtained by crossing out the second row and the third column of this
determinant.   We have the result

$$\begin{vmatrix} 6 & 2 & -4 \\ 0 & 2 & 3 \\ 2 & 1 & 7 \end{vmatrix}$$

and you can verify that this minor equals 94.

The **cofactor of an element** of a determinant is the minor of that element preceded by an appropriate sign. To determine the sign, consider the following checkerboard pattern.

$$
\begin{array}{cccc}
+ & - & + & - & \cdots \\
- & + & - & + & \cdots \\
+ & - & + & - & \cdots \\
- & + & - & + & \cdots \\
\cdot & \cdot & \cdot & \cdot \\
\cdot & \cdot & \cdot & \cdot \\
\cdot & \cdot & \cdot & \cdot
\end{array}
$$

We observe that the sign of the cofactor of an element can be determined by proceeding to this element from the first element in the first row, along rows or down columns, but *not on diagonals*, and alternating signs starting with $+$. It does not matter what path you use. For example, the cofactor of the element -3 in the determinant shown on page 241 equals -94 because its minor equals 94 and it always takes an odd number of steps to reach this element starting from the element 6 in row 1.

The evaluation of a determinant by expanding it by minors consists of selecting any row or column of that determinant, forming the product of each element in that row or column by its cofactor, and adding the products so formed. This method of expansion reduces the problem of expanding an nth order determinant to that of expanding n determinants of order $n - 1$. If some of the elements of a row or column of the original determinant equal zero, the work can be reduced by selecting that row or column for the expansion.

Example 12.7. Use minors to expand the determinant

$$
\begin{vmatrix}
-4 & 3 & 2 & 1 \\
-6 & 1 & 0 & 4 \\
5 & 2 & -7 & 0 \\
1 & 3 & 0 & 0
\end{vmatrix}
$$

and evaluate it.

Solution: We choose the last row for expansion, because it has two zeros. (Note that we could just as well have chosen the third or fourth column.) The cofactor of the first element in the last row is

$$
- \begin{vmatrix}
3 & 2 & 1 \\
1 & 0 & 4 \\
2 & -7 & 0
\end{vmatrix} = -93
$$

The cofactor of the second element in the last row is

$$+ \begin{vmatrix} -4 & 2 & 1 \\ -6 & 0 & 4 \\ 5 & -7 & 0 \end{vmatrix} = -30$$

It is not necessary to find the cofactors of the remaining elements of the last row. (Why?) The determinant equals

$$1 \cdot (-93) + 3 \cdot (-30) = -183$$

Now we can state a rule for solving a system of n linear equations in n variables by the use of determinants. This rule, known as *Cramer's rule*, requires that we form a set of $n + 1$ determinants, where each determinant uses n of the $n + 1$ columns of the augmented matrix of the system. The value of a given variable in the solution is obtained from the quotient of two of these determinants. The denominator determinant is always the determinant of the coefficient matrix, and the numerator determinant is formed by replacing the column of coefficients corresponding to that variable by the last column of the augmented matrix.

As an example of the application of Cramer's rule, we solve the system

$$\begin{aligned} x - 3y + 4z &= 11 \\ 3x + y - z &= 4 \\ 2x - 3y + 2z &= 7 \end{aligned}$$

The augmented matrix of this system is

$$\begin{bmatrix} 1 & -3 & 4 & 11 \\ 3 & 1 & -1 & 4 \\ 2 & -3 & 2 & 7 \end{bmatrix}$$

and the solution is given by

$$x = \frac{\begin{vmatrix} 11 & -3 & 4 \\ 4 & 1 & -1 \\ 7 & -3 & 2 \end{vmatrix}}{\Delta} \qquad y = \frac{\begin{vmatrix} 1 & 11 & 4 \\ 3 & 4 & -1 \\ 2 & 7 & 2 \end{vmatrix}}{\Delta}$$

$$z = \frac{\begin{vmatrix} 1 & -3 & 11 \\ 3 & 1 & 4 \\ 2 & -3 & 7 \end{vmatrix}}{\Delta}$$

where

$$\Delta = \begin{vmatrix} 1 & -3 & 4 \\ 3 & 1 & -1 \\ 2 & -3 & 2 \end{vmatrix}$$

Note that Δ is the determinant of the coefficient matrix of the system. *To obtain* x, the numerator determinant is found by replacing the *first column* of Δ by the last column of the augmented matrix; *to obtain* y, we replace the *second column* of Δ by the last column of the augmented matrix; and *to obtain* z, we replace the *third column* of Δ by the last column of the augmented matrix. Expansion of the resulting determinants gives the solution

$$x = \frac{-42}{-21} = 2$$

$$y = \frac{-21}{-21} = 1$$

$$z = \frac{-63}{-21} = 3$$

If Δ were equal to zero in the preceding example, it would not have been possible to use Cramer's rule to find a solution because division by zero is excluded. Thus, it is possible to determine whether a system of n linear equations in n variables has a unique solution by examining the determinant of the coefficient matrix of the system. The system has a unique solution if and only if this determinant is different from zero.

PROBLEMS A

1. Find the determinants of the following matrices.

(a) $\begin{bmatrix} 3 & 4 \\ 5 & 6 \end{bmatrix}$
(b) $\begin{bmatrix} -1 & 2 \\ 5 & 7 \end{bmatrix}$

(c) $\begin{bmatrix} 4 & -2 \\ 3 & 5 \end{bmatrix}$
(d) $\begin{bmatrix} 1 & -3 \\ -3 & 9 \end{bmatrix}$

(e) $\begin{bmatrix} 1 & 0 & 0 \\ 0 & 1 & 0 \\ 0 & 0 & 1 \end{bmatrix}$
(f) $\begin{bmatrix} 1 & 0 & 2 \\ 3 & 0 & 4 \\ 1 & 2 & 0 \end{bmatrix}$

(g) $\begin{bmatrix} 2 & -3 & 0 \\ 1 & 4 & -5 \\ 3 & 1 & 2 \end{bmatrix}$
(h) $\begin{bmatrix} 3 & 5 & 7 \\ 9 & 2 & 1 \\ -5 & 6 & -3 \end{bmatrix}$

2. Expand the following determinants by minors and evaluate:

(a) $\begin{vmatrix} 3 & 0 & 5 \\ 4 & 2 & -1 \\ 3 & 6 & 7 \end{vmatrix}$
(b) $\begin{vmatrix} 2 & 1 & -3 \\ 7 & 4 & -5 \\ -2 & 1 & 1 \end{vmatrix}$

(c) $\begin{vmatrix} 6 & 4 & 2 \\ 2 & 1 & 3 \\ -3 & -2 & -1 \end{vmatrix}$ (d) $\begin{vmatrix} 1 & 3 & 0 & 1 \\ 4 & 2 & 9 & 6 \\ -1 & -3 & 0 & 2 \\ 6 & 0 & 1 & 3 \end{vmatrix}$

(e) $\begin{vmatrix} 2 & 3 & 5 & 0 \\ 1 & 2 & 0 & 7 \\ -4 & 0 & 2 & 5 \\ 0 & 4 & 1 & 6 \end{vmatrix}$ (f) $\begin{vmatrix} 1 & 2 & 3 & -4 \\ 5 & 3 & -2 & 1 \\ 1 & -3 & 5 & 8 \\ -5 & 1 & 2 & 3 \end{vmatrix}$

(g) $\begin{vmatrix} 1 & 1 & 0 & 0 & 0 \\ 1 & 0 & 1 & 0 & 0 \\ 1 & 0 & 0 & 1 & 0 \\ 1 & 0 & 0 & 0 & 1 \\ 1 & 1 & 1 & 1 & 1 \end{vmatrix}$

3. Use Cramer's rule to solve those of the following systems that have a unique solution.

(a) $\begin{aligned} 3x + 2y &= 5 \\ x + 5y &= 1 \end{aligned}$ (b) $\begin{aligned} 2x - 6y &= 3 \\ 7x + y &= -1 \end{aligned}$

(c) $\begin{aligned} x + 2y - z &= -1 \\ -3x + 5y + 2z &= 4 \\ -2x + 7y + z &= 3 \end{aligned}$ (d) $\begin{aligned} x + y - z &= 4 \\ 3x - 2y + z &= 1 \\ 5x + 7y + 4z &= -6 \end{aligned}$

(e) $\begin{aligned} x + 3y - z &= 2 \\ -x + y - 7z &= 4 \\ -x + 5y - 15z &= -1 \end{aligned}$ (f) $\begin{aligned} x + y + z + w &= 4 \\ x - y - z - w &= -2 \\ x + y - z + w &= 2 \\ x - y &= 0 \end{aligned}$

PROBLEMS B

1. If A and B are 2-by-2 matrices, show that

$$|A \cdot B| = |A| \cdot |B|$$

2. Referring to Problem B-1 at the end of Section 12.1 for the definition of A', prove that

$$|A'| = |A|$$

where A is any 3-by-3 matrix.

3. The **adjoint** of the square matrix A $(Adj\, A)$ is defined to be the transpose of the matrix whose elements are the cofactors of the corresponding elements of A.

(a) Show that $A^{-1} = \dfrac{Adj\,A}{|A|}$, where

$$A = \begin{bmatrix} -1 & 2 & 4 \\ 3 & 1 & 2 \\ 0 & 4 & 2 \end{bmatrix}$$

(b) Solve the system of equations

$$AX = C$$

where A is the matrix in Part (a) of this problem,

$$X = \begin{bmatrix} x \\ y \\ z \end{bmatrix} \quad \text{and} \quad C = \begin{bmatrix} -1 \\ 2 \\ 4 \end{bmatrix}$$

by means of Cramer's rule. Show that this solution leads to the same calculations as the solution of this system by the formula

$$X = A^{-1}C$$

when A^{-1} is calculated as in Part (a).

4. It can be proved that the rank of any matrix equals the number of rows of the biggest square submatrix having a nonvanishing determinant. (Such submatrices are found by crossing out entire rows and/or columns of the original matrix.) Use this theorem to find the rank of the following matrix.

$$\begin{bmatrix} 2 & 1 & -3 & 0 \\ 4 & 0 & 0 & 5 \\ 0 & -2 & 6 & 5 \end{bmatrix}$$

13

Inequalities

13.1 Absolute Inequalities

The inequality relations $<$ (less than) and $>$ (greater than) between two real numbers were introduced in Section 1.8. We observed that $a < b$ is equivalent to the statement "$a - b$ is a negative number," and $a > b$ is equivalent to the statement "$a - b$ is a positive number." In addition, we proved three theorems (Theorems 1.9, 1.10, and 1.11) giving the fundamental properties of the inequality relations. In this section, we shall contrast the properties of the inequality relations with those of the equality relation, and distinguish between absolute and conditional inequalities.

First, we summarize the properties of the inequality relations, and we give one additional property, not yet proved. In the following properties, a, b, and c are real numbers.

Property 1. *If* a $<$ b, *then* b $>$ a.

Property 2. Transitive Law. *If* a $<$ b *and* b $<$ c, *then* a $<$ c.

Property 3. *If* a $<$ b, *then* a $+$ c $<$ b $+$ c.

Property 4. *If* a $<$ b *and* c $>$ 0, *then* ac $<$ bc;
$\quad\quad$ *if* a $<$ b *and* c $<$ 0, *then* ac $>$ bc.

Property 5. *If* a $<$ b *and* c $<$ d, *then* a $+$ c $<$ b $+$ d.

Property 1 follows directly from the definition of the inequality relations, Definition 1.4.   Properties 2, 3, and 4 were proved in Theorems 1.9, 1.10, and 1.11, respectively.   To prove Property 5, we use Property 3 to add c to each side of the inequality $a < b$, obtaining

$$a + c < b + c$$

and to add b to each side of the inequality $c < d$, obtaining

$$b + c < b + d$$

By Property 2

$$a + c < b + d$$

and the proof is complete.

Note that we can use Property 1 to restate each of Properties 2 through 5 in terms of the inequality relation $>$.   For example, Property 2 also can be stated in the form: "If $a > b$ and $b > c$, then $a > c$."

Comparing the properties of the inequality relations with those of the equality relation, given on page 161, we note first that there are no reflexive or symmetric laws for the inequality relations.   (Property 1 should be contrasted with the symmetric law for equalities.)   Second, we note from Property 2 that the inequality relations do obey a transitive law analogous to the transitive law for equalities.   We note from Properties 3 and 4 that, although we can *add* the same quantity to each side of an inequality statement without destroying the original relationship, we may change the relationship when we *multiply* each side by the same quantity.   Finally, Property 5 shows that we can add corresponding sides of inequalities.   For example, if $-3 < 1$ and $1 < 2$, then we have $-3 + 1 < 1 + 2$, or $-2 < 3$.

The fundamental inequality relations $<$ and $>$ can be augmented by the relations $\leq$ (*less than or equal to*) and $\geq$ (*greater than or equal to*). If a and b are real numbers, the statement $a \leq b$ means $a < b$ or $a = b$, and the statement $a \geq b$ means $a > b$ or $a = b$.   Thus, although it is not true that $3 < 3$, it *is* true that $3 \leq 3$.

By applying the properties of the inequality relations $<$ and $>$, together with those of the equality relation, you can show that Properties 1 through 5 listed in this section are true also for the relations $\leq$ and $\geq$.   For example, to prove that "if $a \leq b$, then $a + c \leq b + c$," we divide the argument into two parts.   First, if $a < b$, it follows from Property 3 that $a + c < b + c$.   Second, if $a = b$, it follows from Property 4 for the equality relation that $a + c = b + c$.   Using the definition of the relation $\leq$, we conclude that, if $a \leq b$, then $a + c \leq b + c$.

If **f** and **g** are functions whose ranges consist entirely of real numbers, any statement of the form

$$f(x) < g(x), \quad f(x) > g(x), \quad f(x) \leq g(x), \quad \text{or} \quad f(x) \geq g(x)$$

is called an **inequality.** An inequality, like an equation, need not be a true statement. For example, the inequality $x + 1 < 0$ is satisfied only for real values of x less than -1. In contrast, the inequality $\sqrt{x} \geq 0$ is satisfied for every number x for which $\sqrt{x}$ is defined. If there is at least one value of the variable x for which an inequality is not satisfied, it is called a **conditional inequality.** If an inequality is satisfied for every value of x *for which both f and g are defined*, it is called an **absolute inequality.**

Methods of proving absolute inequalities were illustrated in Examples 1.7 and 1.8 on page 23. In these examples, we used Properties 1 through 4 to rewrite the given inequality in the required form. The following example further illustrates this method of proving absolute inequalities.

Example 13.1. If $a > b > 0$, prove that $a^2 > b^2$.

Solution: Since $a > 0$, we can multiply both sides of the inequality $a > b$ by a to obtain

$$a^2 > ab$$

Similarly, $b > 0$, and we can multiply both sides of the same inequality by b to obtain

$$ab > b^2$$

Applying the Transitive Law, we have

$$a^2 > b^2$$

It is sometimes more convenient to prove an absolute inequality by "working backwards." For example, we could have done Example 13.1 with the following steps:

$$a^2 > b^2$$
$$a^2 - b^2 > 0 \qquad\qquad \text{(Property 3)}$$
$$(a + b)(a - b) > 0$$

The last statement is true because $a + b$ and $a - b$ are positive, and the product of two positive numbers is positive. It is important to note that *this argument does not prove the inequality* a² > b² because we started out by assuming what was to have been proved. To prove this inequality, we must reverse the order of the steps.

To emphasize that we must be able to reverse the order of the steps when proving an inequality by working backwards, we give the following example. Given $x > 2$, it follows from the result of Example 13.1 that $x^2 > 4$. However, the statement $x^2 > 4$ *is not equivalent* to the statement $x > 2$ because x also can be less than -2.

The following is a further example of the foregoing method for proving absolute inequalities.

Example 13.2. If $a > 0$ and $b > 0$, prove that $\sqrt{ab} \leq \dfrac{a+b}{2}$.

Solution: From $a > 0$ and $b > 0$ it follows that $\sqrt{ab} > 0$ and $a + b > 0$. Thus, we can use the result of Example 13.1 to square each side of the inequality $\sqrt{ab} \leq \dfrac{a+b}{2}$, obtaining

$$ab \leq \left(\frac{a+b}{2}\right)^2$$

$$ab \leq \frac{a^2 + 2ab + b^2}{4}$$

$$4ab \leq a^2 + 2ab + b^2$$

$$0 \leq a^2 - 2ab + b^2$$

$$0 \leq (a - b)^2$$

This last statement is true because the square of any real number is non-negative. The order of the steps can be reversed, and the proof is complete.

PROBLEMS A

1. Prove the following inequalities (a and b are real numbers).

(a) $1 + \sqrt{2} > \sqrt{3}$ (b) $\sqrt{7} < 2 + \sqrt{2}$

(c) $\sqrt{5} - \sqrt{3} < \sqrt{2}$ (d) $\sqrt{3} + \sqrt{5} > \sqrt{8}$

(e) $2.64 < \sqrt{7} < 2.65$ (f) $\dfrac{4}{5} < \dfrac{1 + \sqrt{2}}{3} < 1$

(g) If $a < b$, then $-a > -b$ (h) If $a > b > 0$, then $\dfrac{1}{a} < \dfrac{1}{b}$

(i) If $a > b > 0$, then $\sqrt{a} > \sqrt{b}$ (j) $|a| \geq a$

(k) If $a > 0$, then $a + \dfrac{1}{a} \geq 2$ (l) $a^2 + 2ab \leq 2a^2 + b^2$

2. Classify the following inequalities as absolute or conditional (a and b are real numbers).

(a) $a + \sqrt{a} \geq a$ (b) $a + a^2 \geq 1 + a$

(c) $a^2 \geqq 0$ (d) $ab \leq \tfrac{1}{2}(a^2 + b^2)$

(e) $|a|^2 \geq a^2$ (f) $|a - b| \leq |a + b|$

PROBLEMS B

1. If a and b are positive integers, show that $\sqrt{2}$ lies between a/b and $(a + 2b)/(a + b)$.

2. The approximation $\pi \doteq 3.14$ means $3.135 < \pi < 3.145$. If $\sqrt{3} \doteq 1.73$, approximately, give an approximation for $\sqrt{3}\,\pi$. *Hint:* The approximation is *not* $\sqrt{3}\,\pi \doteq 1.73 \cdot 3.14$.

3. Using the approximations $\sqrt{2} \doteq 1.414$ and $\sqrt{5} \doteq 2.236$, how accurately can you calculate $\sqrt{10}$?

13.2 Conditional Inequalities

The **solution set** of a conditional inequality in one variable is the set of all numbers that make the inequality a true statement. To solve a conditional inequality, that is, to find its solution set, we follow a procedure similar to that used in solving equations. Using the properties of the inequality relations, we find an equivalent inequality whose solution set is known. This procedure is illustrated in the following examples.

Example 13.3. Solve the inequality $2x - 5 > 7$.

Solution: Using Property 3 to add 5 to each side, we have

$$2x > 12$$

Using Property 4 to multiply each side by $\frac{1}{2}$, we have

$$x > 6$$

Thus, the solution set consists of all real numbers greater than 6, and it is indicated by the heavy halfline on the axis of real numbers shown below. In this figure, the symbol "(" at the point 6 indicates that this point is *not included* in the solution set.

Example 13.4. Solve the inequality $|x - 1| < 2$.

Solution: $|x - 1| < 2$ means that

$$x - 1 < 2 \quad \text{or} \quad -(x - 1) < 2$$

From the first inequality we obtain $x < 3$, and from the second inequality we obtain $x - 1 > -2$, or $x > -1$. Thus, the solution set consists of all real numbers between -1 and 3, excluding the end-points. This set is indicated by the heavy line segment below.

If a conditional inequality can be written in the form

$$ax + b < 0$$

where a and b are real numbers and $a \neq 0$, it is called a **linear inequality**. If $a > 0$, we can use the method of Example 13.3 to show that the solution set consists of all real numbers less than $-b/a$. If $a < 0$, can you show that the solution set consists of all real numbers *greater than* $-b/a$?

If a conditional inequality can be written in the form

$$ax^2 + bx + c < 0 \quad \text{or} \quad ax^2 + bx + c > 0$$

where a, b, and c are real numbers and $a \neq 0$, it is called a **quadratic inequality**. Many quadratic inequalities can be solved by factoring the quadratic polynomial $ax^2 + bx + c$, and noting what conditions on the factors make the inequality a true statement. For example, consider the inequality

$$x^2 - x - 6 > 0$$

Factoring, we have

$$(x - 3)(x + 2) > 0$$

For the inequality to be a true statement, both factors must be positive or both must be negative. In symbols, either

$$x - 3 > 0 \quad \text{and} \quad x + 2 > 0, \quad \text{or} \quad x - 3 < 0 \quad \text{and} \quad x + 2 < 0$$

The first condition leads to the statement $x > 3$, and the second condition leads to the statement $x < -2$. The solution set $x > 3$ or $x < -2$ is indicated by the heavy half-lines in the following figure.

In general, we can factor the quadratic polynomial

$$ax^2 + bx + c$$

by finding the solutions r_1 and r_2 of the equation

$$ax^2 + bx + c = 0$$

If we first divide each side of the equation by a, so that the coefficient of x^2 equals 1, the resulting polynomial factors into $(x - r_1)(x - r_2)$. If r_1 and r_2 are real numbers, any real solutions of the corresponding quadratic inequality can be obtained by the method illustrated. Care must be taken when you divide by a to reverse the inequality if $a < 0$.

Example 13.5. Find the real solutions of the inequality

$$6x^2 + 7x - 3 < 0$$

Solution: Dividing each side by 6, we have

$$x^2 + \tfrac{7}{6}x - \tfrac{1}{2} < 0$$

Solving the quadratic equation $x^2 + \frac{7}{6}x - \frac{1}{2} = 0$, we have $r_1 = -\frac{3}{2}$ and $r_2 = \frac{1}{3}$. Thus, the original inequality can be written in the form

$$(x + \tfrac{3}{2})(x - \tfrac{1}{3}) < 0$$

This inequality is true if one of the factors is positive and the other is negative, leading to the solution set $-\frac{3}{2} < x < \frac{1}{3}$, which is illustrated below.

If r_1 and r_2 are distinct complex conjugates, the method illustrated is not useful. However, in this case, we note that the equation $ax^2 + bx + c = 0$ has no real solutions, and its graph does not cross the X-axis. Thus, either every real number satisfies the corresponding quadratic inequality or no real number satisfies it. For example, to solve the inequality

$$-2x^2 + 3x - 5 < 0$$

we note that the discriminant of $-2x^2 + 3x - 5 = 0$ is negative, and there are no real solutions. Thus, the graph of this equation lies entirely above or entirely below the X-axis. To determine which alternative is true, we can substitute any convenient value of x into the expression $-2x^2 + 3x - 5$ and note its sign. Choosing $x = 0$, we obtain -5; thus, the graph lies entirely below the X-axis and the inequality $-2x^2 + 3x - 5 < 0$ is satisfied for every real value of x.

In conclusion, we make two remarks to round out our study of quadratic inequalities. The first remark deals with real solutions to inequalities that can be put in the form

$$ax^2 + bx + c \leq 0$$

and the second remark deals with nonreal solutions to quadratic inequalities having real coefficients.

If an inequality is in the form $ax^2 + bx + c \leq 0$, you can find its real solutions by solving the inequality

$$ax^2 + bx + c < 0$$

as illustrated, and adding to the solution set so obtained any real solutions to the equation $ax^2 + bx + c = 0$.

It is possible for an inequality of the form $ax^2 + bx + c < 0$, where a, b, and c are real numbers, to have nonreal numbers in its solution set. To illustrate this statement, consider the inequality

$$x^2 + 1 < 0$$

having the real coefficients

$$a = 1, \quad b = 0, \quad \text{and} \quad c = 1$$

Since there are no real values of x for which x^2 is negative, $x^2 + 1$ cannot be less than zero, and there are no real solutions. However, $2i$ is a solution because

$$(2i)^2 + 1 = -3$$

and $-3 < 0$. In fact, every number of the form ki is a solution if k is a real number satisfying the inequality $|k| > 1$.

PROBLEMS A

1. Solve the following inequalities.

(a) $4x - 8 < 2$

(b) $3x + 2 > 6$

(c) $-\frac{1}{2}x + 3 > \frac{5}{2}$

(d) $4 - \frac{3}{4}x < \frac{1}{4}$

(e) $\frac{3}{8} \leq \frac{1}{8} - x$

(f) $-\frac{1}{4} - \frac{2}{3}x \geq \frac{3}{5}$

(g) $\dfrac{1}{x} > \dfrac{4}{3}$

(h) $\dfrac{x + 2}{x - 1} \leq 3$

(i) $|x| > 1$

(j) $|x - 1| > 1$

(k) $|x - a| \leq b$

(l) $|2x + 3| \geq -4$

2. Solve the following inequalities.

(a) $x^2 - 1 < 0$

(b) $x^2 - 2x - 15 > 0$

(c) $x^2 + 2x - 3 \geq 0$

(d) $x^2 - 5x - 14 \leq 0$

(e) $x^2 > 6x - 8$

(f) $8x \leq -(15 + x^2)$

(g) $2x^2 + 3x - 4 > 0$

(h) $x^2 - 4x + 1 \leq 0$

(i) $x^2 - x + 1 < 0$

(j) $-3x^2 + 4x - 2 < 0$

(k) $2x^2 + 4x + 3 > 0$

(l) $1 - x^2 \geq 2x$

PROBLEMS B

1. Solve the inequality $x^4 - 5x^2 + 4 > 0$.

2. Prove that the inequality $ax^2 + bx + c \geq 0$ is satisfied for all real x if and only if $b^2 - 4ac \leq 0$ and $a > 0$.

3. If a_1, a_2, b_1, and b_2 are real numbers, a special form of *Cauchy's inequality* is

$$(a_1b_1 + a_2b_2)^2 \leq (a_1^2 + a_2^2)(b_1^2 + b_2^2)$$

Prove this inequality by using the inequalities $(a_1x + b_1)^2 \geq 0$ and $(a_2x + b_2)^2 \geq 0$ and the result of Problem 2.

13.3 Graphical Solution of Inequalities

The real solutions of the inequality $f(x) < g(x)$ can be obtained by observing those values of x for which the graph of **f** lies below the graph of **g**. For example, to find the real solutions of the inequality

$$|3x - 5| < 2$$

let

$$f(x) = |3x - 5| \quad \text{and} \quad g(x) = 2$$

The graphs of **f** and **g** are shown in Figure 13.1, and it is evident that the values of x for which the graph of **f** lies below the graph of **g** are given by $1 < x < \frac{7}{3}$.

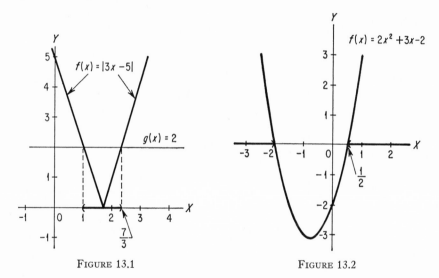

FIGURE 13.1   FIGURE 13.2

The following example illustrates the use of graphical methods in solving quadratic inequalities.

Example 13.6. Find the real solutions of the inequality

$$2x^2 + 3x - 2 > 0$$

Solution: Letting $f(x) = 2x^2 + 3x - 2$ and $g(x) = 0$, we note that the real solutions of this inequality are those values of x for which the graph of the quadratic function lies *above* the X-axis. Graphing **f** in Figure 13.2, and noting that the solutions of the equation $f(x) = 0$ are -2 and $\frac{1}{2}$, we conclude that the real solutions of the inequality are given by $x < -2$ or $x > \frac{1}{2}$.

Graphical methods are particularly useful in solving inequalities involving more than one variable.   For example, the linear inequality

$$ax + by + c < 0$$

in the variables x and y can be solved by graphing the equation $ax + by + c = 0$.   If $b > 0$, every point (x, y) in the plane *below* the line determined by this equation satisfies the given inequality; if $b < 0$, every point (x, y) in the plane *above* the line determined by this equation satisfies the given inequality.

Example 13.7. Solve the inequality $3x + 4y - 5 > 0$.

Solution: The equation $3x + 4y - 5 = 0$ is graphed in Figure 13.3.   The solution set of the inequality consists of all points above the line, or the shaded region of Figure 13.3.   Note that the points on the line itself are excluded.

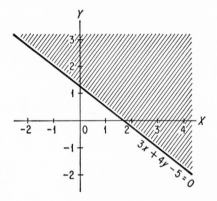

FIGURE 13.3

Sim lar methods are useful in solving systems of inequalities in two variables, as shown in the following examples.

Example 13.8. Solve the system of inequalities:
$$3x + 4y - 5 > 0$$
$$x - y + 1 < 0$$
$$x + 3y - 8 < 0$$

Solution: The graphs of the equations
$$3x + 4y - 5 = 0$$
$$x - y + 1 = 0$$
$$x + 3y - 8 = 0$$

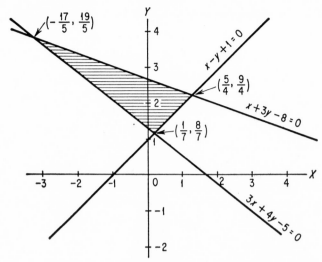

FIGURE 13.4

are shown in Figure 13.4. The region satisfying the three inequalities simultaneously consists of all points (x, y) above the first two lines and below the third line, or the shaded area of Figure 13.4. The coordinates of the vertices of the triangle shown in the figure are obtained by solving the appropriate systems of two linear equations in two variables. For example, the vertex $(\frac{1}{7}, \frac{8}{7})$ is obtained by solving the system

$$3x + 4y - 5 = 0$$
$$x - y + 1 = 0$$

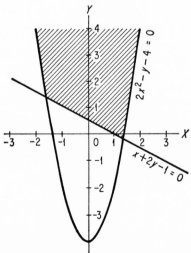

FIGURE 13.5

Example 13.9. Solve the system of inequalities:

$$x + 2y - 1 > 0$$
$$2x^2 - y - 4 < 0$$

Solution: The region satisfying the linear inequality consists of all points (x, y) above the line determined by the equation $x + 2y - 1 = 0$. By trial and error, we find that the region satisfying the quadratic inequality consists of all points (x, y) above the curve determined by the equation

$$2x^2 - y - 4 = 0$$

The region satisfying both inequalities is shown in Figure 13.5.

PROBLEMS A

1. Solve the following inequalities graphically.

(a) $x + 1 > 2$ (b) $-2x \leq 4 + x$
(c) $|x| < 1$ (d) $|x| \geq 2$
(e) $|x - 2| \leq 1$ (f) $|2x - 3| > 5$
(g) $x^2 - 3x + 1 < 0$ (h) $x^2 + 5x - 3 \geq 0$
(i) $2x^2 - 3x + 5 > 0$ (j) $x^2 - 3x + \frac{9}{4} < 0$
(k) $x^2 - 4x + 5 < 0$ (l) $-3x + 5 \geq x^2$

2. Solve the following systems of inequalities graphically.

(a) $x + y < 1$ (b) $2x + 3y \geq 5$
    $x - y > 2$ $-x + 5y \geq 3$

(c) $x + y + 1 < 0$ (d) $x < y$
    $x - y - 1 < 0$ $y < 2$
    $-x + 2y + 1 > 0$ $x + 4y - 2 < 0$

(e) $x^2 + y^2 \leq 1$ (f) $2x + y - 1 > 0$
    $x > 2y$ $x^2 - 4x + 1 \leq 0$

(g) $\frac{x^2}{4} - \frac{y^2}{9} < 1$ (h) $xy \leq 1$
    $x^2 + y^2 > 4$ $y - x > 0$

PROBLEMS B

1. Find the largest value that the expression $x^2 + y^2$ can assume, when x and y are restricted by the inequalities $x + y \leq 4$, $x \geq 0$, and $y \geq 2$.

2. The line segment with end points 0 and 1 is divided into three parts by two points located at x and y, respectively, with $0 < x < y < 1$. What are the conditions on x and y such that the three parts can form a triangle? *Hint:* The sum of any two sides of a triangle is greater than the third.

PART 4

Applications and
Special Topics

In Part IV we group those topics which do not belong to the main stream of our development of algebra and trigonometry. Nevertheless, these topics form an important part of our study because they are concerned with applications of what we have learned, or they deal with ideas essential in further mathematical work.

Although modern emphasis has been placed on the analytic trigonometry that we introduced in Chapters 6 and 7, it is from the science of "triangle measurement" that trigonometry draws its name. The emergence of modern computing equipment frees us from the need to concentrate on the calculations needed to solve triangles, but the main results in Chapter 14 are no less applicable than they used to be.

As your work in mathematics progresses, you will discover the important role that infinite series plays, both as a unifying idea in mathematics and as a useful tool. At best, we can scratch the surface in this book, but you will find that the idea of a limit, presented in Chapter 15, is fundamental in the study of calculus.

The theory of probability, introduced in Chapter 16, is one of the more interesting and challenging areas in mathematics, and it ties together many of the ideas that we have been studying in this book. Much modern research is done in the field of probability theory and in its main field of application, statistics.

259

14

Solution of Triangles

14.1 Introduction

Measurement of an inaccessible length often can be achieved if that length can be regarded as part of a triangle. For example, it is possible to measure the height h of a mountain by laying out a line segment of known length l on level ground near the base of the mountain, and measuring the angles A and B shown in Figure 14.1. The arts of surveying and navigation depend upon just such triangle measurement. It is our purpose in this section to determine what information about a triangle must be known to determine the remaining parts of the triangle.

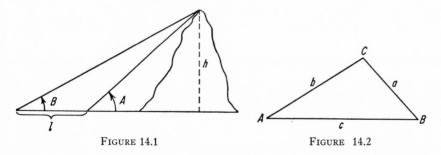

FIGURE 14.1   FIGURE 14.2

A triangle is said to be "solved" when its three angles and its three sides are determined. In the triangle of Figure 14.2, the angles are denoted by the upper case letters A, B, C, and the sides are denoted by the lower case letters a, b, and c. Note that the side opposite the angle A is

261

denoted by a, the side opposite B is denoted by b, and the side opposite C is denoted by c. We shall use this notation throughout the chapter.

To solve a triangle, it is necessary to know at least three of its parts A, B, C, a, b, and c. Often, knowledge of three of these parts makes it possible to determine the rest, and it is our purpose in this chapter to discover and apply laws or formulas that will aid us in finding the remaining three parts.

The sets of three given parts that may determine a triangle fall into one of the following four cases:

Case I. *Given two angles and any side.*

Case II. *Given two sides and an angle opposite one of them.*

Case III. *Given two sides and the included angle.*

Case IV. *Given three sides, such that the sum of any two sides exceeds the third.*

In Cases I, III, and IV, the triangle is uniquely determined; that is, there exists one and only one triangle having the given parts. Case II is special, however, in that there may exist no triangle, there may exist exactly one triangle, or there may exist two triangles having the given parts. The situations that may arise in Case II are illustrated in Figure 14.3. In this figure, h is the altitude of $\triangle ABC$ drawn from the

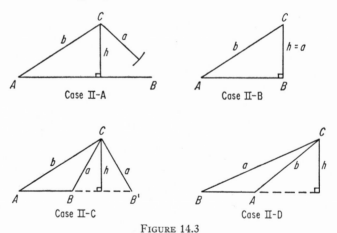

Case II-A   Case II-B

Case II-C   Case II-D

FIGURE 14.3

vertex C, and the given parts are A, a, and b. This figure should enable you to verify the following subdivision of Case II:

Case II-A, a < h. *No triangle is determined.*

Case II-B, a = h. *A right triangle is determined.*

Case II-C, h < a < b. *Two triangles are determined.*

Case II-D, a ≥ b. *One triangle is determined.*

In drawing Figure 14.3, we arbitrarily chose to call the given parts A, a, and b. By changing the letters, but *preserving the correspondence between any angle and its opposite side*, we could have denoted the given parts by B, b, and a, or B, b and c, or C, c, and a, or C, c, and b. In each case, we have two sides and the angle opposite one of them. (If we had been given B, c, and a, for example, the problem would not have belonged to Case II, because B is not opposite either of the sides given.)

Throughout this chapter we shall encounter relations that are true for any triangle, and that can be expressed in different ways by changing the letters. We shall derive such relations by considering only one combination of letters. If we understand that changing the letters in such formulas does not change their validity as long as the correspondence of A to a, B to b, and C to c is preserved, we can avoid needless repetition of proofs.

PROBLEMS A

1. Given the following three parts of $\triangle ABC$, into which case does the triangle-solving problem fall?

(a) a, b, c (b) a, b, C

(c) A, B, a (d) a, b, A

(e) B, a, C (f) b, B, A

(g) C, B, a (h) B, a, c

2. State the four subcases of Case II when the given parts are

(a) B, b, a (b) B, b, c

(c) C, c, a (d) C, c, b

PROBLEMS B

1. If the parts of a quadrilateral are taken to be its four sides, its four angles, and its two diagonals, show that the problem of "solving a quadrilateral" is equivalent to that of solving a triangle.

2. Can you state the problem of "solving an irregular pentagon" in terms of the problem of solving a triangle?

14.2   The Sine and Cosine Laws

In any one of the Cases I through IV, the given triangle can be solved by breaking it up into two right triangles. The resulting work may be somewhat laborious, however, and it is helpful to derive formulas that enable us to solve triangles directly. Among such formulas, the *law of sines* and the *law of cosines* are the most useful, not only in solving triangles, but in discovering other laws of trigonometry.

The **law of sines** is stated in the following theorem.

Theorem 14.1. *If* A, B, C, a, b, *and* c *are the parts of a triangle, then*

$$\frac{a}{\sin A} = \frac{b}{\sin B} = \frac{c}{\sin C}$$

Proof: In Figure 14.4, h is the altitude of $\triangle ABC$ from the vertex C. Thus, $\triangle APC$ and $\triangle BPC$ are right triangles, and, by Definition 6.3, we have

$$\sin A = h/b \quad \text{and} \quad \sin B = h/a$$

or

$$h = b \sin A \quad \text{and} \quad h = a \sin B$$

Thus,

$$a \sin B = b \sin A$$

or

$$\frac{a}{\sin A} = \frac{b}{\sin B}$$

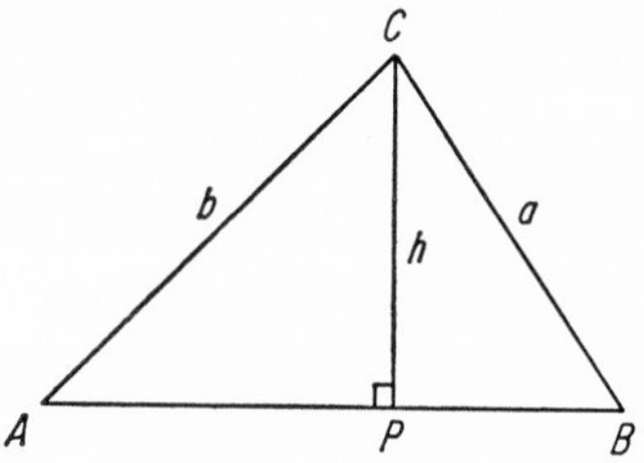

FIGURE 14.4

This last equation says that any two sides of a triangle are proportional to the sines of their opposite angles; thus, it is also true that

$$\frac{a}{\sin A} = \frac{c}{\sin C} \quad \text{and} \quad \frac{b}{\sin B} = \frac{c}{\sin C}$$

The law of sines states that the sides of a triangle are proportional to the *sines* of the opposite angles. This law actually gives the *three* equations

$$\frac{a}{\sin A} = \frac{b}{\sin B}, \quad \frac{a}{\sin A} = \frac{c}{\sin C}, \quad \text{and} \quad \frac{b}{\sin B} = \frac{c}{\sin C}$$

In proving this law, we assumed that B is an acute angle; that is, the altitude drawn from C intersects the base of the triangle. If B is an obtuse angle, the proof proceeds in essentially the same way, and the reader is asked to supply this proof in Problem A-1 at the end of this section.

Since the law of sines relates two sides and two opposite angles, it is particularly useful for solving triangles in Cases I and II. In applying the law of sines to these cases, select that one of the three equations containing the three given parts, and solve for the fourth part. Then, the fifth part is obtained by using the fact that the sum of the angles of a triangle is 180°, and finally, the sixth part is obtained by using a second one of the three equations. The following is an example of the application of the law of sines to Case I.

Example 14.1. Solve the triangle having $A = 30°$, $B = 45°$, and $a = 10$.

Solution: To find b, we use the equation $a/\sin A = b/\sin B$, obtaining

$$\frac{10}{1/2} = \frac{b}{\sqrt{2}/2}$$

or

$$b = 10\sqrt{2}$$

To find C, we use the fact that $A + B + C = 180°$, or

$$C = 180° - A - B = 105°$$

To find c, first we find $\sin C$, obtaining

$$\sin C = \sin (60° + 45°)$$
$$= \sin 60° \cdot \cos 45° + \cos 60° \cdot \sin 45°$$
$$= \frac{\sqrt{3}}{2} \cdot \frac{\sqrt{2}}{2} + \frac{1}{2} \cdot \frac{\sqrt{2}}{2}$$
$$= \frac{\sqrt{6} + \sqrt{2}}{4}$$

To find c, we use the equation $a/\sin A = c/\sin C$, obtaining

$$\frac{10}{1/2} = \frac{c}{(\sqrt{6} + \sqrt{2})/4}$$

or

$$c = 5(\sqrt{6} + \sqrt{2})$$

The following is an example of the application of the sine law to Case II.

Example 14.2. Solve the triangle having $A = 30°$, $a = 5$, and $b = 8$.

Solution: From Figure 14.4, we note that

$$h = b \sin A$$

Thus, in this problem

$$h = 8 \sin 30°$$
$$= 4$$

Thus, $h < a < b$, and there are two triangles determined by the given parts. To find B, we use the equation $a/\sin A = b/\sin B$, obtaining

$$\frac{5}{\frac{1}{2}} = \frac{8}{\sin B}$$

or

$$\sin B = \tfrac{4}{5} = .8000$$

There are two possibilities: either $B = 53° 10'$, or $B = 126° 50'$ to the nearest 10'. First, we select $B_1 = 53° 10'$, and find C_1 and c_1, the remaining parts of the first triangle. We have

$$C_1 = 180° - A_1 - B$$
$$= 96° 50'$$

Thus, $\sin C_1 = \sin (180° - 96° 50') = \sin 83° 10' = .9929$. Using the equation $a/\sin A = c/\sin C$ to find c_1, we have

$$\frac{5}{\frac{1}{2}} = \frac{c_1}{.9929}$$

or

$$c_1 = 9.9$$

to one decimal place. To find the remaining parts of the second triangle, we select $B_2 = 126° 50'$, and find

$$C_2 = 180° - A_2 - B$$
$$= 23° 10'$$

Thus, $\sin C_2 = \sin 23° 10' = .3934$. Using the equation $a/\sin A = c/\sin C$, we have

$$\frac{5}{\frac{1}{2}} = \frac{c_2}{.3934}$$

or

$$c_2 = 3.9$$

to one decimal place.

The **law of cosines** is stated in the following theorem.

Theorem 14.2. *If* A, a, b, *and* c *are parts of a triangle, then*

$$a^2 = b^2 + c^2 - 2bc \cos A$$

Proof: In Figure 14.5, h is the altitude of $\triangle ABC$ from the vertex C. Thus, $\triangle APC$ and $\triangle BPC$ are right triangles, and, by the Pythagorean theorem,

$$h^2 = b^2 - x^2 \quad \text{and} \quad h^2 = a^2 - (c - x)^2$$

Thus,

$$b^2 - x^2 = a^2 - (c - x)^2$$

or

$$a^2 = b^2 + c^2 - 2cx$$

But, from $\triangle APC$ and Definition 6.3, $\cos A = x/b$, or

$$x = b \cos A$$

and we have

$$a^2 = b^2 + c^2 - 2bc \cos A$$

If $A = 90°$, then $\cos A = 0$ and Theorem 14.2 reduces to $a^2 = b^2 + c^2$. Thus, the law of cosines is a generalization of the Pythagorean theorem to triangles other than right triangles. By changing the letters, but pre-

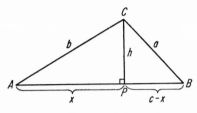

FIGURE 14.5

serving the correspondence between sides and their opposite angles, we obtain the other two forms of the law of cosines.

(14.1) $$b^2 = a^2 + c^2 - 2ac \cos B$$

(14.2) $$c^2 = a^2 + b^2 - 2ab \cos C$$

The reader is asked to prove the law of cosines when B is an obtuse angle in Problem A-2 at the end of this section.

The law of cosines is useful for solving triangles in Cases III and IV. The following is an example of the application of this law to Case III.

Example 14.3. Solve the triangle having $a = 4$, $b = 6$, and $C = 80°$.

Solution: To find c, we use Equation 14.2, obtaining

$$c^2 = 4^2 + 6^2 - 2(4)(6) \cos 80°$$
$$= 52 - 48(.1736)$$
$$= 43.7$$

to one decimal place. Thus, $c = 6.6$. To find A, we use Theorem 14.2, obtaining

$$16 = 36 + 43.7 - 79.2 \cos A$$

or

$$\cos A = .804$$

and

$$A = 36° \, 30'$$

to the nearest 10'. Finally, we find B from the equation $A + B + C = 180°$, or

$$B = 180° - A - C$$
$$= 63° \, 30'$$

The following is an example of the application of the law of cosines to Case IV.

Example 14.4. Solve the triangle having $a = 3$, $b = 5$, and $c = 6$.

Solution: To find A, we use Theorem 14.2, obtaining

$$9 = 25 + 36 - 60 \cos A$$

or

$$\cos A = \tfrac{13}{15}$$

$$= .8667$$

Thus,

$$A = 30° \ 00'$$

to the nearest 10'. To find B, we use Equation 14.1, obtaining $\cos B = \tfrac{5}{9} = .5556$. Thus, $B = 56° \ 10'$ to the nearest 10'. Finally, we find C by using the equation $A + B + C = 180°$, or

$$C = 180° - A - B$$

$$= 93° \ 50'$$

PROBLEMS A

1. Prove the law of sines when B is an obtuse angle; that is, when $\triangle ABC$ looks like the triangle in the accompanying figure.

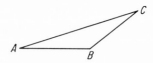

2. Prove the law of cosines when B is an obtuse angle.

3. Solve the triangles having the given parts. (Use slide-rule accuracy, that is, three significant figures, and do not bother to interpolate in Table II.)

(a) $A = 30°$, $B = 75°$, $c = 5$ (b) $A = 45°$, $C = 60°$, $b = 15$
(c) $b = 4$, $c = 5$, $B = 30°$ (d) $a = 10$, $b = 6$, $A = 15°$
(e) $a = 4$, $b = 6$, $c = 8$ (f) $a = \sqrt{5}$, $b = \sqrt{3}$, $c = \sqrt{7}$
(g) $b = 1$, $C = 30°$, $a = 4$ (h) $A = 15°$, $b = \sqrt{6}$, $c = \sqrt{3}$
(i) $B = 60°$, $a = \sqrt{3}$, $b = \tfrac{3}{2}$ (j) $a = 6$, $c = 9$, $B = 52°$
(k) $a = 15$, $b = 25$, $c = 30$ (l) $b = \sqrt{2}$, $c = 7$, $A = 135°$

4. A 50-foot antenna is located at the top of a hill. From a point at the foot of the hill, the angles of elevation to the top and bottom of the antenna are 42° and 38°, respectively. Find the height of the hill.

5. To measure the distance across an unfordable stream from point A to point B, a surveyor locates a point C, on the same side of the stream as point A, and 100 yards from A. The angles BAC and BCA are 50° 10' and 58° 20', respectively. What is the distance across the stream from A to B?

6. A ship, starting out at port A, travels 100 miles and discovers that it is 5° off course. If its destination is 500 miles from A, by how much should the course be altered?

7. What is the perimeter of a parallelogram having a diagonal of 26 inches that makes angles of 18° and 38° with the sides of the parallelogram?

8. In $\triangle ABC$, $B = 2A$. Show that $b/a = 2 \cos A$.

PROBLEMS B

1. A man hears the thunder from a storm 15 seconds after he sees the lightning flash due north from his location. Ten minutes later, the storm is in the northeast, and he hears the thunder 10 seconds after he sees the lightning. If sound travels at the rate of 1100 feet per second, how fast is the storm travelling?

2. Prove the **Law of Tangents:**

$$\frac{a-b}{a+b} = \frac{\tan \frac{1}{2}(A-B)}{\tan \frac{1}{2}(A+B)}$$

To what case or cases is this law most conveniently applied? *Hint:* Let $r = \dfrac{a}{\sin A} = \dfrac{b}{\sin B} = \dfrac{c}{\sin C}$

14.3   The Area of a Triangle

In this section, we shall apply the laws of sines and cosines to find formulas giving the area of any triangle in terms of some of its parts. If we let K represent the area of the triangle shown in Figure 14.6, we know from plane geometry that

$$K = \tfrac{1}{2}ch$$

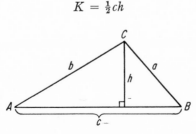

FIGURE 14.6

where c is the base of the triangle and h is its altitude drawn from the vertex C. Using this basic formula, we shall express K in terms of the parts of the triangle given in each of Cases I, III, and IV, on page 262.

In Case I, we are given two angles and any side.   Using the formula $h = b \sin A$, obtained by applying Definition 6.3 to Figure 14.6, we have

(14.3) $$K = \tfrac{1}{2} bc \sin A$$

Using the law of sines to write $b = c \sin B / \sin C$, we have the formula

(14.4) $$K = \frac{c^2 \sin A \sin B}{2 \sin C}$$

which expresses the area of $\triangle ABC$ in terms of its angles and one of its sides.   By rearranging the letters, we also can obtain the following formulas, useful in Case I.

(14.5) $$K = \frac{a^2 \sin B \sin C}{2 \sin A}$$

(14.6) $$K = \frac{b^2 \sin A \sin C}{2 \sin B}$$

Example 14.5. Find the area of the triangle having $a = 4$, $A = 15°$, and $B = 60°$.

Solution: First, we find the remaining angle using the formula $A + B + C = 180°$.   We obtain $C = 105°$.   Substituting in Equation 14.5, we have

$$K = \frac{(4)^2 \sin 60° \sin 105°}{2 \sin 15°}$$

$$= \frac{(16)(.8660)(.9659)}{(2)(.2588)}$$

$$= 25.8$$

to one decimal place.

Equation 14.3 is useful for finding the area of a triangle in Case III. If the given angle is not A, you can change this formula by rearranging the letters to make it applicable in any given Case III problem.

Example 14.6. Find the area of the triangle having $a = 4$, $b = 8$, and $C = 54°$.

Solution: Rewriting Equation 14.3 in the form

$$K = \tfrac{1}{2} ab \sin C$$

and substituting for a, b, and C, we have

$$K = \tfrac{1}{2}(4)(8)(.8090)$$

$$= 12.9$$

to one decimal place.

To find a formula suitable for application to Case IV, first we square each side of Equation 14.3 to obtain

$$K^2 = \tfrac{1}{4}b^2c^2 \sin^2 A$$
$$= \tfrac{1}{4}b^2c^2(1 - \cos^2 A)$$

Using the law of cosines to write

$$\cos A = \frac{b^2 + c^2 - a^2}{2bc}$$

we have

$$K^2 = \tfrac{1}{4}b^2c^2 \left[1 - \frac{(b^2 + c^2 - a^2)^2}{4b^2c^2} \right]$$
$$= \tfrac{1}{16}[4b^2c^2 - (b^2 + c^2 - a^2)^2]$$

The expression $4b^2c^2 - (b^2 + c^2 - a^2)^2$ is the difference between two squares, and it can be factored as follows.

$$4b^2c^2 - (b^2 + c^2 - a^2)^2 = [2bc + (b^2 + c^2 - a^2)][2bc - (b^2 + c^2 - a^2)]$$
$$= [(b^2 + 2bc + c^2) - a^2][a^2 - (b^2 - 2bc + c^2)]$$
$$= [(b + c)^2 - a^2][a^2 - (b - c)^2]$$

Each of the expressions in the brackets can be factored as the difference between two squares, and we obtain

$$4b^2c^2 - (b^2 + c^2 - a^2)^2 = (b + c + a)(b + c - a)(a + b - c)(a - b + c)$$

Substituting in the last formula for K^2, we obtain

(14.7) $$K^2 = \tfrac{1}{16}(a + b + c)(a + b - c)(a - b + c)(-a + b + c)$$

Equation 14.7 can be simplified if we define the **semiperimeter** S of $\triangle ABC$ by the equation

(14.8) $$S = \tfrac{1}{2}(a + b + c)$$

Using Equation 14.8, we can write

$$a + b + c = 2S$$
$$a + b - c = 2(S - c)$$
$$a - b + c = 2(S - b)$$
$$-a + b + c = 2(S - a)$$

Substituting in Equation 14.7, we obtain

(14.9) $$K^2 = S(S - a)(S - b)(S - c)$$

Example 14.7. Find the area of the triangle having $a = 3$, $b = 5$, and $c = 6$.

Solution: Using Equation 14.8 we have

$$S = \tfrac{1}{2}(3 + 5 + 6)$$
$$= 7$$

Substituting in Equation 14.9, we have

$$K^2 = 7(7 - 3)(7 - 5)(7 - 6)$$
$$= 56$$

or

$$K = 7.5$$

to one decimal place.

PROBLEMS A

1. Find the areas of the triangles having the given parts.

(a) $A = 60°$, $B = 45°$, $c = 15$ (b) $a = 5$, $c = 4$, $B = 30°$
(c) $a = 6$, $b = 8$, $c = 4$ (d) $b = 2$, $C = 30°$, $a = 8$
(e) $b = 6$, $c = 9$, $A = 48°$ (f) $a = \sqrt{3}$, $b = \sqrt{6}$, $c = 2$
(g) $B = 20°$, $c = \sqrt{5}$, $a = \tfrac{5}{2}$ (h) $a = \sqrt{3}$, $b = 8$, $C = 120°$
(i) $A = 115°$, $b = 11$, $C = 45°$ (j) $a = b = c = 1$

2. What is the area of a field in the shape of a parallelogram having sides of 1500 feet and 800 feet that make an angle of 75°?

3. How are the areas of two similar triangles related? (Recall that the lengths of corresponding sides have the same ratio in similar triangles.)

PROBLEMS B

1. If a circle, inscribed in a triangle having the semiperimeter s, has radius r, show that

$$K = rs$$

where K is the area of the triangle. *Hint:* The radii of the inscribed circle are perpendicular to the sides of the triangle at the points of contact.

2. Use the results of Problem 1 to prove that the radius of the inscribed circle is given by

$$r = \sqrt{\frac{(s - a)(s - b)(s - c)}{s}}$$

15

Introduction to Series

15.1 Sequences and Series

In this chapter we shall introduce a special kind of a function, called a
sequence, and defined as follows.

Definition 15.1. *A* **sequence** *is a set of elements arranged in a definite
order such that there is a first element, a second element, a third element,
and so forth.*

It is convenient to refer to the first element as a_1, the second element
as a_2, and so forth. Thus, a sequence can be regarded as a function
defined on a domain of natural numbers. Instead of using the usual
functional notation $a(n)$ to stand for that element of the range corresponding to the natural number n, it is customary to use the symbol a_n.

A sequence is said to be **finite** if it has a *last element*. For example, the
sequence 1, 3, 5, 7, 9 is a finite sequence having the last element 9. If
there is no last element of a sequence, it is called an **infinite sequence.**
An infinite sequence often is denoted by listing its first few elements
followed by dots, such as

$$1, \tfrac{1}{2}, \tfrac{1}{3}, \tfrac{1}{4}, \ldots$$

The nth term of this sequence is $1/n$, and the sequence also may be
denoted by the symbol $\{1/n\}$.

If a sequence consists of elements for which the operation of addition is defined, an expression indicating the sum of the terms of the sequence is called a **series.** A series can consist of a finite number of terms, or it can consist of an infinite number of terms. The finite series

$$\tfrac{1}{2} + \tfrac{1}{4} + \tfrac{1}{8} + \tfrac{1}{16}$$

obviously has the sum 15/16. Although it can be shown that the infinite series

$$\tfrac{1}{2} + \tfrac{1}{4} + \tfrac{1}{8} + \dots$$

has the sum 1, *we cannot claim that every infinite series has a sum.* For example, the infinite series

$$1 + 2 + 3 + \dots$$

obviously has no sum. (Why?)

To abbreviate the sum of a series, it is convenient to introduce the summation symbol Σ. For example, the symbol

$$\sum_{n=1}^{3} a_n$$

stands for the sum of the series $a_1 + a_2 + a_3$. In this connection, the subscript n is called the index of summation, and its value identifies the particular term in the sum. The index of summation also can be used to denote an operation to be performed on the terms of the sum. For example, the symbol

$$\sum_{n=1}^{4} a^n$$

stands for the sum of the series $a + a^2 + a^3 + a^4$. We can use symbols other than n to denote the same sum; for example,

$$\sum_{j=1}^{4} a^j$$

also stands for $a + a^2 + a^3 + a^4$.

To denote the sum of an infinite series, when this sum exists, we use the symbol ∞ (infinity) as follows.

$$a_1 + a_2 + a_3 + \dots = \sum_{j=1}^{\infty} a_j$$

Observe that this notation does not imply that ∞ is the last term of the series $a_1 + a_2 + a_3 + \dots$ because this series has no last term. Much confusion can be avoided if you will remember that ∞ *is not a natural number.*

Using the summation notation, we can indicate sums of more complicated series, as shown in the following examples.

$$\sum_{i=1}^{3} a_i^2 = a_1^2 + a_2^2 + a_3^2$$

$$\sum_{j=1}^{5} a_j b_j = a_1 b_1 + a_2 b_2 + a_3 b_3 + a_4 b_4 + a_5 b_5$$

$$\sum_{n=4}^{7} (-1)^n a_n = a_4 - a_5 + a_6 - a_7$$

Three basic properties of the summation symbol $\sum$ are proved in the following theorem.

Theorem 15.1.

(a) *If each term of the series*

$$a_1 + a_2 + \ldots + a_n$$

is added to the corresponding term of the series $b_1 + b_2 + \ldots + b_n$ *then the sum of the resulting series is*

$$\sum_{j=1}^{n} (a_j + b_j)$$

and

$$\sum_{j=1}^{n} (a_j + b_j) = \sum_{j=1}^{n} a_j + \sum_{j=1}^{n} b_j$$

(b) *If each term of the series* $a_1 + a_2 + \ldots + a_n$ *is multiplied by the same constant* k, *then the sum of the resulting series is*

$$\sum_{j=1}^{n} k a_j$$

and

$$\sum_{j=1}^{n} k a_j = k \sum_{j=1}^{n} a_j$$

(c) *If the terms of the series* $a_1 + a_2 + \ldots + a_n$ *all equal* a, *then the sum of the series is formally*

$$\sum_{j=1}^{n} a$$

and

$$\sum_{j=1}^{n} a = na$$

Proof: The proof follows directly from the definition of the summation sign Σ and the properties of addition and multiplication.

(a)　$\displaystyle\sum_{j=1}^{n} (a_j + b_j) = (a_1 + b_1) + (a_2 + b_2) + \ldots + (a_n + b_n)$

$$= (a_1 + a_2 + \ldots + a_n) + (b_1 + b_2 + \ldots + b_n)$$

$$= \sum_{j=1}^{n} a_j + \sum_{j=1}^{n} b_j$$

(b)　$\displaystyle\sum_{j=1}^{n} ka_j = ka_1 + ka_2 + \ldots + ka_n$

$$= k(a_1 + a_2 + \ldots + a_n)$$

$$= k \sum_{j=1}^{n} a_j$$

(c)　$\displaystyle\sum_{j=1}^{n} a = a + a + \ldots + a \quad \text{(n terms)}$

$$= na$$

The following example illustrates Theorem 15.1.

Example 15.1. Prove that

$$\sum_{j=1}^{n} (a_j - k)^2 = \sum_{j=1}^{n} a_j^2 - 2k \sum_{j=1}^{n} a_j + nk^2$$

Solution:

$$\sum_{j=1}^{n} (a_j - k)^2 = \sum_{j=1}^{n} (a_j^2 - 2ka_j + k^2)$$

$$= \sum_{j=1}^{n} a_j^2 + \sum_{j=1}^{n} (-2ka_j) + \sum_{j=1}^{n} k^2 \qquad \text{(Theorem 15.1a)}$$

$$= \sum_{j=1}^{n} a_j^2 - 2k \sum_{j=1}^{n} a_j + \sum_{j=1}^{n} k^2 \qquad \text{(Theorem 15.1b)}$$

$$= \sum_{j=1}^{n} a_j^2 - 2k \sum_{j=1}^{n} a_j + nk^2 \qquad \text{(Theorem 15.1c)}$$

PROBLEMS A

1. Write the first four terms of the sequence whose nth term is given.

(a) $1/n$

(b) $n(n + 1)$

(c) $\dfrac{2^n}{n + 1}$

(d) n^n

(e) $(-1)^n 3^n$

(f) $\dfrac{(-1)^{n-1}}{n^2}$

(g) $(-\tfrac{1}{2})^{2n+1} + (-\tfrac{1}{2})^{2n}$

(h) $n(n - 1)(n - 2) \cdot \ldots \cdot 2 \cdot 1$

2. Guess the nth term of the following series, and express the sum using summation notation.

(a) $1 + 2 + 3 + \ldots + 9$ (b) $\frac{1}{2} + \frac{1}{4} + \frac{1}{8} + \ldots + \frac{1}{256}$

(c) $\frac{1}{2} + \frac{3}{4} + \frac{5}{6} + \frac{7}{8} + \ldots$ (d) $1 + 3 + 5 + 7 + \ldots$

(e) $1 - \frac{1}{4} + \frac{1}{9} - \frac{1}{16} + \ldots$ (f) $-2 + 4 - 6 + 8$

(g) $\left(\dfrac{x}{2}\right)^2 - \left(\dfrac{x}{3}\right)^2 + \left(\dfrac{x}{4}\right)^2 - \ldots + \left(\dfrac{x}{10}\right)^2$

(h) $a + \dfrac{a^3}{1 \cdot 2} + \dfrac{a^5}{1 \cdot 2 \cdot 3} + \dfrac{a^7}{1 \cdot 2 \cdot 3 \cdot 4} + \ldots$

3. Prove the following.

(a) $\displaystyle\sum_{j=1}^{n} (a_j - a) = \sum_{j=1}^{n} a_j - na$

(b) $\displaystyle\sum_{j=1}^{n} (x_j^2 - 1) = \sum_{j=1}^{n} x_j^2 - n$

(c) $\displaystyle\sum_{j=1}^{3} (j + 2)^2 = 50$

(d) $\displaystyle\sum_{j=0}^{5} j(j - 1) = 40$

(e) $\displaystyle\sum_{j=1}^{n} [(-1)^j + (-1)^{j+1}] = 0$

(f) $\displaystyle\sum_{j=1}^{2n} x^j + \sum_{j=1}^{2n} (-x)^j = 2 \sum_{j=1}^{n} x^{2j}$

PROBLEMS B

1. A recursion formula defines a sequence by giving its first term and a rule for finding any other term if one or more of the preceding terms are known.

(a) Write down the first six terms of the sequence defined by the recursion formula

$$a_1 = 1$$
$$a_{n+1} = na_n$$

(b) Find a recursion formula for the sequence

$$a, ar, ar^2, \ldots, ar^{n-1}, \ldots$$

2. The **Fibonacci sequence** has the first term 0, the second term 1, and each other term is the sum of the two preceding terms. Find a recursion formula for the terms of the Fibonacci sequence.

3. The **double summation** $\displaystyle\sum_{j=1}^{n} \sum_{i=1}^{m} a_{ij}$ is defined as follows.

$$\sum_{j=1}^{n} \sum_{i=1}^{m} a_{ij} = a_{11} + a_{21} + \ldots + a_{m1}$$
$$+ a_{12} + a_{22} + \ldots + a_{m2} + \ldots$$
$$+ a_{1n} + a_{2n} + \ldots + a_{mn}$$

(a) Prove that

$$\sum_{j=1}^{n} \sum_{i=1}^{m} a_{ij} = \sum_{j=1}^{n} (a_{1j} + a_{2j} + \ldots + a_{mj})$$

$$= \sum_{i=1}^{m} (a_{i1} + a_{i2} + \ldots + a_{in})$$

(b) Show that

$$\left(\sum_{i=1}^{n} a_i \right)^2 = \sum_{i=1}^{n} a_i^2 + 2 \sum_{j=1}^{n} \sum_{\substack{k=1 \\ (j < k)}}^{n} a_j a_k$$

15.2 Mathematical Induction

The idea of induction is used by people in all walks of life. Generally speaking, induction is the process of using a limited number of specific experiences or observations to draw conclusions about similar situations. Induction involves guesswork, sometimes very imaginative, but it cannot be used to establish the validity of a general conclusion. Thus, we are always revising some of our beliefs in the light of new experience; in particular, scientists are continually revising their theories to conform to newly-discovered facts.

The mathematician makes extensive use of induction to *discover* new theorems, but he cannot use induction to *prove* these theorems. For example, in writing down the difference between the squares of two consecutive natural numbers, we form the following table.

$$2^2 - 1^2 = 3$$
$$3^2 - 2^2 = 5$$
$$4^2 - 3^2 = 7$$

.

.

.

It appears, from this table, that these differences are always odd numbers, in fact, that the difference between the squares of two consecutive natural numbers is the sum of the numbers themselves. This conclusion is correct, but we cannot use the inductive reasoning by which we discovered this law to prove it. We can prove this assertion, however, by noting that

$$(x + 1)^2 - x^2 = 2x + 1 = (x + 1) + x$$

There is a method of *deductive proof* in mathematics which bears some vague similarity to the idea of induction. This method, unfortunately called **mathematical induction,** is particularly useful in proving statements in the form of sequences or series.   It is based on the following axiom for the set of natural numbers.

Axiom of Induction. *Every set of natural numbers includes all natural numbers if*

(a) *it includes the number* 1.

(b) *it includes the number* n + 1 *whenever it includes the number* n.

To illustrate the concept of mathematical induction we consider the following analogy.   If the bowling pins shown in Figure 15.1 are spaced closely enough together, and if the first pin is knocked over, the entire

FIGURE 15.1

row of pins will be knocked over.   Note that there are two essential requirements for all the pins to fall.   First, the leading pin must be knocked over, and second, the pins must be spaced closely enough together so that if any pin falls, the next pin will fall.   If *either* condition is not fulfilled, *all* the pins will not fall.   Note that, if the rth bowling pin is the first pin knocked over, then every pin beginning with the rth pin will fall.   This suggests a theorem that can be proved using the axiom of induction; specifically, it suggests that every set of natural numbers that includes the number r and includes the number $n + 1$, whenever it includes the number $n(n \geq r)$, includes all natural numbers beginning with r.   The reader is asked to prove this theorem in Problem B-1 at the end of this section.

To give an example of the use of mathematical induction, we prove that

$$1 + 2 + \ldots + n = \frac{n(n + 1)}{2}$$

First, we note that the equation is true for $n = 1$; that is, the number 1 is included in the set of all numbers satisfying this equation. Next, we *assume* that the equation is true for some value of n, say $n = k$, and *prove* that this assumption implies that it is true also for $n = k + 1$. By virtue of our assumption, we have

$$1 + 2 + \ldots + k = \frac{k(k + 1)}{2}$$

Adding $k + 1$ to each side of this equation, we have

$$1 + 2 + \ldots + k + (k + 1) = \frac{k(k + 1)}{2} + (k + 1)$$
$$= (k + 1)\left(\frac{k}{2} + 1\right)$$
$$= \frac{(k + 1)(k + 2)}{2}$$

This last statement says that, to get the sum of the first $k + 1$ terms, we multiply $k + 1$ by the next term, $k + 2$, and divide by 2. But the theorem we are proving states that, to get the sum of the first n terms, we multiply n by the next term $n + 1$ and divide by 2. Thus, the theorem is satisfied if $n = k + 1$. Having proved that the number 1 is included in the set of all numbers satisfying this equation, and the number $k + 1$ is included in the set of all natural numbers satisfying this equation *whenever this set includes the number* k, we use the axiom of induction to conclude that the set of numbers satisfying this equation includes *all natural numbers.*

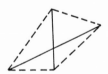 

FIGURE 15.2

Mathematical induction is applicable also in the proof of statements not in the form of equations. For example, we note from Figure 15.2 that a quadrilateral has two diagonals, a pentagon has 5 diagonals, and a hexagon has 9 diagonals. With some clever guesswork, perhaps you can infer from these examples that a convex polygon of n sides has $n(n - 3)/2$

diagonals. As we have seen, this statement is true when n equals 4, 5, and 6. To prove that it is true for all natural numbers, *beginning with* $n = 4$, we assume that it is true for $n = k$, where $k \geq 4$; that is, we assume that a convex polygon of k sides has $k(k-3)/2$ diagonals. To prove that this assumption implies that a convex polygon of $k + 1$ sides has

$$\frac{(k+1)[(k+1)-3]}{2} = \frac{(k+1)(k-2)}{2}$$

diagonals, we add one more side to the k-sided polygon. If we replace one of its sides with a pair of sides, as shown in Figure 15.3, we find that there are $k - 1$ new diagonals. These are all the $k - 2$ lines that can be drawn from the new vertex to the $k - 2$ old vertices *not adjacent to the new vertex*, plus the old side, which is now a diagonal. Thus, there are

$$\frac{k(k-3)}{2} + (k-1)$$

diagonals in the $(k+1)$-sided polygon. Since this expression equals $(k+1)(k-2)/2$, we conclude that, if the statement is true for $n = k$, then it

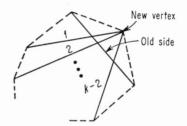

FIGURE 15.3

is true also for $n = k + 1$. Thus, by the theorem stated on page 279, the statement is true for all natural numbers beginning with $n = 4$.

We conclude our discussion of mathematical induction by proving DeMoivre's theorem, Theorem 7.7 on page 146. We have already shown that

$$z^n = r^n (\cos n\theta + i \sin n\theta)$$

when $n = 2$ and $n = 3$. (This theorem is trivially true when $n = 1$.) To prove that this theorem holds for *all* positive integers n, we assume that it holds for $n = k$ and prove that this assumption implies its validity for $n = k + 1$. Multiplying both sides of the equation

$$z^k = r^k (\cos k\theta + i \sin k\theta)$$

by $r(\cos \theta + i \sin \theta)$, we obtain

$$r(\cos \theta + i \sin \theta) \cdot z^k = r(\cos \theta + i \sin \theta) \cdot r^k(\cos k\theta + i \sin k\theta)$$

Using the relation $z = r(\cos \theta + i \sin \theta)$ to write the left-hand side of this equation in the form $z \cdot z^k$, and performing the indicated multiplication on the right-hand side of the equation, we obtain

$$z^{k+1} = r^{k+1}[(\cos \theta \cos k\theta - \sin \theta \sin k\theta) + i(\sin \theta \cos k\theta + \cos \theta \sin k\theta)]$$

By Theorem 7.3,

$$\cos \theta \cos k\theta - \sin \theta \sin k\theta = \cos (\theta + k\theta) = \cos (k + 1)\theta$$

and

$$\sin \theta \cos k\theta + \cos \theta \sin k\theta = \sin (\theta + k\theta) = \sin (k + 1)\theta$$

Hence,

$$z^{k+1} = r^{k+1}[\cos (k + 1)\theta + i \sin (k + 1)\theta]$$

Comparing this result with the statement of DeMoivre's theorem, we observe that this theorem is true for $n = k + 1$ if it is true for $n = k$. By the axiom of induction, we conclude that DeMoivre's theorem is true for every positive integer n.

In summary, we note the distinction between induction and *mathematical* induction. Induction is a method of inference, arguing that all the elements of a set have a given property if every observed member of that set has the given property. Mathematical induction is a method of *deductive proof*, requiring that the set be ordered like the natural numbers, that there exists a first element, and if an element has the given property, the next element has that property.

PROBLEMS A

1. Use mathematical induction to prove the following, where n is a natural number.

(a) $2 + 4 + 6 + \ldots + 2n = n(n + 1)$

(b) $1 + 2 + 4 + \ldots + 2^n = 2^{n+1} - 1$

(c) $\dfrac{1}{1 \cdot 2} + \dfrac{1}{2 \cdot 3} + \dfrac{1}{3 \cdot 4} + \ldots + \dfrac{1}{n(n + 1)} = \dfrac{n}{n + 1}$

(d) $1^2 + 2^2 + 3^2 + \ldots + n^2 = \dfrac{n(n + 1)(2n + 1)}{6}$

(e) $\displaystyle\sum_{j=1}^{n} (4j - 3) = n(2n - 1)$

(f) $\displaystyle\sum_{j=1}^{n} j^3 = \dfrac{n^2(n + 1)^2}{4}$

(g) $\displaystyle\sum_{j=1}^{n-1} 2^j = 2^n - 2$

(h) $\displaystyle\sum_{j=0}^{n-1} (-\tfrac{1}{2})^j = \tfrac{2}{3}[1 - (-\tfrac{1}{2})^n]$

(i) $a^{2n} - b^{2n}$ has the factor $(a + b)$ for all n.

(j) $a^{2n-1} + b^{2n-1}$ has the factor $(a + b)$ for all n.
(k) $2^n \geq 1 + n$ for all n.
(l) 3^n is an odd number for all n.

2. Given n distinct points, no three of which are collinear, prove that $n(n - 1)/2$ distinct lines are determined.

3. A square is inscribed in a unit square by joining the midpoints of the unit square with straight-line segments. A third square is found from the second square in the same way, and so on. Prove by mathematical induction that the area of the nth square so formed is $(\frac{1}{2})^{n-1}$.

4. Attempt to prove the following false statements for all natural numbers n by mathematical induction and note why the proof fails.

(a) $1 + 2 + 3 + \ldots + n = 2^{n-1} + n - 1$

(b) $1 - 1 + 1 - \ldots + (-1)^{n-1} = 1$

(c) $\sum_{j=1}^{n} 2^j = 2(2^n - 1)$

(d) $\sum_{j=1}^{n} 2j = n^2 + n + 2$

PROBLEMS B

1. Prove the theorem mentioned on page 279; that is, prove that every set of natural numbers that includes the number r and includes the number $n + 1$ whenever it includes the number $n(n \geq r)$ includes all natural numbers beginning with r.

2. Prove by mathematical induction that the infinite sequence $\{n^2\}$ can be obtained from the infinite sequence of natural numbers $\{n\}$ by leaving out each second term of $\{n\}$ and summing the first n terms of the resulting sequence. *Hint:* There are three sequences involved. Write down several terms of each.

3. To "prove" by mathematical induction that all natural numbers are equal, we observe first that the statement is true (by default) when $n = 1$. Now, we assume that the statement is true for any k natural numbers $a_1, a_2 \ldots, a_k$. If we include an additional natural number, any k of them are equal by our assumption. Thus, for example,

$$a_1 = a_2 = \ldots = a_k$$

and

$$a_2 = a_3 = \ldots = a_{k+1}$$

This implies that

$$a_1 = a_2 = \ldots = a_k = a_{k+1}$$

and the theorem is proved. Criticize this "proof."

15.3 The Binomial Theorem

An important finite series, having many applications in mathematics, is obtained by expanding the product $(a + b)^n$, where n is a natural number. To make some reasonable guess about the expansion of this product, we examine the results of multiplying n factors $(a + b)$ for a few small values of n. Successive multiplication by $a + b$ gives the following table for $n = 1, 2, 3$, and 4.

n	$(a + b)^n$
1	$a + b$
2	$a^2 + 2ab + b^2$
3	$a^3 + 3a^2b + 3ab^2 + b^3$
4	$a^4 + 4a^3b + 6a^2b^2 + 4ab^3 + b^4$

Now, we use inductive reasoning to *guess* at a result for any positive-integer value of n. To begin, we notice that the first term is a^nb^0, the second term is a coefficient times $a^{n-1}b^1, \ldots$, the $(j + 1)$st term is a coefficient times $a^{n-i}b^i$. Furthermore, there are $n + 1$ terms, corresponding to values of j from $j = 0$ to $j = n$. Next, we notice that there is some regularity in the coefficients. To observe this regularity better, we construct the following table of coefficients.

n						
1			1	1		
2		1	2	1		
3		1	3	3	1	
4	1	4	6	4	1	
5	1	5	10	10	5	1

. . . .

We observe that any number in this table can be expressed as the sum of the two closest numbers in the row above it. The only exceptions to this rule are the first and last numbers in each row, which equal 1 in every case. To check this rule, we have used it to write down the coefficients for $n = 5$, and you can verify by multiplying $(a + b)^4$ by $a + b$ that the underscored coefficients are correct for $n = 5$. The array of numbers obtained by applying the foregoing rule is called **Pascal's triangle.**

Let us digress for the moment, and study some of the mathematical properties of numbers satisfying the rule for the construction of Pascal's triangle. It is possible, although difficult, to use the rule defining Pascal's triangle to find an expression for the $(j + 1)$st number in the nth row of

Pascal's triangle.   Using the symbol $\binom{n}{j}$ to stand for this number, it can be shown that

(15.1) $$\binom{n}{j} = \frac{n(n-1) \cdot \ldots \cdot (n-j+1)}{j(j-1) \cdot \ldots \cdot 2 \cdot 1} \quad (j = 1, 2, \ldots, n-1)$$

(We shall momentarily postpone our discussion of the value of $\binom{n}{j}$ when $j = 0$ and $j = n$.)   For example, to find the third number in the fifth row of Pascal's triangle, we note that $j = 2$ and $n = 5$, and we have

$$\binom{5}{2} = \frac{5 \cdot 4}{2 \cdot 1} = 10$$

Equation 15.1 can be simplified by introducing the notation

$$n! = n(n-1) \cdot \ldots \cdot 2 \cdot 1$$

The symbol $n!$, read "n-factorial," stands for the product of the first n natural numbers.   For example

$$1! = 1, \quad 2! = 2 \cdot 1 = 2, \quad 3! = 3 \cdot 2 \cdot 1 = 6, \quad \text{etc.}$$

Using the factorial notation, we can write Equation 15.1 in the form

(15.2) $$\binom{n}{j} = \frac{n!}{j!(n-j)!} \quad (j = 1, 2, \ldots, n-1)$$

To prove the equivalence of Equations 15.1 and 15.2, we note that $n!$ can be written in the form

$$n! = n(n-1) \cdot \ldots \cdot (n-j+1)(n-j)(n-j-1) \cdot \ldots \cdot 2 \cdot 1$$

However

$$(n-j)(n-j-1) \cdot \ldots \cdot 2 \cdot 1 = (n-j)!$$

Therefore, we have

$$n! = n(n-1) \cdot \ldots \cdot (n-j+1) \cdot (n-j)!$$

or

$$n(n-1) \cdot \ldots \cdot (n-j+1) = \frac{n!}{(n-j)!}$$

Finally, we have

$$\binom{n}{j} = \frac{n(n-1) \cdot \ldots \cdot (n-j+1)}{j(j-1) \cdot \ldots \cdot 2 \cdot 1} = \frac{n!}{j!(n-j)!}$$

To illustrate the use of Equation 15.2 in evaluating the number $\binom{n}{j}$, we evaluate $\binom{7}{3}$. By Equation 15.2 we have

$$\binom{7}{3} = \frac{7!}{3!(7-3)!}$$

$$= \frac{7 \cdot 6 \cdot 5 \cdot 4 \cdot 3 \cdot 2 \cdot 1}{3 \cdot 2 \cdot 1 \cdot 4 \cdot 3 \cdot 2 \cdot 1}$$

$$= \frac{7 \cdot 6 \cdot 5}{3 \cdot 2 \cdot 1}$$

$$= 35$$

To use symbols of the form $\binom{n}{j}$ to represent *any* number in Pascal's triangle, we shall introduce the convention $\binom{n}{0} = \binom{n}{n} = 1$. Use of this convention implies that

$$\frac{n!}{0!\,n!} = 1$$

which is true only if *we define* 0! *to equal* 1. Using this definition of 0!, we can extend Equation 15.2 to include $j = 0$ and $j = n$.

Now we can prove that Equation 15.2 gives the correct formula for calculating the $(j+1)$st number in the nth row of Pascal's triangle. Recall that the rule defining Pascal's triangle states that any number is the sum of the two closest numbers in the row above it, except that the first and last numbers in any row equal 1. Denoting the number in question by $\binom{n+1}{j}$, we have the following theorem.

Theorem 15.2. $\binom{n}{j-1} + \binom{n}{j} = \binom{n+1}{j}$

Proof:

$$\binom{n}{j-1} + \binom{n}{j} = \frac{n!}{(j-1)!(n-j+1)!} + \frac{n!}{j!(n-j)!}$$

To obtain a common denominator, we multiply the numerator and denominator of the first fraction by j and the numerator and denominator of the second fraction by $n - j + 1$, obtaining

$$\binom{n}{j-1} + \binom{n}{j} = \frac{jn!}{j(j-1)!(n-j+1)!} + \frac{(n-j+1)n!}{j!(n-j+1)(n-j)!}$$

$$= \frac{jn!}{j!(n-j+1)!} + \frac{(n-j+1)n!}{j!(n-j+1)!}$$

$$= \frac{(n+1)n!}{j!(n-j+1)!}$$

$$= \frac{(n+1)!}{j!(n-j+1)!}$$

$$= \binom{n+1}{j}$$

The following theorem is helpful in evaluating $\binom{n}{j}$ when j is large.

Theorem 15.3. $\binom{n}{j} = \binom{n}{n-j}$

Proof:

$$\binom{n}{n-j} = \frac{n!}{(n-j)![n-(n-j)]!}$$

$$= \frac{n!}{(n-j)!j!}$$

$$= \frac{n!}{j!(n-j)!}$$

$$= \binom{n}{j}$$

Note that Theorem 15.3 establishes the symmetry of the numbers in any given row of Pascal's triangle. You might already have observed this symmetry. To illustrate this theorem, we evaluate $\binom{10}{8}$, obtaining

$$\binom{10}{8} = \binom{10}{2} = \frac{10 \cdot 9}{2 \cdot 1} = 45$$

Now, we are ready to resume our guesswork concerning the result of expanding $(a + b)^n$, where n is any natural number. Summarizing our previous conclusions, we guess that this expansion has the following properties.

1. There are $n + 1$ terms.

2. The $(j + 1)$st term is $\binom{n}{j} a^{n-j} b^j$.

Thus, we guess the following result, where n is a natural number.

$$(15.3) \qquad (a + b)^n = \sum_{j=0}^{n} \binom{n}{j} a^{n-j} b^j$$

So far, we have used induction to *guess* at the result expressed in Equation 15.3. Now, we use mathematical induction to *prove* that Equation 15.3 is correct.

Theorem 15.4. Binomial Theorem. *If* n *is a natural number and* a *and* b *are elements of a set for which addition and multiplication are uniquely defined, then*

$$(a + b)^n = \sum_{j=0}^{n} \binom{n}{j} a^{n-j} b^j$$

Proof: We have already shown that the theorem is true for $n = 1$. (In fact, we know that it is true for $n = 1, 2, 3, 4,$ and 5.) Assuming that the theorem holds for $n = k$, we have

$$(a + b)^k = \sum_{j=0}^{k} \binom{k}{j} a^{k-j} b^j$$

Multiplying both sides of this equation by $a + b$, we have

$$(a + b)^{k+1} = a \sum_{j=0}^{k} \binom{k}{j} a^{k-j} b^j + b \sum_{j=0}^{k} \binom{k}{j} a^{k-j} b^j$$

$$= \sum_{j=0}^{k} \binom{k}{j} a^{k-j+1} b^j + \sum_{j=0}^{k} \binom{k}{j} a^{k-j} b^{j+1} \qquad \text{(Theorem 15.1 b)}$$

$$= \binom{k}{0} a^{k+1} + \binom{k}{1} a^k b + \binom{k}{2} a^{k-1} b^2 + \ldots + \binom{k}{j} a^{k-j+1} b^j + \ldots + \binom{k}{k} a b^k$$
$$+ \binom{k}{0} a^k b + \binom{k}{1} a^{k-1} b^2 + \ldots + \binom{k}{j-1} a^{k-j+1} b^j + \ldots + \binom{k}{k-1} a b^k + \binom{k}{k} b^{k+1}$$

Adding corresponding terms, we obtain

$$(a + b)^{k+1} = \binom{k}{0} a^{k+1} + \sum_{j=1}^{k} \left[\binom{k}{j-1} + \binom{k}{j} \right] a^{k-j+1} b^j + \binom{k}{k} b^{k+1}$$

Using Theorem 15.2 to add the coefficients in the brackets, we have

$$(a + b)^{k+1} = \binom{k}{0} a^{k+1} + \sum_{j=1}^{k} \binom{k+1}{j} a^{k-j+1} b^j + \binom{k}{k} b^{k+1}$$

Noting that

$$\binom{k}{0} = \binom{k+1}{0} = 1 \quad \text{and} \quad \binom{k}{k} = \binom{k+1}{k+1} = 1$$

we can put the first and the last terms under the summation sign, and write

$$(a + b)^{k+1} = \sum_{j=0}^{k+1} \binom{k + 1}{j} a^{k-i+1} b^i$$

Comparing this result with the equation

$$(a + b)^n = \sum_{j=0}^{n} \binom{n}{j} a^{n-i} b^i$$

we note that the theorem is true for $n = k + 1$ if it is true for $n = k$, and we use the axiom of induction to conclude that the theorem is true for all natural numbers.

Theorem 15.4 can be used to expand positive-integer powers of binomials of the form $a + b$ whether a and b are numbers, polynomials, or any other expressions for which addition and multiplication are uniquely defined. The following example illustrates this application.

Example 15.2. Expand $\left(x\sqrt{y} + \dfrac{x^2}{y} \right)^8$, and identify the fourth term.

Solution: Much labor can be avoided with the use of the summation notation. Substituting $a = x\sqrt{y}$ and $b = x^2/y$ in Theorem 15.4, we have

$$\left(x\sqrt{y} + \frac{x^2}{y} \right)^8 = \sum_{j=0}^{8} \binom{8}{j} (x\sqrt{y})^{8-i} \left(\frac{x^2}{y} \right)^i$$

$$= \sum_{j=0}^{8} \binom{8}{j} x^{8+i} y^{4-(3i/2)}$$

The fourth term is found by setting $j = 3$, and we have

$$\binom{8}{3} x^{11} y^{-1/2} = \frac{56 x^{11}}{\sqrt{y}}$$

The following example illustrates the use of the binomial theorem to expand a positive-integer power of a multinomial.

Example 15.3. Expand $(2x - y + 3z)^3$.

Solution: Using the associative law of addition to write $2x - y + 3z$ in the form $(2x - y) + 3z$, we have

$$[(2x - y) + 3z]^3 = \sum_{j=0}^{3} \binom{3}{j} (2x - y)^{3-i} (3z)^i$$

$$= (2x - y)^3 + 3(2x - y)^2 (3z)$$
$$+ 3(2x - y)(3z)^2 + (3z)^3$$

Using the binomial theorem to expand the different powers of $2x - y$, we have

$$[(2x - y) + 3z]^3 = (2x)^3 + 3(2x)^2(-y) + 3(2x)(-y)^2 + (-y)^3$$
$$+ 3[(2x)^2 + 2(2x)(-y) + (-y)^2](3z)$$
$$+ 3(2x - y)(3z)^2$$
$$+ (3z)^3$$
$$= 8x^3 - 12x^2y + 6xy^2 - y^3$$
$$+ 36x^2z - 36xyz + 9y^2z$$
$$+ 54xz^2 - 27yz^2$$
$$+ 27z^3$$

PROBLEMS A

1. Evaluate the following coefficients.

(a) $\binom{10}{3}$ (b) $\binom{12}{4}$ (c) $\binom{9}{7}$

(d) $\binom{17}{15}$ (e) $\binom{4}{0}$ (f) $\binom{6}{6}$

2. Use Equation 15.2 to prove the following.

(a) $\dfrac{n!}{r!} = (n - r)! \binom{n}{r}$

(b) $\binom{n}{r + 1} \Big/ \binom{n}{r} = \dfrac{n - r}{r + 1}$

(c) $\binom{n}{j} + \binom{n + 1}{j} = \dfrac{2n - j + 2}{n - j + 1} \binom{n}{j}$

(d) $\binom{n + j}{j} = \binom{n + j}{n}$

3. Expand the following using summation notation, and identify the fourth term.

(a) $(x + 2y)^5$ (b) $(2a + 3b)^6$

(c) $(2 - x)^9$ (d) $(2x - 1)^7$

(e) $(x^2y - \sqrt{xy})^{10}$ (f) $\left(\dfrac{x}{y} - \dfrac{y}{x}\right)^8$

(g) $(2^z + 3^v)^6$ (h) $(\sin x - \cos x)^5$

4. Use the binomial theorem to write the following complex numbers in the form $a + bi$.

(a) $(1 + i)^4$ (b) $(2 - 3i)^3$

(c) $(-\tfrac{1}{2} + i)^5$ (d) $(\sqrt{2} + 2i)^5$

5. Use the binomial theorem to calculate the following, correct to three decimal places.

(a) $(1.01)^5$ (b) $(2.002)^8$
(c) $(.999)^{10}$ (d) $(-.95)^7$

6. Expand the following.

(a) $(x + y + z)^4$ (b) $(x + y - z + u)^3$

PROBLEMS B

1. Prove the following recursion formulas (see Problem B-1, end of Section 15.1) for the sequence of binomial coefficients.

(a) $\dbinom{n}{j+1} = \dfrac{n-j}{j+1}\dbinom{n}{j}$ (b) $\dbinom{n+1}{j} = \dfrac{n+1}{n-j+1}\dbinom{n}{j}$

2. Prove that $\displaystyle\sum_{j=0}^{n}\binom{n}{j} = 2^n$. *Hint:* Use the binomial theorem.

3. We can use Equation 15.1 to define $\dbinom{n}{j}$ for values of n other than natural numbers. For example

$$\binom{\frac{1}{2}}{3} = \frac{(\frac{1}{2})(\frac{1}{2}-1)(\frac{1}{2}-2)}{3\cdot 2\cdot 1} = \frac{1}{16}$$

and

$$\binom{-1}{4} = \frac{(-1)(-1-1)(-1-2)(-1-3)(-1-4)}{5\cdot 4\cdot 3\cdot 2\cdot 1} = -1$$

Using this definition, it can be proved that

$$(a+b)^n = \sum_{j=0}^{\infty}\binom{n}{j}a^{n-i}b^i$$

for *any rational number* n. (If n is a natural number, the sum has finitely many terms — otherwise it has infinitely many terms.) Use this result to

(a) evaluate $\sqrt[3]{(1.001)^2}$ to four decimal places.

(b) show that $\sqrt{1+x}$ is approximately equal to $1 + x/2$ if $|x|$ is small.

15.4 Progressions

In this section, we introduce two special sequences, called arithmetic and geometric progressions. First, we study the **arithmetic progression.**

Definition 15.2. *An* **arithmetic progression** *is a sequence such that the difference between any two successive terms is the same constant.*

Any finite arithmetic progression can be represented by the sequence

$$a, a + d, a + 2d, \ldots, a + (n - 1)d$$

In this sequence, a is called the **first term**, and d is called the **common difference.** The jth term of the arithmetic progression is given by the formula

(15.4) $$a_j = a + (j - 1)d \quad (j = 1, 2, \ldots, n)$$

For example, the sequence

$$1, 3, 5, 7, \ldots, (2n - 1)$$

is an arithmetic progression having the first term $a = 1$, and the common difference $d = 2$. The jth term of this progression is

$$a_j = 1 + 2(j - 1) = 2j - 1 \quad (j \leq n)$$

A further application of Equation 15.4 is given in the following example.

Example 15.4. If the third term of an arithmetic progression equals 0 and the eleventh term equals -4, find the common difference.

Solution: We are given $a_3 = 0$ and $a_{11} = -4$. Substituting into Equation 15.4, we obtain

$$0 = a + 2d$$

$$-4 = a + 10d$$

Solving this system of equations, we obtain $a = 1$ and $d = -\frac{1}{2}$.

Now we shall find an expression for the sum of the first n terms of the series $a_1 + a_2 + \ldots + a_n$, where $a_1, a_2, \ldots, a_n$ is an arithmetic progression. Using Equation 15.4, we can write S_n, the sum of this series, in the following form.

$$S_n = \sum_{j=1}^{n} a_j = \sum_{j=1}^{n} [a + (j - 1)d]$$

Using Theorem 15.1, we have

$$S_n = \sum_{j=1}^{n} a + \sum_{j=1}^{n} (j - 1)d$$

$$= na + d \sum_{j=1}^{n} j - nd$$

$$= n(a - d) + d \sum_{j=1}^{n} j$$

However, $\sum_{j=1}^{n} j = 1 + 2 + \ldots + n$, and on page 280 we proved that this sum equals $n(n+1)/2$. Thus

$$S_n = n(a - d) + d\frac{n(n+1)}{2}$$

$$= \frac{n}{2}[2a - 2d + (n+1)d]$$

or

(15.5) $$S_n = \tfrac{1}{2}n[2a + (n-1)d]$$

The following example illustrates the use of Equation 15.5.

Example 15.5. Find the sum of the first 12 positive multiples of 3.

Solution: The first 12 positive multiples of 3 can be written in the form $\{3j\}$, where $j = 1, 2, \ldots, 12$. They form an arithmetic progression with $a = 3$ and $d = 3$. The required sum is

$$S_{12} = \tfrac{12}{2}(2 \cdot 3 + 11 \cdot 3)$$

$$= 234$$

Now we study the **geometric progression.**

Definition 15.3. *A* **geometric progression** *is a sequence such that the quotient of any two successive terms is the same constant.*

Any finite geometric progression can be represented by the sequence

$$a, ar, ar^2, \ldots, ar^{n-1}$$

In this sequence, a is the **first term** and r is called the **common ratio.** The jth term of the geometric progression is given by the formula

(15.6) $$a_j = ar^{j-1} \quad (j = 1, 2, \ldots, n)$$

For example, the sequence

$$1, \tfrac{1}{3}, \tfrac{1}{9}, \ldots, (\tfrac{1}{3})^{n-1}$$

is a geometric progression having the first term $a = 1$ and the common ratio $r = \tfrac{1}{3}$. The jth term of this progression is

$$a_j = 1 \cdot (\tfrac{1}{3})^{j-1} = 3^{1-j} \quad (j \leq n).$$

A further application of Equation 15.6 is given in the following example.

Example 15.6. If the second term of a geometric progression equals $-\sqrt{3}/2$ and the ninth term equals $\sqrt{3}/256$, find the common ratio.

Solution: We are given $a_2 = -\sqrt{3}/2$ and $a_9 = \sqrt{3}/256$. Substituting in Equation 15.6, we obtain

$$\frac{-\sqrt{3}}{2} = ar$$

$$\frac{\sqrt{3}}{256} = ar^8$$

Solving the first equation for a and substituting the result into the second equation, we obtain

$$\frac{\sqrt{3}}{256} = \frac{-\sqrt{3}}{2r} r^8$$

or

$$r^7 = -\tfrac{1}{128}$$

Since $-\tfrac{1}{128} = (-\tfrac{1}{2})^7$, we have $r^7 = (-\tfrac{1}{2})^7$, or $r = -\tfrac{1}{2}$.

Now we shall find an expression for the sum of the first n terms of the series $a_1 + a_2 + \ldots + a_n$, where $a_1, a_2, \ldots, a_n$ is a geometric progression. Using Equation 15.6, we can write S_n, the sum of this series, in the following form.

$$S_n = \sum_{j=1}^{n} ar^{i-1}$$

Multiplying both sides by r, we have

$$rS_n = r\sum_{j=1}^{n} ar^{i-1} = \sum_{j=1}^{n} ar^{i}$$

Subtracting rS_n from S_n, we have

$$(1-r)S_n = \sum_{j=1}^{n} ar^{i-1} - \sum_{j=1}^{n} ar^{i}$$

$$= a\sum_{j=1}^{n} (r^{i-1} - r^{i})$$

If we write out the terms of $\sum_{j=1}^{n} (r^{i-1} - r^{i})$, we have

$$\sum_{j=1}^{n} (r^{i-1} - r^{i}) = (1-r) + (r-r^2) + \ldots + (r^{n-1} - r^n)$$

$$= 1 + (-r + r) + (-r^2 + r^2) + \ldots$$
$$+ (-r^{n-1} + r^{n-1}) - r^n$$

$$= 1 - r^n$$

Thus,

$$(1 - r)S_n = a(1 - r^n)$$

or

(15.7) $$S_n = \frac{a(1 - r^n)}{1 - r} \quad (r \neq 1)$$

(Can you find a formula for S_n if $r = 1$?)

The following example illustrates the use of Equation 15.7.

Example 15.7. A square of side 1 is subdivided into four equal squares of side $\frac{1}{2}$. One of the resulting squares is subdivided into four equal squares, and so on, as shown in Figure 15.4. Find the sum of the areas of the first five squares.

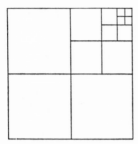

FIGURE 15.4

Solution: A square in any subdivision has $\frac{1}{4}$ the area of a square in the preceding subdivision. Thus, the areas form a geometric progression with $a = 1$ and $r = \frac{1}{4}$. The required sum is

$$S_5 = \frac{1 \cdot [1 - (\frac{1}{4})^5]}{1 - \frac{1}{4}}$$

$$= \frac{1 - \frac{1}{1024}}{1 - \frac{1}{4}}$$

$$= \frac{1024 - 1}{1024 - 256}$$

$$= \frac{1023}{768}$$

PROBLEMS A

1. Which of the following sequences, as far as recorded, are arithmetic progressions? Which are geometric progressions? Find the next two terms of those sequences that are progressions.

(a) $3, 7, 11, 15, \ldots$ (b) $8, -1, -10, -19, \ldots$

(c) $3, 9, 17, 81, \ldots$ (d) $1, -\frac{1}{2}, -\frac{1}{4}, -\frac{1}{8}, \ldots$

(e) $0, 1, 2, 4, 8, \ldots$ (f) $1, -1, 1, -1, \ldots$

(g) $-\frac{1}{2}, \frac{1}{2}, \frac{3}{2}, \frac{5}{2}, \ldots$ (h) $0, -1, 2, -3, \ldots$

(i) $a, a + b, a + 2b, \ldots$ (j) $x - y, x + y, x + 3y, \ldots$

(k) $\dfrac{x}{y}, \dfrac{y}{x}, (y/x)^3, (y/x)^5, \ldots$ (l) $1, x, 2x, 3x, \ldots$

2. Write the first four terms of the arithmetic progression having the following properties

(a) $a = 2, d = -2$ (b) $a_2 = 4, d = 3$

(c) $a_3 = -4, a_5 = 2$ (d) $a_7 = 10, a_{12} = 0$

3. Write down the first four terms of the geometric progression having the, following properties

(a) $a = 3, r = \frac{2}{3}$ (b) $a_9 = 1, r = 5$

(c) $a_3 = 8, a_8 = -256$ (d) $a_5 = 1, a_{10} = -1$

4. Identify whether the sequence is an arithmetic progression or a geometric progression and find the indicated sum.

(a) $1 + 3 + 5 + \ldots + 99$ (b) $1 - 2 - 5 - \ldots - 29$

(c) $1 + \frac{1}{4} + \frac{1}{16} + \ldots + \frac{1}{4096}$ (d) $-\frac{1}{2} + \frac{1}{4} - \frac{1}{8} + \ldots - \frac{1}{512}$

(e) $-\frac{1}{3}, 2, -12, \ldots, -15{,}552$ (f) $-\frac{1}{2} + \frac{1}{2} + \frac{3}{2} + \ldots + \frac{19}{2}$

(g) $(x - y) + (x + y) + (x + 3y) + \ldots + (x + 11y)$

(h) $a/b + b/a + (b/a)^3 + \ldots + (b/a)^{15}$

5. Find the sum of the first twenty positive odd integers.

6. If an automobile valued at \$2,800 depreciates each year by an amount equal to 40 per cent of its value at the beginning of the year, what is its value after seven years?

PROBLEMS B

1. Write down the first eight terms of

(a) the arithmetic progression with $a_3 = -a_6$ and $a_5 = 1 + a_8$.

(b) the geometric progression with $a_8 = 10^7$ $a_j = 100a_{j-2}$ and $a_j a_{j+1} < 0$.

2. The "half-life" of a radioactive substance is defined to be the time required for half of any given amount to change its form. Given twenty grams of a substance having a half-life of two days, how much is unchanged after 30 days?

3. What can be said about the sequence resulting from

(a) multiplying each element of an arithmetic progression by the same constant.

(b) adding the same constant to each element of an arithmetic progression. Prove your conjectures.

4. Do Problem 3 when the original sequence is a geometric progression.

5. What happens to a geometric progression when each element is raised to the same power? Prove your conjecture.

15.5 Limits

In Section 15.1 a sequence was said to be infinite if it does not have a last term.   However, as n increases, the terms of a sequence sometimes become closer and closer to some fixed number.   For example, the sequence

$$-\tfrac{1}{2}, \tfrac{1}{4}, -\tfrac{1}{8}, \tfrac{1}{16}, \ldots$$

has the nth term $a_n = (-\tfrac{1}{2})^n$, and you can see that a_n approaches zero as n increases.   Note that this does not mean that the last term of the sequence $\{(-\tfrac{1}{2})^n\}$ is zero; what is meant is that *the terms of the sequence become arbitrarily close to zero as* n *becomes sufficiently large.*

To put the phrases "arbitrarily close" and "sufficiently large" on a more rigorous basis, we consider the graph shown in Figure 15.5.   From this graph, we observe that, given a positive number ϵ, we can find a

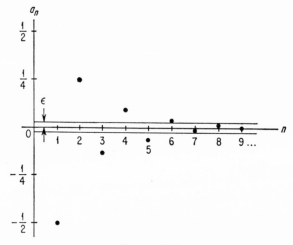

FIGURE 15.5

natural number N such that, for every value of n greater than or equal to N, the distance between $(-\tfrac{1}{2})^n$ and 0 is less than ϵ.   For example, if we are given $\epsilon = 0.01$, then $|(-\tfrac{1}{2})^n - 0| < 0.01$ for every $n \geq 7$.

The property illustrated above is defined formally as follows.

Definition 15.4. *The infinite sequence* $\{a_n\}$ *is said to have the* **limit L** *if, for every positive number* ϵ *there exists a natural number* N, *such that*

$$|a_n - L| < \epsilon$$

whenever n $\geq$ N.   *In symbols, we write*

$$\lim_{n \to \infty} a_n = L$$

If an infinite sequence $\{a_n\}$ has a limit, we call $\{a_n\}$ a **convergent sequence**; otherwise, we say that $\{a_n\}$ is a **divergent sequence**.

Definition 15.4 gives the conditions for the existence of a limit, but it does not tell us how to find a limit. To obtain the limit of a convergent sequence, we examine the behavior of the nth term as n becomes large. For example, the nth term of the infinite sequence

$$\tfrac{2}{1}, \tfrac{3}{2}, \tfrac{4}{3}, \tfrac{5}{4}, \ldots$$

is given by

$$a_n = \frac{n+1}{n}$$

To determine the behavior of a_n as n becomes large, we write

$$a_n = 1 + \frac{1}{n}$$

As n becomes large, $1/n$ tends to zero; thus, $1 + 1/n$ tends to 1, and we write

$$\lim_{n\to\infty} \frac{n+1}{n} = 1$$

To give an example of a divergent sequence, we consider the infinite sequence

$$1, 0, 1, 0, \ldots$$

having the nth term

$$a_n = 1 \quad \text{if } n \text{ is odd}$$

$$a_n = 0 \quad \text{if } n \text{ is even}$$

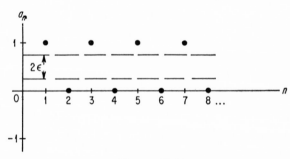

FIGURE 15.6

If we choose a value of ϵ less than $\tfrac{1}{2}$, we observe from Figure 15.6 that there is no natural number N such that *all* points on the graph for which $n \geq N$ lie inside a band of width 2ϵ.

In the following examples, we apply these limiting methods to deter-mine the conditions under which infinite arithmetic and geometric pro-gressions converge.

Example 15.8. Under what conditions does the infinite arithmetic progression $\{a + (n - 1)d\}$ converge?

Solution: If $d \neq 0$, the nth term becomes arbitrarily large and the sequence diverges. If $d = 0$, we get the sequence $\{a\}$, having equal elements, and the sequence obviously has the limit a.

Example 15.9. Under what conditions does the infinite geometric progression $\{ar^{n-1}\}$ converge?

Solution: If $|r| > 1$, the nth term becomes arbitrarily large and the sequence diverges. If $r = 1$, we get the sequence $\{a\}$, having equal elements, and the sequence obviously has the limit a. If $|r| < 1$, the nth term tends to zero as n becomes large, and the sequence has the limit 0.

The concept of the limit of a sequence can be used to determine whether a given infinite series has a sum. For example, given the series

$$1 - \tfrac{1}{2} + \tfrac{1}{4} - \tfrac{1}{8} + \ldots$$

we can construct an infinite sequence $\{S_n\}$ as follows.

$$S_1 = 1$$
$$S_2 = 1 - \tfrac{1}{2}$$
$$S_3 = 1 - \tfrac{1}{2} + \tfrac{1}{4}$$
$$S_4 = 1 - \tfrac{1}{2} + \tfrac{1}{4} - \tfrac{1}{8}$$

.

.

.

The elements of the sequence $\{S_n\}$ are called the **partial sums** of the series $1 - \tfrac{1}{2} + \tfrac{1}{4} - \tfrac{1}{8} + \ldots$. If this infinite series has a sum, the sum is the limit of the sequence of partial sums. We state this definition formally as follows.

Definition 15.5. *The infinite series* $a_1 + a_2 + \ldots$ *is said to have the sum S if*

$$\lim_{n \to \infty} S_n = S$$

where

$$S_n = \sum_{j=1}^{n} a_j$$

Consistent with our terminology for infinite sequences, we say that a series is **convergent** if it has a sum; otherwise it is **divergent**.

Returning to our example, we note that S_n is the sum of a finite geometric series having the first term $a = 1$ and the common ratio $r = -\frac{1}{2}$. From Equation 15.7, we have

$$S_n = \frac{1 - (-\frac{1}{2})^n}{1 - (-\frac{1}{2})}$$

$$= \tfrac{2}{3}[1 - (-\tfrac{1}{2})^n]$$

As n becomes large, $(-\frac{1}{2})^n$ tends to zero; thus, $1 - (-\frac{1}{2})^n$ tends to 1, and we have

$$S = \lim_{n \to \infty} \tfrac{2}{3}[1 - (-\tfrac{1}{2})^n]$$

$$= \tfrac{2}{3}$$

The ideas used in the foregoing example can be applied to find the sum of any convergent infinite geometric series. From Equation 15.7 we have

$$S_n = \frac{a(1 - r^n)}{1 - r} \quad (r \neq 1)$$

If $|r| < 1$, as n becomes large, r^n tends to zero, and we have

(15.8) $$S = \lim_{n \to \infty} S_n = \frac{a}{1 - r} \quad (|r| < 1)$$

An application of Equation 15.8 is illustrated in the following example.

Example 15.10. Express the repeating decimal $.0\overline{21}$ as the quotient of two integers.

Solution:

$$.0\overline{21} = .021 + .00021 + .0000021 + \ldots$$

$$= \frac{21}{10^3} + \frac{21}{10^5} + \frac{21}{10^7} + \ldots$$

This is an infinite geometric series having the first term $a = 21/10^3$ and the common ratio $r = 1/10^2$. Using Equation 15.8 to find its sum, we have

$$S = \frac{21/10^3}{1 - 1/10^2}$$

$$= \frac{21}{10^3 - 10}$$

$$= \frac{21}{990} = \frac{7}{330} \quad \text{(in lowest terms)}$$

PROBLEMS A

1. Find the limit as $n \to \infty$ of any of the following sequences that converge.

(a) $\left\{\dfrac{1}{n-1}\right\}$

(b) $\left\{\dfrac{n-2}{n}\right\}$

(c) $\left\{\dfrac{3-4n}{5}\right\}$

(d) $\{\sqrt{n}\}$

(e) $\left\{\dfrac{n^2}{n!}\right\}$

(f) $\{2^{-n}\}$

(g) $\left\{\dfrac{n+1}{n+2}\right\}$

(h) $\left\{\dfrac{n^2-1}{n+1}\right\}$

(i) $\{n^{-a}\},\ a > 0$

(j) $\left\{\log\dfrac{1}{n}\right\}$

2. Find the sum of any of the following series that converge.

(a) $1 + \frac{1}{2} + \frac{1}{4} + \frac{1}{8} + \ldots$

(b) $-\frac{1}{3} + \frac{1}{6} - \frac{1}{12} + \frac{1}{24} - \ldots$

(c) $1 + 1 + 1 + 1 + \ldots$

(d) $3 + 1 + 3^{-1} + 3^{-2} + \ldots$

(e) $\log 7 + (\log 7)^2 + (\log 7)^3 + \ldots$

(f) $1 - 1 + 1 - 1 + \ldots$

3. Express the following repeating decimals as the quotient of two integers.

(a) $.0\overline{39}$

(b) $1.5\overline{2}$

(c) $1.0\overline{10}$

(d) $.\overline{359}$

(e) $4.21\overline{37}$

(f) $-1.9\overline{041}$

PROBLEMS B

1. Use Definition 15.4 to prove the following theorems.

(a) If $\{a_n\}$ converges, then $\{ca_n\}$ converges, and

$$\lim_{n\to\infty} ca_n = c \lim_{n\to\infty} a_n$$

(b) If $\{a_n\}$ and $\{b_n\}$ converge, then $\{a_n + b_n\}$ converges, and

$$\lim_{n\to\infty} (a_n + b_n) = \lim_{n\to\infty} a_n + \lim_{n\to\infty} b_n.$$

2. Prove that the series $1 + \frac{1}{2} + \frac{1}{3} + \frac{1}{4} + \ldots$ diverges.

Hint: Show that $\displaystyle\sum_{j=2^k+1}^{2^{k+1}} \frac{1}{j} > \frac{1}{2}$ for $k = 1, 2, 3, \ldots$.

3. Comment on the following "proof" that $0 = 1$.

$$S = 1 + 1 + 1 + \ldots$$
$$= 1 + (1 + 1 + 1 + \ldots)$$
$$= 1 + S$$

therefore $S = 1 + S$ and $0 = 1$.

16

Introduction to Probability

16.1 Sets and Events

Probabilities are associated with the outcomes of experiments, such as tossing a coin, drawing a card from a deck of cards, determining the quality of a manufactured product, or crossing two species of plants and observing the characteristics of the offspring. Thus, we speak of the probability of obtaining a head when a coin is tossed, the probability of drawing an ace from a deck of cards, the probability that a manufacturing process will produce a defective item, or the probability that the offspring will be resistant to a certain plant disease. In each experiment, there is a set of all conceivable outcomes, and we are interested in the probability of a particular outcome.

In this chapter, we shall introduce the theory of probability as it applies to experiments having finitely many outcomes. For example, the sets of outcomes of an experiment involving the toss of a single coin or a single die are both finite; the first set has *two* elements, called "heads" and "tails", and the second set has the *six* elements 1, 2, 3, 4, 5, and 6.

In framing a probability problem, the term **sample space** is used to refer to the set of all outcomes. Since we are dealing with finite sample spaces, it is possible to think of the sample space as consisting of a number of distinct elements. For example, the sample space of an experiment consisting of the toss of two coins has the four elements HH, HT, TH, and TT, where H and T stand for "heads" and "tails", respectively. With respect to this sample space, we might be interested in finding the probability that exactly one head appears, that is, the probability of obtaining one of the elements HT or TH. The set $\{HT, TH\}$ is a collection of elements chosen from the sample space $\{HH, HT, TH, TT\}$, and it is called a **subset** of the sample space. More precisely, A is a subset of B if every element of A also is an element of B. It is customary to use the word **event** to stand for a subset of a sample space. Thus, the event that exactly one head appears when two coins are tossed corresponds to the subset $\{HT, TH\}$ of the sample space of this experiment.

In many problems of probability, we are interested in finding the probability of an event consisting of some combination of two or more events. For example, we may wish to know the probability of drawing an ace *and* a king in two draws from a deck of cards, or we may wish to know the probability that the draws will result in two spades *or* two diamonds. In general, if A and B are any two sets, we wish to define new sets A *and* B and A *or* B. It is customary to use the symbols $A \cap B$ and $A \cup B$ to stand for A *and* B, and A *or* B, respectively. The symbol $\cap$ is called "cap," and $\cup$ is called "cup." We can look upon cap and cup as denoting operations on sets in much the same way as we look upon the times and plus signs as denoting operations on numbers.

To visualize the operations on sets, it is helpful to think of the elements of a set as points within some closed curve such as a circle or a rectangle. The sample space, denoted by the letter S, is represented in Figure 16.1 by a rectangle, and the events A and B are represented by circles. Such a representation is called a **Venn diagram;** Venn diagrams are useful in representing many kinds of relations among sets, as shown

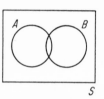

FIGURE 16.1

in Figure 16.2. The Venn diagram representing the statement "A is a subset of B" is shown in Figure 16.2(a). If A and B have *no elements in common* they are called **disjoint sets**, and the Venn diagram representing

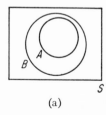 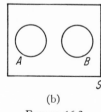 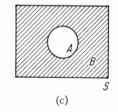

| (a) | (b) | (c) |

FIGURE 16.2

the statement "A and B are disjoint sets" is shown in Figure 16.2(b). If B consists of *all elements in* S *not in* A, then B is called the **complement** of A, and the Venn diagram representing the statement "B is the complement of A" is shown in Figure 16.2(c).

The cap and cup operations are represented by the Venn diagrams of Figure 16.3. From Figure 16.3(a) we observe that the set $A \cap B$ consists of all elements in *both* A *and* B and you can see why $A \cap B$ also is called the **intersection** of A and B. From Figure 16.3(b) we observe that the set $A \cup B$ consists of all elements *either in* A *or in* B, *or in both*, and you can see why $A \cup B$ also is called the **union** of A and B.

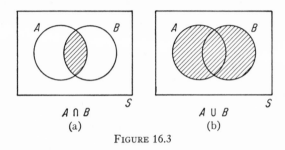

$A \cap B$ $A \cup B$
(a)   (b)
FIGURE 16.3

Using the operations $\cap$ and $\cup$, together with the operation of complementation denoted by $\bar{A}$ ($\bar{A}$ is the complement of A) it is possible to construct an algebra of sets. The algebra of sets, like the algebra of real numbers, is based upon a number of axioms stating the behavior of the elements of the system (sets, in this case) under certain operations ($\cap$, $\cup$, and $^{-}$ in this case). We shall not give a complete axiomatic development of set algebra in this book; rather, we shall compare some of the axioms of set algebra with like axioms for the real number system. In the following axioms, the equal sign connecting two sets means that the elements of both sets are identical.

1. **Commutative Laws.**
$$A \cup B = B \cup A$$
$$A \cap B = B \cap A$$

2. **Associative Laws.**
$$(A \cup B) \cup C = A \cup (B \cup C)$$
$$(A \cap B) \cap C = A \cap (B \cap C)$$

3. **Distributive Laws.**
$$A \cap (B \cup C) = (A \cap B) \cup (A \cap C)$$
$$A \cup (B \cap C) = (A \cup B) \cap (A \cup C)$$

Like the commutative and associative laws of addition and multiplication for real numbers, there are commutative and associative laws of union and intersection for sets. These laws for sets are identical to those for real numbers, except that $\cup$ and $\cap$ replace $+$ and $\cdot$, respectively. However, unlike the system of real numbers, there are *two distributive laws* for the algebra of sets.   The first law, the distributive law of intersection over union, can be compared to the distributive law of multiplication over addition,

$$a(b + c) = ab + ac$$

but the second law, the distributive law of union over intersection, is without parallel in the real number system.   If this second distributive law seems unreasonable, remember that it is an axiom and we do not prove it; however, a comparison of the Venn diagrams in Figure 16.4 shows that it is a reasonable axiom for sets.

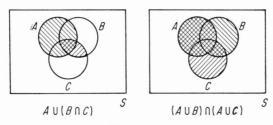

$$A \cup (B \cap C) \qquad\qquad (A \cup B) \cap (A \cup C)$$

FIGURE 16.4

Further comparison of set algebra with the real number system shows that there are sets corresponding to the real numbers 0 and 1.   If we let ϕ stand for the *empty set*, that is, the set consisting of no elements, we have $A \cup \phi = A$ for any set A.   (Can you justify this axiom by means of a Venn diagram?)   Thus, ϕ behaves like the number 0 in that it is the identity element under the operation of union (rather than addition). Furthermore, the sample space S has the property $S \cap A = A$ for all A in S.   (Draw a Venn diagram.)   Thus, S behaves like the number 1 in that it is the identity element under the operation of intersection (rather than multiplication).

In the remainder of this chapter, we shall use the elementary concepts of set algebra to develop the elements of the mathematical theory of probability for finite sample spaces.   It should be pointed out that set algebra has applications other than in probability theory.   For example, set algebra is useful in computer design, and it provides the mathematical foundation for symbolic logic.

PROBLEMS A

1. List the elements of the sample space of the following experiments.
(a) A roll of one die.
(b) A toss of three coins.
(c) A roll of two dice.

(d) Two drawings from a deck consisting of the ace, king, queen, and jack of spades, where the first card is replaced before the second is drawn.

(e) Two drawings from a deck consisting of the ace, king, queen, and jack of spades, where the first card is not replaced before the second is drawn.

2. A bowl contains three tags numbered 1, 2, and 3. Two tags are drawn, the first being replaced before the second is drawn. Let $(2, 1)$, for example, stand for the outcome that tag 2 is obtained on the first draw and tag 1 is obtained on the second draw. If A is the event that the tag 1 is drawn, B is the event that an odd numbered tag is drawn at least once, and C is the event that the sum of the draws is an even number, list the elements of the following sets.

(a) the sample space for both draws. (b) A

(c) B (d) C

(e) $A \cup B$ (f) $B \cap C$

(g) $\bar{B}$ (h) $A \cap C$

(i) $A \cup (B \cap C)$ (j) $\bar{A} \cap (B \cup C)$

3. If S is the set of all points in the plane, A is the set of points for which $x^2 + y^2 < 1$, and B is the set of points for which $x > y$, sketch graphs to indicate the following sets.

(a) A (b) B (c) $\bar{A}$ (d) $\bar{B}$

(e) $A \cup B$ (f) $A \cap B$ (g) $A \cap \bar{B}$ (h) $\bar{A} \cup B$

4. Use Venn diagrams to illustrate the following sets.

(a) $A \cap \bar{B}$ (b) $\overline{A \cup B}$

(c) $\bar{A} \cup \bar{B}$ (d) $\bar{A} \cap \bar{B}$

(e) $A \cap B \cap C$ (f) $A \cup B \cup C$

(g) $(A \cap \bar{B}) \cup (\bar{A} \cap B)$ (h) $A \cap B \cup \bar{C}$

5. Use Venn diagrams to verify the following formulas.

(a) $A = (A \cap B) \cup (A \cap \bar{B})$

(b) $A \cap (B \cup C) = (A \cap B) \cup (A \cap C)$

(c) $\overline{A \cup B} = \bar{A} \cap \bar{B}$

(d) $\overline{A \cap B} = \bar{A} \cup \bar{B}$

PROBLEMS B

1. Prove that A is a subset of B if and only if $A \cap B = A$ by considering any element a in A.

2. Prove that $\bar{\bar{A}} = A$, that is, the complement of the complement of a set is the set itself.

3. Prove that $A \cup A = A \cap A = A$.

16.2 Definition of Probability

If we assign a unique number to every subset A of a sample space S, then we define a function having as its domain the set of subsets of S and as its range a set of numbers. Such a function, defined on a domain of sets, is called a **set function**. For example, if S consists of the elements a, b, and c, it has the eight subsets shown in the following table.

Subsets of S	ϕ	$\{a\}$	$\{b\}$	$\{c\}$	$\{a, b\}$	$\{a, c\}$	$\{b, c\}$	$\{a, b, c\}$
Value of **f**	10	1	-2	3	-1	4	1	2

Now, if we assign a number to each subset, as shown in the table, we define a set function **f** whose domain is the set of subsets shown, and whose range is the set of numbers shown.

The concept of a set function is used to define probabilities. If an event A is a subset of a sample space S, we define $P(A)$, the **probability of the event A**, to be a value of a set function **P**, called a probability function. However, just any set function will not do; for **P** to be a probability function it must satisfy the following axioms.

Axiom 1. $0 \leq P(A) \leq 1$ *for every subset* A *in* S

Axiom 2. P(S) = 1

Axiom 3. *If* A *and* B *are disjoint sets in* S, *then*

$$P(A \cup B) = P(A) + P(B)$$

Axiom 1 states that the range of the probability function **P** consists entirely of real numbers between 0 and 1, inclusive. Thus, no probability can be negative, nor can it exceed 1. Axiom 2 states that the probability of the sample space equals 1. This axiom expresses the idea that the probability of a logically certain event is 1. Axiom 3 establishes that **P** is an *additive* set function; that is, if we form the union of any two disjoint subsets in S, we find the probability of the union by *adding* the probabilities of the individual sets. Using the associative law of union together with mathematical induction, it is possible to extend Axiom 3 to include any number of disjoint sets. Thus, this axiom suggests that we can find the probability of any subset of S by assigning probability "weights" to each element in S consistent with Axioms 1 and 2, and by adding the weights of all elements in that subset.

To illustrate the construction of a probability function, we consider the sample space

$$S = \{HH, HT, TH, TT\}$$

consisting of the outcomes when two coins are tossed. If we assign the probability weight $\frac{1}{4}$ to each of the four elements in S, then Axioms 1 and 2 are satisfied. The probability of the event A, that exactly one head appears when the coins are tossed, is obtained by adding the weights of the elements HT and TH, and we obtain the result

$$P(A) = \tfrac{1}{4} + \tfrac{1}{4} = \tfrac{1}{2}$$

If we assign the weights as follows:

$$P(HH) = \tfrac{1}{2}, \quad P(HT) = \tfrac{1}{8}, \quad P(TH) = \tfrac{1}{8}, \quad P(TT) = \tfrac{1}{4}$$

Axioms 1 and 2 also are satisfied. Thus, this is a legitimate probability function, and we now obtain

$$P(A) = \tfrac{1}{8} + \tfrac{1}{8} = \tfrac{1}{4}$$

There is no question of which answer is correct; either answer is correct, depending upon which assignment of weights more closely approximates the true physical nature of coin tossing. (If the coins are balanced and they are tossed in such a way that neither side is favored, then the assumption of equal weights seems justified, and the correct answer for that physical situation is $P(A) = \tfrac{1}{2}$.) Note that we could not assign the weights as follows:

$$P(HH) = \tfrac{1}{2}, \quad P(HT) = \tfrac{1}{4}, \quad P(TH) = \tfrac{1}{4}, \quad P(TT) = \tfrac{1}{2}$$

because $P(S)$ would equal $\tfrac{3}{2}$ and Axiom 2 would be violated. It can be concluded from this example that the axioms of probability do not tell us how to assign probabilities to events, but they do restrict the possible assignments that can be made.

In order to assign probabilities to events, we use estimates based on experience, or, as we have seen, we make assumptions that seem to fit the physical requirements. An example of the use of estimates based on experience is the use of mortality tables by insurance companies to estimate the probability that an insured risk will survive x years. To estimate the probability that an individual, aged n, will live to be $n + x$, records are kept on a large number of people, and this probability is estimated to be the ratio of the number of people living at age $n + x$ to the number of people living at age n.

The assumption of equal probability weights for the elements of S, called the assumption of *equal likelihood*, sometimes is used to give a "definition" of probability. Thus, if an experiment has n "equally-likely" outcomes among which s are successes, then the probability of a success is "defined" to be s/n. This statement is worthless as a definition of probability because it is circular, that is, it uses the term "equally-likely" in the definition of the word "probability." (Note that "equally-likely" is just another way of saying "equally-probable.") Even so,

Substituting $P(A) - P(A \cap B)$ for $P(A \cap \overline{B})$ and $P(B) - $ for $P(\overline{A} \cap B)$ in the equation for $P(A \cup B)$, we obtain

$$P(A \cup B) = P(A) - P(A \cap B) + P(B) - P(A \cap B) + P($$

or

(16.1) $$P(A \cup B) = P(A) + P(B) - P(A \cap B)$$

Equation 16.1 is called the **general law of addition** for probabi If A and B are mutually exclusive events, $A \cap B = \phi$, and we have that $P(\phi) = 0$; hence, for mutually exclusive events Equation reduces to the **special law of addition** for probabilities, given by Axiom

To make use of Equation 16.1, we must be able to compute $P(A \cap B$ To illustrate this computation, we consider the following example. Fift people were interviewed for a job. Their qualifications are broken down by educational background and experience, as shown in the accompany-ing table.

	College Graduates	Non-College Graduates	
Experienced	7	16	23
Non-Experienced	13	14	27
	20	30	50

Let A stand for the event that the person selected is a college graduate and B stand for the event that the person selected has experience in this job. If we assume that each person has the same probability of selection, namely $\frac{1}{50}$, we can compute $P(A)$, the probability that the person selected will be a college graduate, by taking the ratio of the number of college graduates to the total number of applicants. In this way, we obtain

$$P(A) = \tfrac{20}{50} = .40$$

Similarly, we obtain

$$P(B) = \tfrac{23}{50} = .46$$

To obtain $P(A \cap B)$, the probability that the person selected is both a college graduate and has job experience, we note that there are 7 such cases out of 50, and we obtain

$$P(A \cap B) = \tfrac{7}{50} = .14$$

Now, suppose we want to find the probability that the person selected is experienced, given that he is a college graduate. Now, we are con-cerned with the *reduced sample space* consisting of the college graduates only; it contains 20 members, of whom 7 are experienced. Again assum-ing equal likelihood, we obtain the probability that a person is experi-

this statement does express a rule that can be very useful in computing probabilities, especially in connection with games of chance. Whenever the assumption of equal likelihood seems justified, it follows from the definition of the probability function **P** that $P(A)$ equals s/n, the number of elements in A divided by the number of elements in S. This principle is illustrated in the following examples.

Example 16.1. Find the probability of drawing an ace from a standard deck of cards.

Solution: There are 52 possible outcomes of the drawing, of which 4 are suc-cesses (aces). If all outcomes are equally-likely, the probability of drawing an ace is

$$P(A) = \frac{4}{52} = \frac{1}{13}$$

Example 16.2. Find the probability of rolling a 7 with a pair of dice.

Solution: A die is a cube whose six sides have 1, 2, 3, 4, 5, and 6 spots, respec-tively. If two dice are rolled, there are six outcomes of the second die corre-sponding to each of the six outcomes of the first die, or $6 \cdot 6 = 36$ outcomes in all. Among these outcomes, the following are successes:

First Die	1	2	3	4	5	6
Second Die	6	5	4	3	2	1
Total	7	7	7	7	7	7

Since there are six successes out of 36 outcomes, the required probability equals 6/36, or 1/6.

PROBLEMS A

1. An experiment has four possible outcomes A, B, C, and D. State which of the following are not permissible probability functions and why.

(a) $P(A) = .1, P(B) = .2, P(C) = -.3, P(D) = .4$
(b) $P(A) = .1, P(B) = .2, P(C) = .3, P(D) = .4$
(c) $P(A) = .3, P(B) = .2, P(C) = 1.1, P(D) = 0$
(d) $P(A) = .4, P(B) = .5, P(C) = .3, P(D) = .2$
(e) $P(A) = 0, P(B) = 0, P(C) = 1, P(D) = 0$
(f) $P(A) = .2, P(B) = P(C) = .1, P(D) = .5$

2. If four coins are tossed, what is the probability of the following events? (Assume all elements of the sample space have the same probability.)

(a) no heads   (b) exactly one head
(c) at least three tails   (d) an odd number of heads
(e) at least one head   (f) one head or one tail

3. Referring to Problem 2 on page 306, suppose each tag has the same probability of being drawn.   Find the following probabilities.

(a) $P(A)$ (b) $P(B)$ (c) $P(C)$ (d) $P(\bar{B})$
(e) $P(A \cap C)$ (f) $P(A \cup B)$ (g) $P(\bar{A} \cap C)$ (h) $P(A \cup B \cup C)$

4. The circumference of a wheel is divided into five segments, numbered from 1 to 5 and having lengths of 1, 2, 3, 4, and 5 inches, respectively.   The wheel is spun, and the probability that a pointer intersects a given segment is proportional to its length.   Find the probability that the pointer intersects the following segments.

(a) 3   (b) 1 or 2
(c) an even-numbered segment   (d) an odd-numbered segment

5. A baseball player has 120 hits in 400 times at bat.   Estimate the probability that he will get a hit the next time he comes to bat.

PROBLEMS B

1. Refer the 36 points in the sample space for the roll of two dice to a pair of coordinate axes.   Giving each point the same probability, find the probabilities of the following events.

(a) The sum on the two dice equals $j, j = 2, 3, \dots, 12$.
(b) The difference between the points on the dice equals 2 in absolute value.
(c) The product of the points on the dice is an even number.

2. A rectangular dart board having dimensions a by b has painted on it n nonoverlapping circles, each of radius r.   If the probability that a dart hitting the board will land in a given circle is proportional to its area, what is the probability that a dart hitting the board will not land on one of the circles?

3. Consider the quarter circle shown in the accompanying figure.   A line segment of length l is chosen by selecting a point C on the circumference of the quarter circle having unit radius.   If C is chosen so that the probability that it lies in any given segment of the arc of the quarter circle is proportional to the length of that arc, what is the probability that $l \leq \frac{1}{2}$?   Why doesn't the answer equal $\frac{1}{2}$?

16.3   Addition and Multiplication Laws

Recalling that an event is a subset of a sample space, we define a **compound event** to be any subset of S formed by applying set operations to one or more events in S.   For example, if A and B are events in S, then $\bar{A}, A \cup B$, and $A \cap B$ are compound events in S.

The axioms of probability can be used to obtain theorem w to find the probability of compound events like $\bar{A}$, $\cap B$ when $P(A)$ and $P(B)$ are known.

First, we prove that the probability of the complement (quals 1 minus the probability of the event itself.

Theorem 16.1. $P(\bar{A}) = 1 - P(A)$

Proof:

$$A \cup \bar{A} = S \qquad (F$$

$$P(A \cup \bar{A}) = P(S)$$

Since A and $\bar{A}$ are disjoint sets, we have

$$P(A) + P(\bar{A}) = P(S)$$

$$P(A) + P(\bar{A}) = 1$$

$$P(\bar{A}) = 1 - P(A)$$

As a corollary, we note that $P(\phi) = 0$.   This conclusion f the fact that $\phi = \bar{S}$.

If A and B are disjoint sets, we refer to the corresponding events as **mutually exclusive** events, and Axiom 3 establishes the law of addition of probabilities for mutually exclusive events.   It is possible to extend this law to find $P(A \cup B)$ when A and B are *not* mutually exclusive events.   We can derive the result by considering the diagram shown in Figure 16.5.   From this figure you can see that $A \cup B$ is the union of the *three disjoint sets* $A \cap$ and $\bar{A} \cap B$.   Thus,

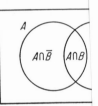

FIGURE 16

$$P(A \cup B) = P(A \cap \bar{B}) + P(A \cap B) + P(\bar{A} \cap B)$$

You can see from the same figure that

$$A = (A \cap \bar{B}) \cup (A \cap B)$$

and

$$B = (\bar{A} \cap B) \cup (A \cap B)$$

Thus,

$$P(A) = P(A \cap \bar{B}) + P(A \cap B)$$

and

$$P(B) = P(\bar{A} \cap B) + P(A \cap B)$$

enced, *given that he is a college graduate*, to be $\frac{7}{20}$ or .35. Using the symbol $P(B|A)$ to denote this probability, we observe that $P(B|A) = .35$ but $P(B) = .46$. Thus, an event can have different probabilities, depending upon the sample space to which it is referred.

Note that $P(B|A)$ was obtained by dividing 7, the number of people who are *both* college graduates and experienced, by 20, the number of college graduates. In fact, we could have written

$$P(B|A) = \frac{\frac{7}{50}}{\frac{20}{50}}$$

Since $P(A \cap B) = \frac{7}{50}$ and $P(A) = \frac{20}{50}$, in this case we have

$$P(B|A) = \frac{P(A \cap B)}{P(A)}$$

Generalizing, we have the following definition.

Definition 16.1. *If* P(A) $\neq$ 0, *the* **conditional probability** *of* B *given* A *is defined by*

$$P(B|A) = \frac{P(A \cap B)}{P(A)}$$

In practice, we can use Definition 16.1 to compute $P(A \cap B)$ when $P(A)$ and $P(B|A)$ are known, as illustrated in the following example.

Example 16.3. Two balls are drawn from a bowl containing one white ball and two red balls. The first ball is *not replaced* prior to drawing the second ball. Find the probability that both balls drawn will be red.

Solution: If A and B denote the events that a red ball is obtained in the first and second draws, respectively, then $P(A \cap B)$ is the required probability. From Definition 16.1 we have

$$P(A \cap B) = P(A)P(B|A)$$

Assuming equal probabilities, we obtain $P(A) = \frac{2}{3}$, since two of the three balls are red. Also, $P(B|A) = \frac{1}{2}$ because, after a red ball is drawn, the bowl contains one white and one red ball.
Thus,

$$P(A \cap B) = \tfrac{2}{3} \cdot \tfrac{1}{2} = \tfrac{1}{3}$$

Note that, had we replaced the first ball prior to drawing the second ball, we would have obtained $P(B|A) = \frac{2}{3}$, which agrees with the *un-conditional probability* of drawing a red ball, $P(B)$. This result is intuitively justified because the probability of drawing a red ball on the second draw no longer depends on the result of the first draw. Thus, we say that A and B are **independent events** if $P(B|A) = P(B)$.

Note that we could have interchanged the letters A and B in the foregoing discussion without altering any of the main ideas. Thus, we can use Definition 16.1 to state the following **general law of multiplication** for probabilities.

(16.2)
$$P(A \cap B) = P(A)P(B|A)$$
$$= P(B)P(A|B)$$

In the special case where A and B are *independent* events,

$$P(B|A) = P(B) \quad \text{and} \quad P(A|B) = P(A)$$

and Equation 16.2 reduces to the following **special law of multiplication** for probabilities.

(16.3)
$$P(A \cap B) = P(A)P(B)$$

The laws of addition and multiplication for probabilities are illustrated in the following examples.

Example 16.4. If the probability that a missile hits a target on a given trial is .60, assuming independence, find the probability that at least one missile hits the target if two missiles are launched.

Solution: If A and B are the events that the first and the second missile, respectively, hit the target, we are given $P(A) = P(B) = .60$, and we are required to find $P(A \cup B)$. Using Equation 16.1, we have

$$P(A \cup B) = P(A) + P(B) - P(A \cap B)$$

Since A and B are independent events,

$$P(A \cap B) = P(A)P(B) = .36$$

and

$$P(A \cup B) = .60 + .60 - .36$$
$$= .84$$

Note that we would have obtained the absurd result $P(A \cup B) = 1.20$ had we forgotten to subtract $P(A \cap B)$.

Example 16.5. Two cards are drawn without replacement from a deck consisting of 13 spades. What is the probability that the ace is not among them?

Solution: Let A and B represent the events that the ace does not appear on the first and second draws, respectively. There are 12 nonaces among the 13 cards, and, assuming equal probabilities, we have

$$P(A) = \frac{12}{13}$$

After drawing a nonace, there are 11 nonaces among the 12 remaining cards, and, again assuming equal probabilities, we have

$$P(B|A) = \frac{11}{12}$$

Using the general law of multiplication, we find the required probability as follows.

$$P(A \cap B) = P(A)P(B|A)$$
$$= \frac{12}{13} \cdot \frac{11}{12}$$
$$= \frac{11}{13}$$

PROBLEMS A

1. If $P(A) = .3$, $P(B) = .4$, and $P(B|A) = .5$, find the following probabilities.

(a) $P(\bar{A})$ (b) $P(A \cap B)$ (c) $P(A \cup B)$
(d) $P(\overline{A \cap B})$ (e) $P(\overline{A \cup B})$ (f) $P(A \cap \bar{B})$

2. If A and B are independent events, with $P(A \cup B) = .9$, $P(A \cap B) = .4$, and $P(A) < P(B)$, find the following probabilities.

(a) $P(\overline{A \cap B})$ (b) $P(\overline{A \cup B})$ (c) $P(A|B)$
(d) $P(A)$ (e) $P(B)$ (f) $P(A \cup \bar{B})$

3. A bowl contains 100 balls of different colors and having different numbers, with the following distribution.

	Red	White
Odd-numbered	15	40
Even-numbered	25	20

If a ball is drawn from the bowl so that each ball has an equal chance of selection, find the probabilities of the following events.

(a) the ball is red   (b) the ball is even-numbered
(c) a red ball drawn is even-   (d) the ball is white and odd-numbered
    numbered
(e) the ball is red or odd-   (f) the ball is red and odd-numbered or
    numbered   white and even-numbered

4. A certain baseball player gets on base (via a hit or a base on balls) 30 per cent of the time. If he hits safely in 28 per cent of his times at bat, what proportion of the time does he get a base on balls?

5. A coin is tossed and a die is thrown. What is the probability of obtaining a head on the coin or a six on the die?

6. A pinochle deck consists of two each of the ace, king, queen, jack, ten, and nine of each suit, or 48 cards in all. What is the probability that two cards drawn from a pinochle deck without replacement will be the king and queen of the same suit?

PROBLEMS B

1. Use an argument like that shown on page 311 to prove that

$$P(A \cup B \cup C) = P(A) + P(B) + P(C) - P(A \cap B)$$
$$- P(A \cap C) - P(B \cap C) + P(A \cap B \cap C)$$

2. If A, B, and C are independent events, use the result of Problem 1 to find $P[(A \cap B) \cup (A \cap C) \cup (B \cap C)]$ where $P(A) = .3$, $P(B) = .5$, and $P(C) = .6$.

3. If $B_1, B_2, \ldots, B_n$ are disjoint subsets such that $B_1 \cup B_2 \cup \ldots \cup B_n = S$, if $P(B_1) = P(B_2) = \ldots = P(B_n)$, and if A is the union of s of these sets, prove that $P(A) = s/n$. How does this theorem relate to the assumption of equal probabilities?

16.4   Permutations and Combinations

When we assign equal probabilities to the elements of a sample space S, we obtain the probability of a given event A in S by counting the elements in A and dividing by the number of elements in S. Often it is difficult to find the number of elements in a set by direct enumeration, and we must resort to more sophisticated methods of counting. In this section, we introduce the concepts of permutations and combinations, and apply these concepts to counting the elements of sets.

First, we consider the problem of constructing a new set C by selecting first an element from the set A and then an element from the set B. For example, let A consist of the *three elements* a_1, a_2, and a_3, and let B consist of the *two elements* b_1 and b_2. The set C consists of all the ordered pairs of elements formed by choosing first an element of A and then an element of B; thus, C consists of the elements

$$(a_1, b_1), \quad (a_1, b_2), \quad (a_2, b_1), \quad (a_2, b_2), \quad (a_3, b_1), \quad \text{and} \quad (a_3, b_2)$$

Note that we listed the elements of C by taking each of the three elements of A together with each of the two elements of B, obtaining $2 \cdot 3$ or 6 elements. A similar argument can be used to prove the following general theorem.

Theorem 16.2. *If sets* A_1, A_2, ..., A_k *have* n_1, n_2, ..., n_k *elements, respectively, the number of ways that we can select first an element from* A_1, *then an element from* A_2, ..., *finally an element from* A_k *is*

$$n_1 \cdot n_2 \cdot \ldots \cdot n_k$$

To give a further illustration of Theorem 16.2, we find the number of outcomes of an experiment consisting first of the toss of a coin, then the roll of a die, and then the selection of a card from a deck of 52 cards. There are two outcomes of the toss of the coin, six outcomes of the roll of the die, and 52 outcomes of the selection of a card; thus, there are $2 \cdot 6 \cdot 52 = 624$ outcomes of the experiment. Note that it would have been a tedious job to enumerate all the outcomes.

Now we consider all possible *arrangements* of the elements of a given set. For example, if a set A consists of the three elements a_1, a_2, and a_3, there are the following six arrangements of these elements.

$$a_1a_2a_3, \quad a_1a_3a_2, \quad a_2a_1a_3, \quad a_2a_3a_1, \quad a_3a_1a_2, \quad \text{and} \quad a_3a_2a_1$$

Each such arrangement of the elements of A is called a **permutation** of the *three* elements of A. It is possible also to consider all possible *permutations of two* elements of A; they are

$$a_1a_2, \quad a_2a_1, \quad a_1a_3, \quad a_3a_1, \quad a_2a_3, \quad \text{and} \quad a_3a_2$$

In general, if A has n elements, we use the symbol $P(n, r)$ to denote the number of permutations of r out of the n elements of A. $P(n, r)$ can be expressed in terms of n and r by means of the following theorem.

Theorem 16.3. *The number of permutations of* r *elements selected from a set containing* n *distinct elements is given by*

$$P(n, r) = \frac{n!}{(n - r)!}$$

Proof: There are n ways to select the first element, $n - 1$ ways to select the second element, and, finally, $n - r + 1$ ways to select the rth element. Each such ordered selection is a permutation of r elements selected from a set containing n elements, and by Theorem 16.2 we have

$$P(n, r) = n(n - 1) \cdot \ldots \cdot (n - r + 1)$$

On page 285 we showed that this product equals $n!/(n - r)!$, and the theorem is proved.

Theorem 16.3 can be used only if the symbols to be arranged are *distinct*. Thus, if we want to determine the number of arrangements of the letters in the word *see*, we cannot use this theorem because two of the letters are identical. If we distinguish between these two letters by giving them subscripts, however, we can use the theorem to conclude that there are 3 ! permutations of the symbols se_1e_2; they are:

$$se_1e_2 \qquad e_1se_2 \qquad e_1e_2s$$

$$se_2e_1 \qquad e_2se_1 \qquad e_2e_1s$$

Now, if we drop the subscripts, we note that there are only three distinct permutations of the letters in the word *see*, namely *see*, *ese*, and *ees*. Since each pair of permutations with subscripts produces only one arrangement without subscripts, the total number of arrangements without subscripts is 3 ! divided by 2 ! or 3.

In general, if there were n letters and n_1 of them were alike, there would be n !$/n_1$! *distinct* arrangements of the n letters. Generalizing further, we observe that each subset of n_j like elements has n_j! permutations which contribute only one distinct arrangement. Thus, the number of arrangements of n elements of which n_1 are alike, a further n_2 are alike, . . . , finally, a further n_k are alike is

(16.4)
$$\frac{n!}{n_1!\, n_2!\cdot \, \ldots \, \cdot \, n_k!}$$

The following examples illustrate Theorem 16.3 and Formula 16.4.

Example 16.6. How many seating arrangements for five people are possible if there are ten seats?

Solution: Each seating arrangement can be regarded as a permutation of people in five seats selected from a set of ten seats. Thus, the number of seating arrangements is

$$P(10, 5) = \frac{10!}{5!}$$

$$= 10 \cdot 9 \cdot 8 \cdot 7 \cdot 6$$

$$= 30,240$$

Example 16.7. How many distinct signals can be made with six flags by displaying them all, if two are white, three are red, and one is blue?

Solution: Using Formula 16.4 with $n = 6$, $n_1 = 2$, $n_2 = 3$, and $n_3 = 1$, we find the number of signals to be

$$\frac{6!}{2!3!1!} = \frac{6 \cdot 5 \cdot 4 \cdot 3 \cdot 2 \cdot 1}{2 \cdot 1 \cdot 3 \cdot 2 \cdot 1 \cdot 1} = 60$$

So far we have been concerned with the order of the elements selected from a given set. If we are concerned only with which elements are selected, without regard to their order, we call such a selection a **combination.** For example, the combinations of two elements, selected from the set $A = \{a_1, a_2, a_3\}$ are

$$\{a_1a_2\}, \quad \{a_1a_3\}, \quad \text{and} \quad \{a_2a_3\}$$

Note that each such combination gives rise to 2 ! permutations; thus, we could have determined the number of combinations without listing them, by dividing $P(3, 2)$ by 2 !. In general, the number of combinations of r elements selected from a set containing n elements is denoted by $C(n, r)$, and for each such combination there are r ! permutations. Thus

$$P(n, r) = r\,!\,C(n, r)$$

or

$$C(n, r) = \frac{P(n, r)}{r!}$$

Substituting $n\,!/(n - r)\,!$ for $P(n, r)$, we obtain

(16.5) $$C(n, r) = \frac{n!}{r!(n - r)!}$$

Comparing Equation 16.5 with Equation 15.2 on page 285, we note that *the number of combinations of* r *elements selected from* n *elements is given by the binomial coefficient* $\binom{n}{r}$.

The properties of $\binom{n}{r}$, derived in Section 15.3, can be used to simplify finding the number of combinations of r elements selected from n elements, as illustrated in the following example.

Example 16.8. How many football teams of 11 players can be selected from a squad consisting of 15 players?

Solution: The required result is $\binom{15}{11}$. Using Theorem 15.3 on page 287, we have

$$\binom{15}{11} = \binom{15}{4}$$

$$= \frac{15 \cdot 14 \cdot 13 \cdot 12}{4 \cdot 3 \cdot 2 \cdot 1}$$

$$= 1365$$

The methods developed in this section are useful in solving many probability problems in which the assumption of equal likelihood can be made, as illustrated in the following examples.

Example 16.9. What is the probability of drawing five cards of the same suit from a deck of cards?

Solution: The sample space consists of $\binom{52}{5}$ possible 52-card hands. The number of such hands consisting of five cards from any given suit is $\binom{13}{5}$. Since there are four suits, there are $4 \cdot \binom{13}{5}$ hands containing five cards of the same suit. Thus, the required probability is

$$\frac{4 \cdot \binom{13}{5}}{\binom{52}{5}} = \frac{4 \cdot \dfrac{13 \cdot 12 \cdot 11 \cdot 10 \cdot 9}{5!}}{\dfrac{52 \cdot 51 \cdot 50 \cdot 49 \cdot 48}{5!}}$$

$$= \frac{4 \cdot 13 \cdot 12 \cdot 11 \cdot 10 \cdot 9}{52 \cdot 51 \cdot 50 \cdot 49 \cdot 48}$$

$$= \frac{33}{16,660}$$

Example 16.10. A jury of 12 is to be selected from a panel consisting of 15 men and 20 women. What is the probability that the jury will have an equal number of men and women?

Solution: The sample space consists of $\binom{35}{12}$ possible juries. If six men are to be on the jury, they can be selected in $\binom{15}{6}$ ways, and the six women can be selected in $\binom{20}{6}$ ways. Thus, there are $\binom{15}{6} \cdot \binom{20}{6}$ juries consisting of six men and six women, and the required probability is

$$\frac{\binom{15}{6} \cdot \binom{20}{6}}{\binom{35}{12}}$$

After some computation, we find the result to be 209/899.

In solving probability problems of the type illustrated in this section, you will find that there can be several different methods of approach to a given problem. If possible, work the problem two or more ways and compare results. A great deal of practice and ingenuity are required to become proficient at solving such problems.

this statement does express a rule that can be very useful in computing probabilities, especially in connection with games of chance. Whenever the assumption of equal likelihood seems justified, it follows from the definition of the probability function **P** that $P(A)$ equals s/n, the number of elements in A divided by the number of elements in S. This principle is illustrated in the following examples.

Example 16.1. Find the probability of drawing an ace from a standard deck of cards.

Solution: There are 52 possible outcomes of the drawing, of which 4 are successes (aces). If all outcomes are equally-likely, the probability of drawing an ace is

$$P(A) = \frac{4}{52} = \frac{1}{13}$$

Example 16.2. Find the probability of rolling a 7 with a pair of dice.

Solution: A die is a cube whose six sides have 1, 2, 3, 4, 5, and 6 spots, respectively. If two dice are rolled, there are six outcomes of the second die corresponding to each of the six outcomes of the first die, or $6 \cdot 6 = 36$ outcomes in all. Among these outcomes, the following are successes:

First Die	1	2	3	4	5	6
Second Die	6	5	4	3	2	1
Total	7	7	7	7	7	7

Since there are six successes out of 36 outcomes, the required probability equals 6/36, or 1/6.

PROBLEMS A

1. An experiment has four possible outcomes A, B, C, and D. State which of the following are not permissible probability functions and why.
(a) $P(A) = .1$, $P(B) = .2$, $P(C) = -.3$, $P(D) = .4$
(b) $P(A) = .1$, $P(B) = .2$, $P(C) = .3$, $P(D) = .4$
(c) $P(A) = .3$, $P(B) = .2$, $P(C) = 1.1$, $P(D) = 0$
(d) $P(A) = .4$, $P(B) = .5$, $P(C) = .3$, $P(D) = .2$
(e) $P(A) = 0$, $P(B) = 0$, $P(C) = 1$, $P(D) = 0$
(f) $P(A) = .2$, $P(B) = P(C) = .1$, $P(D) = .5$

2. If four coins are tossed, what is the probability of the following events? (Assume all elements of the sample space have the same probability.)
(a) no heads   (b) exactly one head
(c) at least three tails   (d) an odd number of heads
(e) at least one head   (f) one head or one tail

3. Referring to Problem 2 on page 306, suppose each tag has the same probability of being drawn. Find the following probabilities.

(a) $P(A)$ (b) $P(B)$ (c) $P(C)$ (d) $P(\bar{B})$
(e) $P(A \cap C)$ (f) $P(A \cup B)$ (g) $P(\bar{A} \cap C)$ (h) $P(A \cup B \cup C)$

4. The circumference of a wheel is divided into five segments, numbered from
1 to 5 and having lengths of 1, 2, 3, 4, and 5 inches, respectively. The wheel
is spun, and the probability that a pointer intersects a given segment is proportional to its length. Find the probability that the pointer intersects the
following segments.

(a) 3   (b) 1 or 2

(c) an even-numbered segment   (d) an odd-numbered segment

5. A baseball player has 120 hits in 400 times at bat. Estimate the probability
that he will get a hit the next time he comes to bat.

PROBLEMS B

1. Refer the 36 points in the sample space for the roll of two dice to a pair of
coordinate axes. Giving each point the same probability, find the probabilities
of the following events.

(a) The sum on the two dice equals $j, j = 2, 3, \ldots, 12$.
(b) The difference between the points on the dice equals 2 in absolute value.
(c) The product of the points on the dice is an even number.

2. A rectangular dart board having dimensions a by b has painted on it n
nonoverlapping circles, each of radius r. If the probability that a dart hitting
the board will land in a given circle is proportional to its area, what is the
probability that a dart hitting the board will not land on one of the circles?

3. Consider the quarter circle shown in the accompanying
figure. A line segment of length l is chosen by selecting a
point C on the circumference of the quarter circle having
unit radius. If C is chosen so that the probability that it
lies in any given segment of the arc of the quarter circle is
proportional to the length of that arc, what is the probability that $l \leq \frac{1}{2}$? Why doesn't the answer equal $\frac{1}{2}$?

16.3   Addition and Multiplication Laws

Recalling that an event is a subset of a sample space, we define a **compound event** to be any subset of S formed by applying set operations to
one or more events in S. For example, if A and B are events in S, then
$\bar{A}, A \cup B$, and $A \cap B$ are compound events in S.

The axioms of probability can be used to obtain theorems that show how to find the probability of compound events like $\bar{A}$, $A \cup B$, and $A \cap B$ when $P(A)$ and $P(B)$ are known.

First, we prove that the probability of the complement of any event equals 1 minus the probability of the event itself.

Theorem 16.1. $P(\bar{A}) = 1 - P(A)$

Proof:

$$A \cup \bar{A} = S \qquad \text{(Figure 16.2c)}$$

$$P(A \cup \bar{A}) = P(S)$$

Since A and $\bar{A}$ are disjoint sets, we have

$$P(A) + P(\bar{A}) = P(S) \qquad \text{(Axiom 3)}$$

$$P(A) + P(\bar{A}) = 1 \qquad \text{(Axiom 2)}$$

$$P(\bar{A}) = 1 - P(A)$$

As a corollary, we note that $P(\phi) = 0$. This conclusion follows from the fact that $\phi = \bar{S}$.

If A and B are disjoint sets, we refer to the corresponding events as **mutually exclusive** events, and Axiom 3 establishes the law of addition of probabilities for mutually exclusive events. It is possible to extend this law to find $P(A \cup B)$ when A and B are *not* mutually exclusive events. We can derive the result by considering the diagram shown in Figure 16.5. From this figure you

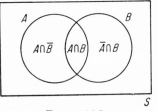

FIGURE 16.5

can see that $A \cup B$ is the union of the *three disjoint sets* $A \cap \bar{B}$, $A \cap B$, and $\bar{A} \cap B$. Thus,

$$P(A \cup B) = P(A \cap \bar{B}) + P(A \cap B) + P(\bar{A} \cap B)$$

You can see from the same figure that

$$A = (A \cap \bar{B}) \cup (A \cap B)$$

and

$$B = (\bar{A} \cap B) \cup (A \cap B)$$

Thus,

$$P(A) = P(A \cap \bar{B}) + P(A \cap B)$$

and

$$P(B) = P(\bar{A} \cap B) + P(A \cap B)$$

Substituting $P(A) - P(A \cap B)$ for $P(A \cap \overline{B})$ and $P(B) - P(A \cap B)$ for $P(\overline{A} \cap B)$ in the equation for $P(A \cup B)$, we obtain

$$P(A \cup B) = P(A) - P(A \cap B) + P(B) - P(A \cap B) + P(A \cap B)$$

or

(16.1) $$P(A \cup B) = P(A) + P(B) - P(A \cap B)$$

Equation 16.1 is called the **general law of addition** for probabilities. If A and B are mutually exclusive events, $A \cap B = \phi$, and we have seen that $P(\phi) = 0$; hence, for mutually exclusive events Equation 16.1 reduces to the **special law of addition** for probabilities, given by Axiom 3.

To make use of Equation 16.1, we must be able to compute $P(A \cap B)$. To illustrate this computation, we consider the following example. Fifty people were interviewed for a job. Their qualifications are broken down by educational background and experience, as shown in the accompanying table.

	College Graduates	Non-College Graduates	
Experienced	7	16	23
Non-Experienced	13	14	27
	20	30	50

Let A stand for the event that the person selected is a college graduate and B stand for the event that the person selected has experience in this job. If we assume that each person has the same probability of selection, namely $\frac{1}{50}$, we can compute $P(A)$, the probability that the person selected will be a college graduate, by taking the ratio of the number of college graduates to the total number of applicants. In this way, we obtain

$$P(A) = \tfrac{20}{50} = .40$$

Similarly, we obtain

$$P(B) = \tfrac{23}{50} = .46$$

To obtain $P(A \cap B)$, the probability that the person selected is both a college graduate and has job experience, we note that there are 7 such cases out of 50, and we obtain

$$P(A \cap B) = \tfrac{7}{50} = .14$$

Now, suppose we want to find the probability that the person selected is experienced, given that he is a college graduate. Now, we are concerned with the *reduced sample space* consisting of the college graduates only; it contains 20 members, of whom 7 are experienced. Again assuming equal likelihood, we obtain the probability that a person is experienced, *given that he is a college graduate,* to be $\frac{7}{20}$ or .35.   Using the symbol $P(B|A)$ to denote this probability, we observe that $P(B|A) = .35$ but $P(B) = .46$.   Thus, an event can have different probabilities, depending upon the sample space to which it is referred.

Note that $P(B|A)$ was obtained by dividing 7, the number of people who are *both* college graduates and experienced, by 20, the number of college graduates.   In fact, we could have written

$$P(B|A) = \frac{\frac{7}{50}}{\frac{20}{50}}$$

Since $P(A \cap B) = \frac{7}{50}$ and $P(A) = \frac{20}{50}$, in this case we have

$$P(B|A) = \frac{P(A \cap B)}{P(A)}$$

Generalizing, we have the following definition.

Definition 16.1. *If* $P(A) \neq 0$, *the* **conditional probability** *of* B *given* A *is defined by*

$$P(B|A) = \frac{P(A \cap B)}{P(A)}$$

In practice, we can use Definition 16.1 to compute $P(A \cap B)$ when $P(A)$ and $P(B|A)$ are known, as illustrated in the following example.

Example 16.3. Two balls are drawn from a bowl containing one white ball and two red balls.   The first ball is *not replaced* prior to drawing the second ball.   Find the probability that both balls drawn will be red.

Solution: If A and B denote the events that a red ball is obtained in the first and second draws, respectively, then $P(A \cap B)$ is the required probability. From Definition 16.1 we have

$$P(A \cap B) = P(A)P(B|A)$$

Assuming equal probabilities, we obtain $P(A) = \frac{2}{3}$, since two of the three balls are red.   Also, $P(B|A) = \frac{1}{2}$ because, after a red ball is drawn, the bowl contains one white and one red ball.
Thus,

$$P(A \cap B) = \frac{2}{3} \cdot \frac{1}{2} = \frac{1}{3}$$

Note that, had we replaced the first ball prior to drawing the second ball, we would have obtained $P(B|A) = \frac{2}{3}$, which agrees with the *un-conditional probability* of drawing a red ball, $P(B)$.   This result is intuitively justified because the probability of drawing a red ball on the second draw no longer depends on the result of the first draw.   Thus, we say that A and B are **independent events** if $P(B|A) = P(B)$.

Note that we could have interchanged the letters A and B in the fore-going discussion without altering any of the main ideas. Thus, we can use Definition 16.1 to state the following **general law of multiplication** for probabilities.

$$(16.2) \qquad P(A \cap B) = P(A)P(B|A)$$
$$= P(B)P(A|B)$$

In the special case where A and B are *independent* events,

$$P(B|A) = P(B) \quad \text{and} \quad P(A|B) = P(A)$$

and Equation 16.2 reduces to the following **special law of multiplication** for probabilities.

$$(16.3) \qquad P(A \cap B) = P(A)P(B)$$

The laws of addition and multiplication for probabilities are illustrated in the following examples.

Example 16.4. If the probability that a missile hits a target on a given trial is .60, assuming independence, find the probability that at least one missile hits the target if two missiles are launched.

Solution: If A and B are the events that the first and the second missile, respectively, hit the target, we are given $P(A) = P(B) = .60$, and we are required to find $P(A \cup B)$. Using Equation 16.1, we have

$$P(A \cup B) = P(A) + P(B) - P(A \cap B)$$

Since A and B are independent events,

$$P(A \cap B) = P(A)P(B) = .36$$
and
$$P(A \cup B) = .60 + .60 - .36$$
$$= .84$$

Note that we would have obtained the absurd result $P(A \cup B) = 1.20$ had we forgotten to subtract $P(A \cap B)$.

Example 16.5. Two cards are drawn without replacement from a deck consisting of 13 spades. What is the probability that the ace is not among them?

Solution: Let A and B represent the events that the ace does not appear on the first and second draws, respectively. There are 12 nonaces among the 13 cards, and, assuming equal probabilities, we have

$$P(A) = \frac{12}{13}$$

After drawing a nonace, there are 11 nonaces among the 12 remaining cards, and, again assuming equal probabilities, we have

$$P(B|A) = \frac{11}{12}$$

Using the general law of multiplication, we find the required probability as follows.

$$P(A \cap B) = P(A)P(B|A)$$
$$= \frac{12}{13} \cdot \frac{11}{12}$$
$$= \frac{11}{13}$$

PROBLEMS A

1. If $P(A) = .3$, $P(B) = .4$, and $P(B|A) = .5$, find the following probabilities.
(a) $P(\bar{A})$ (b) $P(A \cap B)$ (c) $P(A \cup B)$
(d) $P(\overline{A \cap B})$ (e) $P(\overline{A \cup B})$ (f) $P(A \cap \bar{B})$

2. If A and B are independent events, with $P(A \cup B) = .9$, $P(A \cap B) = .4$, and $P(A) < P(B)$, find the following probabilities.
(a) $P(\overline{A \cap B})$ (b) $P(\overline{A \cup B})$ (c) $P(A|B)$
(d) $P(A)$ (e) $P(B)$ (f) $P(A \cup \bar{B})$

3. A bowl contains 100 balls of different colors and having different numbers, with the following distribution.

	Red	White
Odd-numbered	15	40
Even-numbered	25	20

If a ball is drawn from the bowl so that each ball has an equal chance of selection, find the probabilities of the following events.
(a) the ball is red
(b) the ball is even-numbered
(c) a red ball drawn is even-numbered
(d) the ball is white and odd-numbered
(e) the ball is red or odd-numbered
(f) the ball is red and odd-numbered or white and even-numbered

4. A certain baseball player gets on base (via a hit or a base on balls) 30 per cent of the time. If he hits safely in 28 per cent of his times at bat, what proportion of the time does he get a base on balls?

5. A coin is tossed and a die is thrown. What is the probability of obtaining a head on the coin or a six on the die?

6. A pinochle deck consists of two each of the ace, king, queen, jack, ten, and nine of each suit, or 48 cards in all. What is the probability that two cards drawn from a pinochle deck without replacement will be the king and queen of the same suit?

PROBLEMS B

1. Use an argument like that shown on page 311 to prove that

$$P(A \cup B \cup C) = P(A) + P(B) + P(C) - P(A \cap B)$$
$$- P(A \cap C) - P(B \cap C) + P(A \cap B \cap C)$$

2. If A, B, and C are independent events, use the result of Problem 1 to find $P[(A \cap B) \cup (A \cap C) \cup (B \cap C)]$ where $P(A) = .3$, $P(B) = .5$, and $P(C) = .6$.

3. If B_1, B_2, ..., B_n are disjoint subsets such that $B_1 \cup B_2 \cup ... \cup B_n = S$, if $P(B_1) = P(B_2) = ... = P(B_n)$, and if A is the union of s of these sets, prove that $P(A) = s/n$. How does this theorem relate to the assumption of equal probabilities?

16.4   Permutations and Combinations

When we assign equal probabilities to the elements of a sample space S, we obtain the probability of a given event A in S by counting the elements in A and dividing by the number of elements in S. Often it is difficult to find the number of elements in a set by direct enumeration, and we must resort to more sophisticated methods of counting. In this section, we introduce the concepts of permutations and combinations, and apply these concepts to counting the elements of sets.

First, we consider the problem of constructing a new set C by selecting first an element from the set A and then an element from the set B. For example, let A consist of the *three elements* a_1, a_2, and a_3, and let B consist of the *two elements* b_1 and b_2. The set C consists of all the ordered pairs of elements formed by choosing first an element of A and then an element of B; thus, C consists of the elements

$$(a_1, b_1), \quad (a_1, b_2), \quad (a_2, b_1), \quad (a_2, b_2), \quad (a_3, b_1), \quad \text{and} \quad (a_3, b_2)$$

Note that we listed the elements of C by taking each of the three elements of A together with each of the two elements of B, obtaining $2 \cdot 3$ or 6 elements. A similar argument can be used to prove the following general theorem.

Theorem 16.2. *If sets* A_1, A_2, . . . , A_k *have* n_1, n_2, . . . , n_k *elements, respectively, the number of ways that we can select first an element from* A_1, *then an element from* A_2, . . . , *finally an element from* A_k *is*

$$n_1 \cdot n_2 \cdot \ldots \cdot n_k$$

To give a further illustration of Theorem 16.2, we find the number of outcomes of an experiment consisting first of the toss of a coin, then the roll of a die, and then the selection of a card from a deck of 52 cards. There are two outcomes of the toss of the coin, six outcomes of the roll of the die, and 52 outcomes of the selection of a card; thus, there are $2 \cdot 6 \cdot 52 = 624$ outcomes of the experiment. Note that it would have been a tedious job to enumerate all the outcomes.

Now we consider all possible *arrangements* of the elements of a given set. For example, if a set A consists of the three elements a_1, a_2, and a_3, there are the following six arrangements of these elements.

$$a_1a_2a_3, \quad a_1a_3a_2, \quad a_2a_1a_3, \quad a_2a_3a_1, \quad a_3a_1a_2, \quad \text{and} \quad a_3a_2a_1$$

Each such arrangement of the elements of A is called a **permutation** of the *three* elements of A. It is possible also to consider all possible *permutations of two* elements of A; they are

$$a_1a_2, \quad a_2a_1, \quad a_1a_3, \quad a_3a_1, \quad a_2a_3, \quad \text{and} \quad a_3a_2$$

In general, if A has n elements, we use the symbol $P(n, r)$ to denote the number of permutations of r out of the n elements of A. $P(n, r)$ can be expressed in terms of n and r by means of the following theorem.

Theorem 16.3. *The number of permutations of* r *elements selected from a set containing* n *distinct elements is given by*

$$P(n, r) = \frac{n!}{(n - r)!}$$

Proof: There are n ways to select the first element, $n - 1$ ways to select the second element, and, finally, $n - r + 1$ ways to select the rth element. Each such ordered selection is a permutation of r elements selected from a set containing n elements, and by Theorem 16.2 we have

$$P(n, r) = n(n - 1) \cdot \ldots \cdot (n - r + 1)$$

On page 285 we showed that this product equals $n!/(n - r)!$, and the theorem is proved.

Theorem 16.3 can be used only if the symbols to be arranged are *distinct*. Thus, if we want to determine the number of arrangements of the letters in the word *see*, we cannot use this theorem because two of the letters are identical.   If we distinguish between these two letters by giving them subscripts, however, we can use the theorem to conclude that there are 3 ! permutations of the symbols se_1e_2; they are:

$$se_1e_2 \qquad e_1se_2 \qquad e_1e_2s$$

$$se_2e_1 \qquad e_2se_1 \qquad e_2e_1s$$

Now, if we drop the subscripts, we note that there are only three distinct permutations of the letters in the word *see*, namely *see*, *ese*, and *ees*. Since each pair of permutations with subscripts produces only one arrangement without subscripts, the total number of arrangements without subscripts is 3 ! divided by 2 ! or 3.

In general, if there were n letters and n_1 of them were alike, there would be n !/n_1 ! *distinct* arrangements of the n letters.   Generalizing further, we observe that each subset of n_j like elements has n_j! permutations which contribute only one distinct arrangement.   Thus, the number of arrangements of n elements of which n_1 are alike, a further n_2 are alike, . . . , finally, a further n_k are alike is

(16.4)
$$\frac{n!}{n_1!\, n_2!\cdot\, \ldots\, \cdot\, n_k!}$$

The following examples illustrate Theorem 16.3 and Formula 16.4.

Example 16.6. How many seating arrangements for five people are possible if there are ten seats?

Solution: Each seating arrangement can be regarded as a permutation of people in five seats selected from a set of ten seats.   Thus, the number of seating arrangements is

$$P(10,\, 5) = \frac{10!}{5!}$$

$$= 10 \cdot 9 \cdot 8 \cdot 7 \cdot 6$$

$$= 30,240$$

Example 16.7. How many distinct signals can be made with six flags by displaying them all, if two are white, three are red, and one is blue?

Solution: Using Formula 16.4 with $n = 6$, $n_1 = 2$, $n_2 = 3$, and $n_3 = 1$, we find the number of signals to be

$$\frac{6!}{2!3!1!} = \frac{6 \cdot 5 \cdot 4 \cdot 3 \cdot 2 \cdot 1}{2 \cdot 1 \cdot 3 \cdot 2 \cdot 1 \cdot 1} = 60$$

So far we have been concerned with the order of the elements selected from a given set. If we are concerned only with which elements are selected, without regard to their order, we call such a selection a **combination**. For example, the combinations of two elements, selected from the set $A = \{a_1, a_2, a_3\}$ are

$$\{a_1 a_2\}, \quad \{a_1 a_3\}, \quad \text{and} \quad \{a_2 a_3\}$$

Note that each such combination gives rise to 2 ! permutations; thus, we could have determined the number of combinations without listing them, by dividing $P(3, 2)$ by 2 !. In general, the number of combinations of r elements selected from a set containing n elements is denoted by $C(n, r)$, and for each such combination there are r ! permutations. Thus

$$P(n, r) = r\,!C(n, r)$$

or

$$C(n, r) = \frac{P(n, r)}{r!}$$

Substituting $n\,!/(n - r)\,!$ for $P(n, r)$, we obtain

(16.5)
$$C(n, r) = \frac{n!}{r!(n - r)!}$$

Comparing Equation 16.5 with Equation 15.2 on page 285, we note that *the number of combinations of* r *elements selected from* n *elements is given by the binomial coefficient* $\binom{n}{r}$.

The properties of $\binom{n}{r}$, derived in Section 15.3, can be used to simplify finding the number of combinations of r elements selected from n elements, as illustrated in the following example.

Example 16.8. How many football teams of 11 players can be selected from a squad consisting of 15 players?

Solution: The required result is $\binom{15}{11}$. Using Theorem 15.3 on page 287, we have

$$\binom{15}{11} = \binom{15}{4}$$

$$= \frac{15 \cdot 14 \cdot 13 \cdot 12}{4 \cdot 3 \cdot 2 \cdot 1}$$

$$= 1365$$

The methods developed in this section are useful in solving many probability problems in which the assumption of equal likelihood can be made, as illustrated in the following examples.

Example 16.9. What is the probability of drawing five cards of the same suit from a deck of cards?

Solution: The sample space consists of $\binom{52}{5}$ possible 52-card hands. The number of such hands consisting of five cards from any given suit is $\binom{13}{5}$. Since there are four suits, there are $4 \cdot \binom{13}{5}$ hands containing five cards of the same suit. Thus, the required probability is

$$\frac{4 \cdot \binom{13}{5}}{\binom{52}{5}} = \frac{4 \cdot \dfrac{13 \cdot 12 \cdot 11 \cdot 10 \cdot 9}{5!}}{\dfrac{52 \cdot 51 \cdot 50 \cdot 49 \cdot 48}{5!}}$$

$$= \frac{4 \cdot 13 \cdot 12 \cdot 11 \cdot 10 \cdot 9}{52 \cdot 51 \cdot 50 \cdot 49 \cdot 48}$$

$$= \frac{33}{16,660}$$

Example 16.10. A jury of 12 is to be selected from a panel consisting of 15 men and 20 women. What is the probability that the jury will have an equal number of men and women?

Solution: The sample space consists of $\binom{35}{12}$ possible juries. If six men are to be on the jury, they can be selected in $\binom{15}{6}$ ways, and the six women can be selected in $\binom{20}{6}$ ways. Thus, there are $\binom{15}{6} \cdot \binom{20}{6}$ juries consisting of six men and six women, and the required probability is

$$\frac{\binom{15}{6} \cdot \binom{20}{6}}{\binom{35}{12}}$$

After some computation, we find the result to be 209/899.

In solving probability problems of the type illustrated in this section, you will find that there can be several different methods of approach to a given problem. If possible, work the problem two or more ways and compare results. A great deal of practice and ingenuity are required to become proficient at solving such problems.

PROBLEMS A

1. If there are 6 routes from New York to Chicago and 4 routes from Chicago to Los Angeles, how many routes are there from New York to Los Angeles by way of Chicago?

2. If there are 4 bridges across a river, in how many ways can a person cross the river and return if (a) he may use the same bridge twice, (b) he may not use the same bridge twice?

3. If there are x outcomes whenever an experiment is performed once, how many ordered outcomes are there when the experiment is performed n times?

4. In how many ways can three pictures be arranged horizontally on a wall if there are 10 pictures to choose from?

5. How many signals can be made from 5 flags by arranging flags of different colors on a vertical pole if (a) 3 flags are to be used, (b) any number of flags from 1 to 5 can be used, (c) all 5 flags are to be used but the red flag is always to be placed on top?

6. In how many ways can the letters of the word "probability" be arranged?

7. In how many ways can the letters of the word "acquire" be arranged so that the letter q is followed by the letter u?

8. Out of 10 ties and 5 belts, in how many ways can a man choose (a) a tie and a belt to wear? (b) 3 ties and 2 belts to pack for a trip?

9. An automobile dealer requires 4 sedans, 2 hard tops, and a convertible to fill his orders. If the distributor has available 12 sedans, 9 hard tops, and 5 convertibles, how many choices of 7 cars are available to the dealer?

10. (a) How many triangles are determined by 6 points, no three of which are colinear? (b) How many quadrilaterals are determined? (c) How many triangles are determined if there is one set of three colinear points?

In the following problems, assume that all selections have the same probability.

11. If two letters are chosen from the word "chance," what is the probability that they are vowels?

12. Five cards are drawn from a deck of 52 cards. Find the probabilities of the following hands.

(a) four of a kind   (b) two pairs
(c) three of one kind and two   (d) five spades
     of another
(e) three of a kind   (f) no face cards (ace, king, queen, or jack)

13. A bowl contains 3 red balls, 5 white balls, and 2 black balls. If three balls are drawn, what is the probability that (a) exactly one is black, (b) at least two are white, (c) all are of the same color?

14. A box contains 10 tickets numbered from 1 to 10, inclusive. (a) if all 10 tickets are drawn, one after another, what is the probability that their numbers appear in consecutive order, (b) if 5 tickets are drawn, what is the probability of obtaining five consecutive numbers in their natural order?

15. A poker player has 4 cards of the same suit and is to receive one more card. What is the probability of getting a flush (5 cards of the same suit) if (a) all other cards are unknown to the player, (b) he looks around and sees that 5 other cards of that suit already have been turned up?

16. If five couples play bridge, what is the probability that each man has his own wife as a partner?

17. A closet contains five pairs of shoes. If four shoes are chosen, what is the probability that there is no complete pair among them?

18. Six letters are selected from the word "football" in a given order. What is the probability that the word "ball" appears?

19. Each of 3 people chooses a number from 1 to 10. What is the probability that the sum of the numbers chosen is an even number?

20. A jury of 12 is to be chosen from a panel of 20 people. If Mr. and Mrs. Jones are on the panel, what is the probability that they will not both be on the jury?

PROBLEMS B

1. Find the number of ways that 5 different toys can be distributed among 3 children if there is no restriction as to how many toys each child can receive.

2. Prove that the number of ways that r indistinguishable objects can be distributed among n boxes is $\binom{n + r - 1}{r}$ if there is no restriction as to how many objects can be put in any box. *Hint:* If there are 4 objects and 3 boxes, we can use two bars to separate the 4 objects. For example 0|00|0 is an assignment of one object to the first box, 2 to the second box, and one to the third box.

3. Two boxes contain 4 red balls and 6 white balls, and 7 red balls and 3 white balls, respectively. Simultaneously, a ball is drawn from each box and placed in the other box. Then, one ball is drawn from each box. Find the probability that the last two balls drawn are of the same color.

16.5   The Binomial Distribution

An important class of probability problems deals with a set of "trials" of an event. For example, we may want to know the probability of obtaining 3 heads and 7 tails in 10 tosses of a balanced coin, or the probability that 25 out of 40 voters will favor a given candidate, or the probability that 8 out of 10 light bulbs will last at least 100 hours. In each case, we have a given number of "trials" and we are interested in obtaining a certain number of "successes."

The problem can be stated more generally if we let n denote the number of trials, that is, n denotes the number of distinct opportunities for a success to occur, and if we let x denote the number of successes in n trials. The solution to the problem of finding the number of successes in n trials depends upon what assumptions we make about the trials. For example, if we toss a coin n times, calling "heads" a success, it is reasonable to assume that the probability of a success is the same from trial to trial (it equals $\frac{1}{2}$). Furthermore, the coin has no memory, and we assume that the outcomes of n trials are independent. Loosely speaking, independence of more than two trials means that the outcome of any given trial is not influenced by the outcome of the preceding trials. More precisely, we generalize the special law of multiplication and say that the events $A_1, A_2, \ldots, A_k$ are **completely independent** if the probability of the intersection of any subset of these events equals the product of the probabilities of the events in that subset.

The assumptions that seem reasonable for coin tossing also apply to a wide variety of other problems. Thus, we give such trials a special name (after the mathematician who did much early work with them) and define them formally as follows.

Definition 16.2. *A sequence of* n *trials is called a sequence of* **Bernoulli trials** *if*

(a) *there are only two possible outcomes of any given trial*

(b) *the probability of success is constant from trial to trial*

(c) *the* n *trials are completely independent.*

According to Definition 16.2, n rolls of a die do not form a sequence of Bernoulli trials because there are six possible outcomes of a given roll. Two drawings, *without replacement*, from a bowl containing 5 white balls and 5 red balls do not form a sequence of Bernoulli trials because successive drawings are not independent. Examples of sequences of trials that reasonably well approximate the assumptions of Bernoulli trials are the selection of balls from a bowl of red and white balls *with replacement*, and the set of hits and misses when a rifleman shoots at a target.

Returning to the problem of finding the probability of x success in n trials, we shall obtain a solution by a simple application of the laws of probability to the case of Bernoulli trials. Denoting a success by the letter S and a failure by the letter F, first we consider any *fixed* arrangement of x success and $n - x$ failures. For simplicity, suppose the x successes occurred first, followed by the $n - x$ failures, as follows.

$$\underbrace{S, S, \ldots, S,}_{x} \underbrace{F, F, \ldots, F}_{n - x}$$

If the probability of a success on any given trial is p, then, by Theorem 16.1, the probability of a failure is $1 - p$. From the assumption of independence, we conclude that the probability of x successes and $n - x$ failures *in a given order* is the product of x factors p and $n - x$ factors $1 - p$, or $p^x(1 - p)^{n-x}$.

To obtain the probability of x successes and $n - x$ failures *in any order*, first we use the preceding argument to conclude that each such sequence has the probability $p^x(1 - p)^{n-x}$. Next, we note that there are $n!/x!(n - x)!$ or $\binom{n}{x}$ such sequences because each sequence is a different permutation of n letters, of which x are S's and $n - x$ are F's. Now the occurrences of any two such sequences are mutually exclusive events; thus, the probability that one or the other will occur is the sum of the individual probabilities of occurrence. Hence, the probability of x successes in n Bernoulli trials is the sum of $\binom{n}{x}$ terms, each equal to $p^x(1 - p)^{n-x}$. If we denote this probability by the symbol $P(x; n, p)$, we have

$$(16.6) \qquad P(x; n, p) = \binom{n}{x} p^x(1 - p)^{n-x} \quad (x = 0, 1, 2, \ldots n)$$

The symbol $P(x; n, p)$ in Equation 16.6 emphasizes that we are seeking the probability of x successes, and we have n trials with a probability p of success on a given trial. The function defined by Equation 16.6 is called the **binomial distribution** and an application is illustrated in the following example.

Example 16.11. Find the probability of rolling two fives in six rolls of a balanced die.

Solution: Assuming that the six outcomes of a given roll are equally-likely, the probability of a five on a given roll is $\frac{1}{6}$. Thus, we have $x = 2$, $n = 6$, and $p = \frac{1}{6}$, and

$$P(2; 6, \tfrac{1}{6}) = \binom{6}{2}(\tfrac{1}{6})^2(\tfrac{5}{6})^4$$

$$= 15 \cdot \frac{5^4}{6^6}$$

$$= \frac{9375}{46,656}$$

The binomial distribution is an example of a class of functions called **probability distribution functions.** For a function **f** to be a probability distribution function, it must satisfy the following properties.

1. $f(x) \geq 0$ (for all x in the domain of **f**)

2. $\underset{\text{all } x}{\Sigma} f(x) = 1$

These properties are required for $f(x)$ to be interpretable as a probability. The first property is derived from Axiom 1 for a probability function, and the second property is derived from Axioms 2 and 3.

Referring to the binomial distribution, we note that $P(x; n, p) \geq 0$ for every x in the domain $x = 0, 1, 2, \ldots, n$. To prove that

$$\sum_{x=0}^{n} P(x; n, p) = 1$$

we expand $[(1 - p) + p]^n$ in a binomial series, obtaining

$$[(1 - p) + p]^n = \sum_{x=0}^{n} \binom{n}{x} (1 - p)^{n-x} p^x$$

Since $(1 - p) + p = 1$, the left-hand side of this equation equals 1 but the right-hand side is the sum of all the values of the binomial distribution, and the proof is complete. It is the property illustrated here, namely that $P(x; n, p)$ is the xth term (counting from 0) in the binomial expansion of $[(1 - p) + p]^n$ that gives the binomial distribution its name.

The binomial distribution can be used to find the probability of *at least* x successes in n trials, or *at most* x successes in n trials. For example, the probability of at least x successes is given by the sum

$$P(x; n, p) + P(x + 1; n, p) + \ldots + P(n; n, p)$$

The special law of addition for probabilities can be used here because obtaining x and $x + 1$ successes, for example, are mutually exclusive events. This application is illustrated in the following examples.

Example 16.12. Find the probability of obtaining at least four heads when five coins are tossed.

Solution: We have $n = 5$ and $p = \frac{1}{2}$. The required probability is given by

$$\sum_{x=4}^{5} P(x; 5, \tfrac{1}{2}) = \binom{5}{4}(\tfrac{1}{2})^4(\tfrac{1}{2}) + \binom{5}{5}(\tfrac{1}{2})^5(\tfrac{1}{2})^0$$

$$= 5\,(\tfrac{1}{2})^5 + (\tfrac{1}{2})^5$$

$$= \frac{3}{16}$$

Example 16.13. If a manufacturing process produces 95 per cent acceptable items, find the probability of obtaining less than 9 acceptable items in a batch of 10 items.

Solution: We have $n = 10$ and $p = .95$. Rather than compute the sum $\sum_{x=0}^{8} P(x; 10, .95)$, it is easier to compute the probability of obtaining at least 9 acceptable items and subtract the result from 1. (Can you justify this procedure?) We obtain

$$1 - \sum_{x=9}^{10} P(x; 10, .95) = 1 - \binom{10}{9}(.95)^9(.05)^1 - \binom{10}{10}(.95)^{10}$$

$$= 1 - (.5)(.95)^9 - (.95)^{10}$$

$$= 1 - (1.45)(.95)^9$$

$$= .086$$

PROBLEMS A

1. Evaluate the following.

(a) $P(3; 4, \frac{1}{2})$ (b) $P(2; 5, \frac{1}{3})$

(c) $P(9; 10, \frac{1}{10})$ (d) $P(7; 9, .8)$

(e) $P(0; 4, .6)$ (f) $P(5; 5, .2)$

(g) $P(0; n, p)$ (h) $P(n; n, p)$

2. Find the probability of obtaining (a) exactly 2 heads, (b) exactly 5 heads, (c) at most 3 heads, (d) at least 3 heads in 10 tosses of a balanced coin.

3. If a lot of 20 tubes contains two defectives, can you use the binomial distribution to calculate the probability that a sample of 5 tubes contains exactly one defective (a) if the sample is drawn without replacement, (b) if the sample is drawn with replacement? Calculate this probability for the appropriate one of these two cases.

4. A true-false test contains ten questions and a passing grade is obtained if seven or more questions are answered correctly. If you flip a coin to determine your answers, what is your probability of passing?

5. What is the probability of throwing a seven at last once in five throws with a pair of dice?

6. A marksman hits a target 9 times out of every 10 shots. Find the probability that he will hit the target (a) 4 times in a row, (b) n times in a row.

7. A bowl contains 7 red balls and 3 white balls. If 5 balls are drawn, with replacement, show that the most likely number of red balls is 4.

PROBLEMS B

1. Prove the following recursion formula for the binomial distribution.

$$P(x + 1; n, p) = \frac{n - x}{x + 1} \cdot \frac{p}{1 - p} \cdot P(x; n, p)$$

2. Use the formula of Problem 1 to calculate all the values of $P(x; 10, \frac{1}{3})$.

3. If a bowl contains a red balls and b white balls, and n balls are selected *without replacement*, prove that the probability that x of them will be red is given by

$$H(x; n, a, b) = \frac{\binom{a}{x}\binom{b}{n - x}}{\binom{a + b}{n}} \qquad (x = 0, 1, 2, \ldots, n)$$

4. The function **H** of Problem 3 is called the **hypergeometric distribution.** To prove that **H** is a probability distribution function, it must be shown that

$$\sum_{x=0}^{n} \binom{a}{x}\binom{b}{n - x} = \binom{a + b}{n}$$

Prove this by equating the coefficients of t^z on both sides of the identity

$$(1 + t)^{a+b} = (1 + t)^a (1 + t)^b$$

5. A sample of 10 items is drawn without replacement from a lot containing 20 items, of which 4 are defective. Compute the probability of obtaining at most 2 defectives in the sample in two ways. First, use the hypergeometric distribution of Problem 3, then, although it is incorrect, use the binomial distribution with $n = 10$ and $p = .2$. Compare your answers. Why are they reasonably close and under what conditions would the two results have been even closer?

Appendix

Answers to Alternate Problems

A.1(a) 2, (c) 7, (e) 1, (g) 15, (i) -10. 2(a) $a - b + c$, (c) $a - 2b$, (e) $-abcd$, (g) $-ca + cb$, (i) $-xu + xv + yu - yv$, (k) 0.
3(a) $(x + y)a$, (c) $-(x + y)a$, (e) $(x + y - 5)z$, (g) $(y + b)(x + a)$.
4(a) -2, (c) 2, (e) b $\quad (a \neq 0, c \neq 0)$, (g) $\frac{2}{3}$, (i) a/b $\quad (a \neq 0, b \neq 0)$, (k) a $\quad (b + c \neq 0)$.

Section 1.6

A.1(a) $.\overline{3}$, (c) $3.\overline{142857}$, (e) $7.\overline{8}$. 2(a) $\frac{1}{4}$, (c) $437/10{,}000$.
3(a) rational, (c) rational, (e) irrational.
B.3 $13{,}499/99{,}900$.

Section 1.7

B.1 four.

Section 1.8

A.1 -3, $-\frac{1}{8}$, $\frac{3}{4}$, 1.1, 2. 5 yes. 7 no.

B.1(a) no, (c) no (0 is not a negative number), (e) no.
2(a) 1, (c) no, (e) 0.

Section 1.9

A.1(a) 2, (c) 8, (e) 5, (g) 60, (i) $\frac{3}{2}$. 2(a) 2, -2, (c) none,
(e) 3, -3. 3(a) $x = -2, 2$, (c) $x = -1, 3$.

Section 2.1

A.1 2, 3, 5, 7, 11, 13, 17, 19, 23, 29. 2(a) composite, (c) prime.
3(a) 1, 2, 4, 8, (c) prime, (e) 1, 2, 3, 4, 6, 8, 12, 24. 4(a) 36, (c) 135,
(e) 48. 5(a) not rel. prime, (c) rel. prime, (e) not rel. prime.

Section 2.2

A.1(a) equal, (c) unequal, (e) equal. 2(a) $\frac{5}{6}$, (c) $-\frac{1}{12}$, (e) $\frac{28}{15}$,
(g) $(a^2 - b^2)/ab$, (i) b/a, (k) $\frac{25}{24}$, (m) $\frac{93}{40}$, (0) 2. 3(a) $\frac{3}{2}$, (c) $1 + b/a$,
(e) $ab/(a + b)$.

Section 2.3

A.1(a) $2/a^3$, (c) $3u^2/v^3$, (e) $1/(x - 2)$, (g) $a^{2m}b^{xm}$, (i) $uv/(u + v)$,
(k) $(y^{2b} + y^{2a})/y^{a+b}$.

Section 2.4

A.1(a) 2, (c) $\frac{64}{343}$, (e) .2. 2(a) x^2, (c) $x/3$, (e) $a^{1/2}$, (g) $2a^{1/8}b^{3/8}$,
(i) $3x^{-2/3}$. 3(a) $-2\sqrt{2}$, (c) $2a^{1/6}b(1 - 3a^{1/2}b)$, (e) $3(\sqrt{3} - \sqrt{2})$,
(g) $(x - \sqrt{xy})/(x - y)$, (i) $\sqrt{xy(x + y)}/xy$.

Section 2.6

A.1(a) $5 - 5x^2 - 3x^3$, (c) $3x - 3x^2 - x^3$, (e) $1 - x$,
(g) $12 + x - 9x^2 + 2x^3$, (i) $7 + 4x + 12x^2 + 16x^3 - 7x^4 + 3x^5$,
(k) $1 + x + x^2 + 2x^3 + x^4 + x^5 + x^6$. 2(a) 0,
(c) $25x^6 - 70x^5 + 79x^4 - 52x^3 + 23x^2 - 6x + 1$,
(e) $-5x^3 - 7x^2 - 3x - 1$. 3(a) m, (c) $m + 1$, (e) $2m$.
B.1(a) $-x^3 + x^2 - 2x - 2$, (c) $5 - (x^2 - 2x + 3)^3$.

Section 2.8

A.1(a) $x - 1$, (c) $x - 1 + (3x - 2)/(x^2 - 2x + 2)$, (e) $-y^3 - 2$.
3(a) $3x + 7 + 17/(x - 3)$, (c) $-2x^2 - 10x - 27 - 86/(x - 3)$,
(e) $2x^2 + 4x - 6 - 2/(x + \frac{1}{2})$.

Section 2.9

A.1(a) $6(x + 2)$, (c) $2xy(4 - xy + 2y)$, (e) $(a - 2b)(a + 2b)$,
(g) $(y + 2)(y + 5)$, (i) $(3x + 1)(2x - 5)$, (k) $(y + 3)^3$,
(m) $(u - x - 2y)(u^2 + ux + 2uy + x^2 + 4xy + 4y^2)$,
(o) $2(3r - 5u)(s - t)$, (q) $(w + x - y + z)(w + x + y - z)$,
(s) $(u + v)^2(u - v)^2$, (u) $(x^a + 2y^{3b})(x^{2a} - 2x^a y^{3b} + 4y^{6b})$,
(w) $(3u + 2v)(3u - 2v - 3a + 3b)/(a - b)^2$. 2(a) $-1/(x + y)$,
(c) $x/3$, (e) $(3x + 2)/2(x + 4)$, (g) $-1/xy(x + y)$, (i) $1/(x + 1)$,
(k) $\dfrac{x^3 - y^3 + 1}{(x - y - 1)(x^2 + xy + y^2)}$ 3(a) $(21x - 5)/7x^2$,
(c) $(x^2 + 1)(x - 1)/x^4$, (e) $3(u - 1)/(u + 2)$, (g) $x + 1$,
(i) $y(y - 2)/(y + 1)(y + 3)$, (k) $(x + 2y)/2y$.
B.1 $a(x - a)(x + 1/a)$. 3. $(x + iy)(x - iy)$,   where $i = \sqrt{-1}$.

Section 3.1

A.1(a) $5 - i$, (c) 8, (e) $18 + i$, (g) $21 + 59i$, (i) $5 - 12i$,
(k) $-\dfrac{1}{2} + \dfrac{\sqrt{3}}{2} i$, (m) 0, (o) $4 - 10i$. 2(a) -1, (c) i. 3(a) $(8, 12)$,
(c) $(-30, 45)$, (e) $(4, 0)$.

Section 3.2

A.1(a) $-\sqrt{5} - 2\sqrt{5}\, i$, (c) $-\frac{3}{2} + \frac{7}{2}i$, (e) $\frac{1}{2} - \frac{1}{2}i$, (g) $3 + 2i$,
(i) $-\frac{11}{2} + \frac{13}{2}i$, (k) $1 - \dfrac{\sqrt{3}}{3} + (\frac{1}{3} + \sqrt{3})i$, (m) $\frac{6}{61} - \frac{5}{61}i$.

Section 3.3

A.1(a) 5, (c) $\sqrt{13}/6$, (e) 2, (g) $\sqrt{2}$.

Section 4.1

A.1(a) all real numbers, all real numbers, $f(x) = -x$.
2(a) $\{-1, 0, 1\}$, (c) $\phi(x) \geq 0$, (e) $h(x) > 0$, (g) $0 \leq f(u) \leq 1$.   3(a) 0,
(c) $y^2 - 2y + 1$, (e) $x^2 + 2(h - 1)x$, (g) $x^2 + 2x + 1$.   4(a) $x \geq 1$,
(c) all real numbers, (e) $x \leq 0$.   5(a) 2, (c) x^2.
   B.3(a) $x^2 + 1$, (c) $|x + 1/x|$, $x \neq 0$.

Section 4.2

A.1 $\frac{5}{2}$.   3. $\frac{3}{2}$.   5. $+10\%$.   7. $1/x + 1/y = (x + y)/xy$.
9. one is inversely proportional to the other.
11. $s = \sqrt{90{,}000(t + \frac{1}{2})^2 + 62{,}500t^2}$, $t \geq 0$.
   B.1. $r_2 = r_1(1 + s/d)$.

Section 4.3

A.2(a) $x < -1$, (c) $x < 1$.

Section 4.4

A.4(a) $(x + 1)^2 - 1$, (c) $-(x - 1)^2$, (e) $5(x - 1)^2 + 10$.

Section 5.1

A.2(a) 1.23, (c) 2.58, (e) 0.71,   5. 0.30 amp.

Section 5.2

A.1(a) 2, (c) 81, (e) 2, (g) $\frac{1}{4}$.   2(a) 0.778, (c) 0.398, (e) 0.0792,
(g) 2.097, (i) 0, (k) $-.111$, (m) -1, (o) 1.47, (q) 1.699.

Section 5.3

A.1(a) $2.5 \cdot 10$, (c) $3.476 \cdot 10^6$, (e) $1.5 \cdot 10^{-2}$, (g) $5 \cdot 10^0$, (i) $-3.7005 \cdot 10$.
2(a) 2.1038, (c) $9.5490 - 10$, (e) 3.7924, (g) $7.3404 - 10$, (i) 12.7043.
3(a) 753, (c) 0.00553, (e) $4.56 \cdot 10^{-15}$.

Section 5.4

A.1(a) 0.2613, (c) 3.5792, (e) 1.2941, (g) 1.0009, (i) $8.6271 - 10$.
2(a) 32.05, (c) 4753, (e) 0.6308, (g) $1.498 \cdot 10^{-11}$, (i) 0.7468.
3(a) 1.723, (c) -1.588.

Section 5.5

A.1(a) 755, (c) 34,900, (e) $2.931 \cdot 10^9$, (g) 50,400, (i) 0.841,
(k) 0.05662, (m) 2.468, (o) 0.0007906.

Section 6.1

A.2(a) $24°18'$, (c) $-87°40'48''$.

Section 6.2

A.1(a) $\pi/6$, (c) $3\pi/2$, (e) $\pi/12$, (g) $2\pi/45$, (i) $-2\pi/3$, (k) -2π.
2(a) $30°$, (c) $120°$, (e) $360°/\pi$, (g) $146.7°/\pi$, (i) $-337.68°/\pi$.
3(a) $(-1, 0)$, (c) $\left(-\dfrac{\sqrt{2}}{2}, \dfrac{\sqrt{2}}{2}\right)$, (e) $\left(\dfrac{\sqrt{2}}{2}, -\dfrac{\sqrt{2}}{2}\right)$, (g) $\left(\dfrac{\sqrt{3}}{2}, \dfrac{1}{2}\right)$,
(i) $\left(\dfrac{1}{2}, \dfrac{\sqrt{3}}{2}\right)$, (k) $\left(-\dfrac{\sqrt{2}}{2}, \dfrac{\sqrt{2}}{2}\right)$.
5.   9.23 radians.

Section 6.3

	sin t	cos t	tan t	csc t	sec t	cot t
A.1(a)	4/5	3/5	4/3	5/4	5/3	3/4
(c)	1	0	—	1	—	0
2(a)	0	-1	0	—	-1	—
(c)	$\sqrt{2}/2$	$-\sqrt{2}/2$	-1	$\sqrt{2}$	$-\sqrt{2}$	-1
(e)	$-\sqrt{2}/2$	$\sqrt{2}/2$	-1	$-\sqrt{2}$	$\sqrt{2}$	-1
(g)	$1/2$	$-\sqrt{3}/2$	$-\sqrt{3}/3$	2	$-2\sqrt{3}/3$	$-\sqrt{3}$
(i)	$\sqrt{2}/2$	$-\sqrt{2}/2$	-1	$\sqrt{2}$	$-\sqrt{2}$	-1
(k)	$-1/2$	$\sqrt{3}/2$	$-\sqrt{3}/3$	-2	$2\sqrt{3}/3$	$-\sqrt{3}$

3(a) $0 < t < \pi/2$, (c) $\pi < t < 3\pi/2$.
B.1 $-\pi, 0, \pi$.   3 sin, tan, csc, cot.

Section 6.5

A.1(a) 0.5200, (c) 3.376, (e) 1.087, (g) 0.3153, (i) 2.131, (k) 2.972.
2(a) 0.4189, (c) 0.1818, (e) 0.1440.   3(a) 74°29′, (c) 359°49′,
(e) 180°04′.

B.1 $0 < t < 0.3927$.

Section 6.6

A.1(a) $B = 57°, b = 18.5, c = 22.0$, (c) $B = 53°39′, b = 13.4$,
$c = 16.6$,   (e) $A = 85°04′$, $B = 4°56′$, $a = 96.0$.   3 0.485.   5 43.8″.
7 14.5″.   9 140.5′.

B.1 18.1′.

Section 7.1

A.1(a) $(\sqrt{6} + \sqrt{2})/4$, (c) $2 + \sqrt{3}$, (e) $-1/2$, (g) $-2 - \sqrt{3}$.
3 $\sin u \cos v - \cos u \sin v$.   5 $(\cot u \cot v - 1)/(\cot u + \cot v)$.

B.1(a) even, (c) odd, (e) odd.   3 $\sin u \cos v \cos w +$
$\cos u \sin v \cos w + \cos u \cos v \sin w - \sin u \sin v \sin w$.

Section 7.2

A.1(a) $\sqrt{2 + \sqrt{3}}/2$, (c) $(\sqrt{6} + \sqrt{2})/4$, (e) $2/\sqrt{2 - \sqrt{2}}$,
(g) $\sqrt{2 - \sqrt{2 + \sqrt{3}}}/2$.   3 $4 \tan t(1 - \tan^2 t)/(1 - 6 \tan^2 t + \tan^4 t)$.

Section 7.4

A.1(a) $4\pi, 1$, (c) $\pi, 2$, (e) $\pi, 3$.
B.3 2π.

Section 7.5

A.2(a) $\left(\dfrac{\sqrt{3}}{2}, \dfrac{1}{2}\right)$, (c) $(-1, \sqrt{3})$, (e) $(0, -1)$, (g) $(-\tfrac{1}{2}, 0)$,
(i) $(1, 0)$, (k) $(0, -2)$.   3(a) $(1, 0)$, (c) $\left(\sqrt{2}, \dfrac{\pi}{4}\right)$, (e) $\left(2, \dfrac{\pi}{6}\right)$,
(g) $\left(2, \dfrac{5\pi}{4}\right)$, (i) $(0, 0)$.

B.3 Line through origin, making angle θ_0 with X-axis.   5 $x = 5$.

Section 7.6

A.1(a) $5\sqrt{2}\left(\cos\dfrac{7\pi}{4}+i\sin\dfrac{7\pi}{4}\right)$, (c) $2\left(\cos\dfrac{\pi}{6}+i\sin\dfrac{\pi}{6}\right)$,

(e) $2\left(\cos\dfrac{\pi}{2}+i\sin\dfrac{\pi}{2}\right)$, (g) $6(\cos 0 + i\sin 0)$,

(i) $5(\cos .9273 + i\sin .9273)$.   2(a) $6 + 6\sqrt{3}\,i$,
(c) $-1.2856 - 1.5320i$, (e) $-i$, (g) -64, (i) $-16\sqrt{3} - 16i$.

3(a) $R = 5, \theta_k = \dfrac{\pi}{9} + \dfrac{2k\pi}{3}$, $k = 0, 1, 2$, (c) $R = 2, \theta_k = \dfrac{7\pi}{16} + \dfrac{2k\pi}{4}$,

$k = 0, 1, 2, 3$, (e) $\pm\dfrac{\sqrt{2}}{2}\pm\dfrac{\sqrt{2}}{2}i$, (g) $i, \pm\dfrac{\sqrt{3}}{2}-\dfrac{1}{2}i$, (i) $R = 2^{1/6}$,

$\theta_k = \dfrac{\pi}{12} + \dfrac{2k\pi}{3}$, $k = 0, 1, 2$.

B.1 $\pm 2 \pm 2i$.

Section 8.1

A.1(a) $x = [f(x) - 1]/2$, $-3 \le f(x) \le 3$, (c) $u = 1/f(u)$, $f(u) > 0$,
(e) $x = \log_2 f(x)$, $f(x) > 0$, (g) undefined.
B.1 Symmetric about the line making an angle of $45°$ with the X-axis.

Section 8.2

A.1(a) $\pi/2$, (c) $\pi/3$, (e) $-\pi/4$, (g) $-\pi/4$, (i) 0.8465.
2(a) $\sqrt{2}/2$, (c) -1, (e) 0, (g) $\pi/3$.

Section 9.1

A.1(a) 2, (c) 1, (e) 4.   2(a) Yes, (c) yes, (e) no, (g) no.   3(a) Yes,
(c) yes, (e) no, (g) yes.   4(a) 5, (c) 9/10, (e) 4, (g) $\{-3, -2\}$,
(i) -3, (k) $\{0, 1\}$.   5(a) $-v/g$, (c) $2F/(a + b)$, (e) 1.

B.1 $\left\{2^{1/p}\left[\cos\dfrac{2k\pi}{p}+i\sin\dfrac{2k\pi}{p}\right]\right\}$, $k = 0, 1, \ldots, p - 1$.

3 If $g(x) = 0$ implies that $f(x) = 0$.

Section 9.2

A.1 13, 14.   3 $20.   5 30.   7 $54.   9 225 miles.
B.1 8:43.64.   3 120/13 min.

Section 9.4

A.1(a) $\dfrac{\pi}{2} + 2k\pi$, (c) $\dfrac{5\pi}{6} + 2k\pi$, $\dfrac{13\pi}{6} + 2k\pi$,

(e) $\dfrac{\pi}{3} + k\pi$, $\dfrac{2\pi}{3} + k\pi$, (g) $\dfrac{3\pi}{2} + 2k\pi$, (i) $\dfrac{3\pi}{4} + 2k\pi$, $\dfrac{5\pi}{4} + 2k\pi$,

(k) $\dfrac{\pi}{3} + 2k\pi$, $\dfrac{5\pi}{3} + 2k\pi$, (m) $\dfrac{\pi}{2} + k\pi$, $\dfrac{7\pi}{6} + 2k\pi$, $\dfrac{11\pi}{6} + 2k\pi$,

(o) $k\pi$.

B.1 $2k\pi$, $\dfrac{\pi}{2} + 2k\pi$.   3 $\sqrt{2}/2$.   5 $\tfrac{1}{2}$.

Section 9.5

A.2(a) 4, (c) $-\tfrac{1}{2}$.

Section 10.1

A.1(a) $\{0, 1\}$, (c) $\{1\}$, (e) $\{-3, 0\}$, (g) $\{-\tfrac{2}{3}, 2\}$, (i) $\{-\tfrac{1}{4}, \tfrac{7}{3}\}$,
(k) $\{-1, \tfrac{1}{6}\}$. 2(a) $\{-1, 3\}$, (c) $\{1 - \sqrt{2}, 1 + \sqrt{2}\}$,

(e) $\left\{-\dfrac{3}{2} - \dfrac{\sqrt{7}}{2}\,i, \; -\dfrac{3}{2} + \dfrac{\sqrt{7}}{2}\,i\right\}$, (g) $\{\tfrac{2}{3}, 1\}$,

(i) $\left\{\dfrac{3}{2} - \dfrac{\sqrt{19}}{2}, \dfrac{3}{2} + \dfrac{\sqrt{19}}{2}\right\}$, (k) $\{1 - \sqrt{2}\,i, 1 + \sqrt{2}\,i\}$.

4(a) $x = -y$, (c) $x = [-By - C \pm \sqrt{(By + c)^2 - 4AD}]/2A$,
(e) $t = (-v_0 \pm \sqrt{v_0^2 + 2\,gs})/g$. 5 18, 24. 7 4 or 6. 9 7, 8. 11 12'.
B.1 $\{-2, 1 + i\}$.

Section 10.2

A.1(a) Real and distinct, (c) distinct complex conjugates, (e) real and
distinct, (g) real and equal, (i) distinct complex conjugates.
2(a) $x^2 - 2x - 3 = 0$, (c) $15x^2 - 13x + 2 = 0$, (e) $x^2 - 4x + 1 = 0$,
(g) $x^2 - 4x + 13 = 0$, (i) $x^2 - 2ax + (a^2 + b^2) = 0$. 3(a) $-2, 2$,
(c) $|k| > \tfrac{3}{2}$.
B.1(a) $(x - i)(x + i)$, (c) $(kx - 1)(x + k - 1)$.

Section 10.3

A.1(a) $\{-2, 2, -i, i\}$, (c) $\{-\frac{1}{3}, \frac{1}{2}\}$, (e) $\{1, 1024\}$, (g) $\{\frac{17}{2}, \frac{353}{81}\}$,
(i) no solutions, (k) $\left\{\dfrac{\pi}{2} + 2k\pi, \dfrac{7\pi}{6} + 2k\pi, \dfrac{11\pi}{6} + 2k\pi\right\}$.   2(a) $\{14\}$,
(c) $\{\frac{17}{16}\}$, (e) $\{4\}$, (g) $\{-1 - \sqrt{13}, -1 + \sqrt{13}\}$.

B.1 $\pm\sqrt{\dfrac{\pi}{2} + k\pi}$.

Section 10.4

A.1(a) 5, (c) 1135.   2(a) 2959, (c) $37 + 32i$.   3(a) 8, (c) $-\frac{5}{24}$.
B.1 n even.

Section 10.5

A.1(a) -1, -1, (c) -1, $-i$.   2(a) $\{1, i, -i\}$, (c) $\{1, 1, 1, 1\}$.

Section 10.6

A.1(a) $(x - 2)(x + 3)(x - 4)$, (c) $(x + 2)(x^2 - 2x + 5)$,
(e) $(x - 4)(x + 2)(x^2 - 6x + 58)$, (g) $(x + 9)(x^2 - 2\sqrt{3}\,x + 5)$,
(i) $(x^2 - 2x + 2)(x^2 + 4x + 13)$.   2(a) $-i, 2$, (c) $1 - i$,
$\dfrac{1}{2} + \dfrac{\sqrt{5}}{2}, \dfrac{1}{2} - \dfrac{\sqrt{5}}{2}$, (e) $-1 - 2i, -1 + 2i, -1 - 2i$.
3(a) Rational, (c) rational, (e) not all real.   4(a) $\{-1, 1, 2\}$,
(c) $\{-\frac{3}{2}, i, -i\}$, (e) $\{-2, -2, 2, 2\}$, (g) $\{-1, 0, 2, \frac{5}{2}\}$,
(i) $\{-2, -1, \frac{3}{4}, 1\}$.

Section 11.1

A.1(a) $(14, 1)$, (c) $(-4, 2)$, (e) $(\sqrt{3}, 0)$, (g) $(-\frac{2}{13}, \frac{3}{26})$,
(i) $(3, 2 - 3\sqrt{2})$, (k) $(\frac{117}{29}, \frac{72}{29})$.   2(a) $(\frac{1}{2}, 1)$, (c) $(\frac{1}{200}, 20)$.
3 $\frac{19}{2}, \frac{15}{2}$.   5 \$0.20.
B.1 $a = -\frac{5}{2}, b = -\frac{11}{2}$.

Section 11.2

A.1(a) Dependent, (c) dependent, (e) consistent and independent. 2(a) Dependent, (c) dependent, (e) consistent and independent. 3(a) (i) any $k \neq -\frac{2}{3}$, (ii) $-\frac{2}{3}$, (iii) none, (c) (*i*) any $k \neq -1$, (*ii*) none, (*iii*) -1.

B.1 $x = (k - 4)/3, y = (40 - k)/3, k = 13, 16, 19, 22, 25, 28, 31$.

Section 11.3

A.1(a) $(\frac{5}{2}, \frac{1}{2}, \frac{5}{2})$, (c) $(3, \frac{3}{2}, -4)$, (e) $(-\frac{65}{24}, \frac{1}{24}, -\frac{13}{24})$, (g) dependent, (i) $(0, -9, -10, -7)$. 2(a) $x = -(z + 1)/3$, $y = (z - 5)/3$, (c) $x = (53z - 17)/29, y = (2z + 1)/29$. 3 $0.30.

B.1(a) $(1, 7), (2, 4), (3, 1)$, (b) $(3, 3, 3)$.

Section 11.4

A.2(a) $(3, 3)$, $(-\frac{3}{2}, \frac{3}{4})$,

(c) $\left(\dfrac{6 + 2\sqrt{74}}{5}, \dfrac{83 + 6\sqrt{74}}{25}\right), \left(\dfrac{6 - 2\sqrt{74}}{5}, \dfrac{83 - 6\sqrt{74}}{25}\right)$,

(e) $(\sqrt{19}, \sqrt{3}\, i), (\sqrt{19}, -\sqrt{3}\, i), (-\sqrt{19}, \sqrt{3}\, i), (-\sqrt{19}, -\sqrt{3}\, i)$, (g) $(1, 1), (-1, -1)$, (i) $(4, -2), (-4, 2), (1, -3), (-1, 3)$, (k) $(0, 2\, i), (0, -2\, i), (2, 4), (-2, -4)$. 3 $7, 12$.

B.1(a) $\left(\dfrac{1 + \sqrt{5}}{2}, \dfrac{1 - \sqrt{5}}{2}\right), \left(\dfrac{1 - \sqrt{5}}{2}, \dfrac{1 + \sqrt{5}}{2}\right)$,

$(-3 + \sqrt{11}\, i, -3 - \sqrt{11}\, i), (-3 - \sqrt{11}\, i, -3 + \sqrt{11}\, i)$, (b) $(3, 1), (-1, -3)$.

Section 12.1

A.1(a) Square, (c) row, (e) all three, (g) column. 3 $x = \pm i, y = \pm \sqrt{2}$.

B.1(a) $\begin{bmatrix} 1 & 4 & 7 \\ 2 & 5 & 8 \\ 3 & 6 & 9 \end{bmatrix}$, (b) n-by-1 column matrix.

Section 12.2

A.1(a) $\begin{bmatrix} -1 & 2 \\ 1 & 0 \end{bmatrix}$ (c) $\begin{bmatrix} a-b & 0 & 5 \\ b & a+5b & 0 \end{bmatrix}$

2(a) $\begin{bmatrix} 1 \\ 2 \\ 0 \end{bmatrix}$ (c) $[11 \quad 4 \quad 10 \quad -1]$

5(a) $[16]$ (c) $\begin{bmatrix} -4 & 20-\sqrt{2} & 4\sqrt{20}+2\sqrt{2} \\ -2-3\sqrt{8} & 8 & \sqrt{20}-6 \\ -2\sqrt{5}+7\sqrt{8} & 5\sqrt{5}-7 & 24 \end{bmatrix}$

(e) $\begin{bmatrix} 0 & 0 \\ 0 & 0 \end{bmatrix}$ (g) $\begin{bmatrix} 0 \\ 0 \\ 0 \end{bmatrix}$

Section 12.3

A.1(a) $(2, 1)$, (c) $(\frac{2}{5}, \frac{3}{7})$, (e) $(5, 5)$, (g) $(1, 1, 1)$.
2(a) Unique solution, (c) unique solution, (e) unique solution.
B.1(a) $(-4, -9)$, (b) $x'' = x - 12y$, $y'' = 6x + 23y$.

Section 12.4

A.1(a) $\begin{bmatrix} 1 & -\frac{3}{2} \\ 0 & \frac{1}{2} \end{bmatrix}$ (c) $\begin{bmatrix} -\frac{1}{3} & \frac{2}{3} \\ \frac{2}{3} & -\frac{1}{3} \end{bmatrix}$

(e) $\begin{bmatrix} 1 & -1 \\ 1 & 0 \end{bmatrix}$ (g) $\begin{bmatrix} 1 & -\frac{1}{2} & -\frac{1}{12} \\ 0 & \frac{1}{4} & -\frac{5}{24} \\ 0 & 0 & \frac{1}{6} \end{bmatrix}$

B.1 $X = B^{-1}CA^{-1}$. $3\begin{bmatrix} \frac{10}{89} & -\frac{1}{89} \\ -\frac{1}{89} & \frac{9}{89} \end{bmatrix}$

Section 12.5

A.1(a) -2, (c) 26, (e) 1, (g) 77. 2(a) 150, (c) 0, (e) -441,
(g) -3. 3(a) $(\frac{23}{13}, -\frac{2}{13})$, (c) no unique solution, (e) no unique solution.
B.3(a) $A^{-1} = \begin{bmatrix} -\frac{1}{7} & \frac{2}{7} & 0 \\ -\frac{1}{7} & -\frac{1}{21} & \frac{1}{3} \\ \frac{2}{7} & \frac{2}{21} & -\frac{1}{6} \end{bmatrix}$ (b) $X = \begin{bmatrix} \frac{5}{7} \\ \frac{29}{21} \\ -\frac{16}{21} \end{bmatrix}$

Section 13.1

A.2(a) Absolute, (c) conditional, (e) absolute.
B.3 $\sqrt{10} \doteq 3.16$.

Section 13.2

A.1(a) $x < \frac{5}{2}$, (c) $x < 1$, (e) $x \leq -\frac{1}{4}$, (g) $0 < x < \frac{3}{4}$,
(i) $x < -1$ or $x > 1$, (k) $x \geq a - b$ or $x \leq a + b$.
2(a) $-1 < x < 1$, (c) $x \leq -3$ or $x \geq 1$, (e) $x < 2$ or $x > 4$,
(g) $x < (-3 - \sqrt{41})/4$ or $x > (-3 + \sqrt{41})/4$,
(i) no real solutions, (k) all real x.
B.1 $x < -2$, $-1 < x < 1$, $x > 2$.

Section 13.3

B.1 16.

Section 14.1

A.1(a) IV, (c) I, (e) I, (g) I.

Section 14.2

A.3(a) $a = 2.588$, $b = 5$, $C = 75°$, (c) $a_1 = 7.45$, $A_1 = 111°20'$,
$C_1 = 38°40'$, $a_2 = 1.21$, $A_2 = 8°40'$, $C_2 = 141°20'$, (e) $A = 28°80'$,
$B = 46°40'$, $C = 104°30'$, (g) $c = 3.18$, $A = 140°40'$, $B = 9°20'$,
(i) $c = \sqrt{3}/2$, $A = 90°00'$, $C = 30°00'$, (k) $A = 29°50'$, $B = 56°20'$,
$C = 93°50'$. 5 89.8 yd. 7 52.6''.
B.1 1170 ft/min.

Section 14.3

A.1(a) 71.2, (c) $3\sqrt{15}$, (e) 20.1, (g) .956, (i) 113.
3 The ratio of the areas is the square of the ratio of the sides.

Section 15.1

A.1(a) $1, \frac{1}{2}, \frac{1}{3}, \frac{1}{4}$, (c) $1, \frac{4}{3}, 2, \frac{16}{5}$, (e) $-3, 9, -27, 81$,

(g) $\frac{1}{8}, \frac{1}{32}, \frac{1}{128}, \frac{1}{512}$.   2(a) $n(n \le 9), 0(n > 9), \sum\limits_{j=1}^{9} j$,

(c) $(2n - 1)/2n, \sum\limits_{j=1}^{\infty} (2j - 1)/2j$,

(g) $(-1)^{n+1}[x/(n + 1)](n \le 9), 0(n > 9)^2, \sum\limits_{j=2}^{10} (-1)^j(x/j)^2$.

B.1(a) $1, 1, 2, 6, 24, 120$, (b) $a_1 = a, a_{n+1} = ra_n$.

Section 15.3

A.1(a) 120, (c) 36, (e) 1.   3(a) $\sum\limits_{j=0}^{5} \binom{5}{j} x^{5-j}(2y)^j, 80x^2y^3$,

(c) $\sum\limits_{j=0}^{9} \binom{9}{j} 2^{9-j}(-x)^j, -5376x^3$, (e) $\sum\limits_{j=0}^{10} \binom{10}{j} (-1)^j x^{20-3j/2} y^{10-j/2}$,

$-120x^{31/2}y^{17/2}$, (g) $\sum\limits_{j=0}^{6} \binom{6}{j} 2^{(6-j)x} 3^{jy}, 20(2^x3^y)^3$.

4(a) -4, (c) $-\dfrac{41}{32} - \dfrac{19}{16}i$.   5(a) 1.051, (c) 0.990.

6(a) $x^4 + y^4 + z^4 + 4x^3y + 4x^3z + 6x^2y^2 + 12x^2yz + 6x^2z^2 + 4xy^3 + 12xy^2z + 12xyz^2 + 4xz^3 + 4y^3z + 6y^2z^2 + 4yz^3$.

B.3(a) 1.0007.

Section 15.4

A.1(a) A.P., $19, 23$, (c) not a progression, (e) not a progression,
(g) A.P., $\frac{7}{2}, \frac{9}{2}$, (i) A.P., $a + 3b, a + 4b$, (k) G.P., $(y/x)^7, (y/x)^9$.
2(a) $2, 0, -2, -4$, (c) $-10, -7, -4, -1$.   3(a) $3, 2, \frac{4}{3}, \frac{8}{9}$,
(c) $2, -4, 8, -16$.   4(a) 2500, (c) $5461/4096$, (e) $-39{,}991/3$,
(g) $7x + 35y$.   5 400.
   B.1(a) $\frac{7}{6}, \frac{5}{6}, \frac{1}{2}, \frac{1}{6}, -\frac{1}{6}, -\frac{1}{2}, -\frac{5}{6}, -\frac{7}{6}$, (b) $-1, 10, -10^2, 10^3, -10^4$,
$10^5, -10^6, 10^7$.   3(a) $a' = ka, d' = kd$, (b) $a' = a + k, d' = d$.
5. $a' = a^p, r' = r^p$.

Section 15.5

A.1(a) 0, (c) diverges, (e) 0, (g) 1, (i) 0.   2(a) 2, (c) diverges,
(e) $\log 7/(1 - \log 7)$.   3(a) $\frac{13}{330}$, (c) $100/99$, (e) $10{,}429/2475$.

Section 16.1

A.1(a) $\{1, 2, 3, 4, 5, 6\}$, (c) $\{(i, j)\}$, $i = 1, \ldots, 6$,
$j = 1, \ldots, 6$ (36 elements),
(e) $\{AK, AQ, AJ, KA, KQ, KJ, QA, QK, QJ, JA, JK, JQ\}$.
2(a) $\{(1, 1), (1, 2), (1, 3), (2, 1), (2, 2), (2, 3), (3, 1), (3, 2), (3, 3)\}$,
(c) $\{(1, 1), (1, 2), (1, 3), (2, 1), (2, 3), (3, 1), (3, 2), (3, 3)\}$,
(e) $\{(1, 1), (1, 2), (1, 3), (2, 1), (2, 3), (3, 1), (3, 2), (3, 3)\}$,
(g) $\{(2, 2)\}$, (i) $\{(1, 1), (1, 2), (1, 3), (2, 1), (3, 1), (3, 3)\}$.

Section 16.2

A.1(a) No, $P(C) < 0$, (c) no, $P(C) > 1$, (e) yes.
2(a) $\frac{1}{16}$, (c) $\frac{5}{16}$, (e) $\frac{15}{16}$.   3(a) $\frac{5}{9}$, (c) $\frac{5}{9}$, (e) $\frac{1}{3}$, (g) $\frac{2}{9}$.
4(a) $\frac{1}{5}$, (c) $\frac{2}{5}$.   5 0.3.
B.1(a) $(j - 1)/36$, $j = 2, \ldots, 7$, $(12 - j + 1)/36$, $j = 8, \ldots, 12$,
(b) $\frac{2}{9}$, (c) $\frac{3}{4}$.   3 $\frac{1}{3}$.

Section 16.3

A.1(a) 0.7, (c) 0.55, (e) 0.45.   2(a) 0.6, (c) 0.5, (e) 0.8.
3(a) 0.4, (c) 0.625, (e) 0.8.   5 $\frac{7}{12}$.

Section 16.4

A.1 24.   3 x^n.   5(a) 60, (b) 325, (c) 24.   7 720.   9 89, 100.
11 1/180.   12(a) 1/4165, (c) 6/4165, (e) 88/4165.   13(a) 7/15,
(b) 1/2, (c) 11/120.   15(a) 3/16, (b) 4/43.   17 8/21.   19 1/2.
B.1 243.   3 292/625.

Section 16.5

A.1(a) 1/4, (c) $9 \cdot 10^{-9}$, (e) 0.0256, (g) $(1 - p)^n$.   3(a) No,
(b) 0.32805.   5 4651/7776.
B.5 0.708, 0.678.

Table 1   Appendix   345

TABLE 1

Common Logarithms

n	0	1	2	3	4	5	6	7	8	9
1.0	.0000	.0043	.0086	.0128	.0170	.0212	.0253	.0294	.0334	.0374
1.1	.0414	.0453	.0492	.0531	.0569	.0607	.0645	.0682	.0719	.0755
1.2	.0792	.0828	.0864	.0899	.0934	.0969	.1004	.1038	.1072*	.1106
1.3	.1139	.1173	.1206	.1239	.1271	.1303	.1335	.1367	.1399	.1430
1.4	.1461	.1492	.1523	.1553	.1584	.1614	.1644	.1673	.1703	.1732
1.5	.1761	.1790	.1818	.1847	.1875	.1903	.1931	.1959	.1987	.2014
1.6	.2041	.2068	.2095	.2122	.2148	.2175	.2201	.2227	.2253	.2279
1.7	.2304	.2330	.2355	.2380	.2405	.2430	.2455	.2480	.2504	.2529
1.8	.2553	.2577	.2601	.2625	.2648	.2672	.2695	.2718	.2742	.2765
1.9	.2788	.2810	.2833	.2856	.2878	.2900	.2923	.2945	.2967	.2989
2.0	.3010	.3032	.3054	.3075	.3096	.3118	.3139	.3160	.3181	.3201
2.1	.3222	.3243	.3263	.3284	.3304	.3324	.3345	.3365	.3385	.3404
2.2	.3424	.3444	.3464	.3483	.3502	.3522	.3541	.3560	.3579	.3598
2.3	.3617	.3636	.3655	.3674	.3692	.3711	.3729	.3747	.3766	.3784
2.4	.3802	.3820	.3838	.3856	.3874	.3892	.3909	.3927	.3945	.3962
2.5	.3979	.3997	.4014	.4031	.4048	.4065	.4082	.4099	.4116	.4133
2.6	.4150	.4166	.4183	.4200	.4216	.4232	.4249	.4265	.4281	.4298
2.7	.4314	.4330	.4346	.4362	.4378	.4393	.4409	.4425	.4440	.4456
2.8	.4472	.4487	.4502	.4518	.4533	.4548	.4564	.4579	.4594	.4609
2.9	.4624	.4639	.4654	.4669	.4683	.4698	.4713	.4728	.4742	.4757
3.0	.4771	.4786	.4800	.4814	.4829	.4843	.4857	.4871	.4886	.4900
3.1	.4914	.4928	.4942	.4955	.4969	.4983	.4997	.5011	.5024	.5038
3.2	.5051	.5065	.5079	.5092	.5105	.5119	.5132	.5145	.5159	.5172
3.3	.5185	.5198	.5211	.5224	.5237	.5250	.5263	.5276	.5289	.5302
3.4	.5315	.5328	.5340	.5353	.5366	.5378	.5391	.5403	.5416	.5428
3.5	.5441	.5453	.5465	.5478	.5490	.5502	.5514	.5527	.5539	.5551
3.6	.5563	.5575	.5587	.5599	.5611	.5623	.5635	.5647	.5658	.5670
3.7	.5682	.5694	.5705	.5717	.5729	.5740	.5752	.5763	.5775	.5786
3.8	.5798	.5809	.5821	.5832	.5843	.5855	.5866	.5877	.5888	.5899
3.9	.5911	.5922	.5933	.5944	.5955	.5966	.5977	.5988	.5999	.6010
4.0	.6021	.6031	.6042	.6053	.6064	.6075	.6085	.6096	.6107	.6117
4.1	.6128	.6138	.6149	.6160	.6170	.6180	.6191	.6201	.6212	.6222
4.2	.6232	.6243	.6253	.6263	.6274	.6284	.6294	.6304	.6314	.6325
4.3	.6335	.6345	.6355	.6365	.6375	.6385	.6395	.6405	.6415	.6425
4.4	.6435	.6444	.6454	.6464	.6474	.6484	.6493	.6503	.6513	.6522
4.5	.6532	.6542	.6551	.6561	.6571	.6580	.6590	.6599	.6609	.6618
4.6	.6628	.6637	.6646	.6656	.6665	.6675	.6684	.6693	.6702	.6712
4.7	.6721	.6730	.6739	.6749	.6758	.6767	.6776	.6785	.6794	.6803
4.8	.6812	.6821	.6830	.6839	.6848	.6857	.6866	.6875	.6884	.6893
4.9	.6902	.6911	.6920	.6928	.6937	.6946	.6955	.6964	.6972	.6981
5.0	.6990	.6998	.7007	.7016	.7024	.7033	.7042	.7050	.7059	.7067
5.1	.7076	.7084	.7093	.7101	.7110	.7118	.7126	.7135	.7143	.7152
5.2	.7160	.7168	.7177	.7185	.7193	.7202	.7210	.7218	.7226	.7235
5.3	.7243	.7251	.7259	.7267	.7275	.7284	.7292	.7300	.7308	.7316
5.4	.7324	.7332	.7340	.7348	.7356	.7364	.7372	.7380	.7388	.7396

TABLE 1. (Cont.)

Common Logarithms

n	0	1	2	3	4	5	6	7	8	9
5.5	.7404	.7412	.7419	.7427	.7435	.7443	.7451	.7459	.7466	.7474
5.6	.7482	.7490	.7497	.7505	.7513	.7520	.7528	.7536	.7543	.7551
5.7	.7559	.7566	.7574	.7582	.7589	.7597	.7604	.7612	.7619	.7627
5.8	.7634	.7642	.7649	.7657	.7664	.7672	.7679	.7686	.7694	.7701
5.9	.7709	.7716	.7723	.7731	.7738	.7745	.7752	.7760	.7767	.7774
6.0	.7782	.7789	.7796	.7803	.7810	.7818	.7825	.7832	.7839	.7846
6.1	.7853	.7860	.7868	.7875	.7882	.7889	.7896	.7903	.7910	.7917
6.2	.7924	.7931	.7938	.7945	.7952	.7959	.7966	.7973	.7980	.7987
6.3	.7993	.8000	.8007	.8014	.8021	.8028	.8035	.8041	.8048	.8055
6.4	.8062	.8069	.8075	.8082	.8089	.8096	.8102	.8109	.8116	.8122
6.5	.8129	.8136	.8142	.8149	.8156	.8162	.8169	.8176	.8182	.8189
6.6	.8195	.8202	.8209	.8215	.8222	.8228	.8235	.8241	.8248	.8254
6.7	.8261	.8267	.8274	.8280	.8287	.8293	.8299	.8306	.8312	.8319
6.8	.8325	.8331	.8338	.8344	.8351	.8357	.8363	.8370	.8376	.8382
6.9	.8388	.8395	.8401	.8407	.8414	.8420	.8426	.8432	.8439	.8445
7.0	.8451	.8457	.8463	.8470	.8476	.8482	.8488	.8494	.8500	.8506
7.1	.8513	.8519	.8525	.8531	.8537	.8543	.8549	.8555	.8561	.8627
7.2	.8573	.8579	.8585	.8591	.8597	.8603	.8609	.8615	.8621	.8627
7.3	.8633	.8639	.8645	.8651	.8657	.8663	.8669	.8675	.8681	.8686
7.4	.8692	.8698	.8704	.8710	.8716	.8722	.8727	.8733	.8739	.8745
7.5	.8751	.8756	.8762	.8768	.8774	.8779	.8785	.8791	.8797	.8802
7.6	.8808	.8814	.8820	.8825	.8831	.8837	.8842	.8848	.8854	.8859
7.7	.8865	.8871	.8876	.8882	.8887	.8893	.8899	.8904	.8910	.8915
7.8	.8921	.8927	.8932	.8938	.8943	.8949	.8954	.8960	.8965	.8971
7.9	.8976	.8982	.8987	.8993	.8998	.9004	.9009	.9015	.9020	.9025
8.0	.9031	.9036	.9042	.9047	.9053	.9058	.9063	.9069	.9074	.9079
8.1	.9085	.9090	.9096	.9101	.9106	.9112	.9117	.9122	.9128	.9133
8.2	.9138	.9143	.9149	.9154	.9159	.9165	.9170	.9175	.9180	.9186
8.3	.9191	.9196	.9201	.9206	.9212	.9217	.9222	.9227	.9232	.9238
8.4	.9243	.9248	.9253	.9258	.9263	.9269	.9274	.9279	.9284	.9289
8.5	.9294	.9299	.9304	.9309	.9315	.9320	.9325	.9330	.9335	.9340
8.6	.9345	.9350	.9355	.9360	.9365	.9370	.9375	.9380	.9385	.9390
8.7	.9395	.9400	.9405	.9410	.9415	.9420	.9425	.9430	.9435	.9440
8.8	.9445	.9450	.9455	.9460	.9465	.9469	.9474	.9479	.9484	.9489
8.9	.9494	.9499	.9504	.9509	.9513	.9518	.9523	.9528	.9533	.9538
9.0	.9542	.9547	.9552	.9557	.9562	.9566	.9571	.9576	.9581	.9586
9.1	.9590	.9595	.9600	.9605	.9609	.9614	.9619	.9624	.9628	.9633
9.2	.9638	.9643	.9647	.9652	.9657	.9661	.9666	.9671	.9675	.9680
9.3	.9685	.9689	.9694	.9699	.9703	.9708	.9713	.9717	.9722	.9727
9.4	.9731	.9736	.9741	.9745	.9750	.9754	.9759	.9763	.9768	.9773
9.5	.9777	.9782	.9786	.9791	.9795	.9800	.9805	.9809	.9814	.9818
9.6	.9823	.9827	.9832	.9836	.9841	.9845	.9850	.9854	.9859	.9863
9.7	.9868	.9872	.9877	.9881	.9886	.9890	.9899	.9899	.9903	.9908
9.8	.9912	.9917	.9921	.9926	.9930	.9934	.9939	.9943	.9948	.9952
9.9	.9956	.9961	.9965	.9969	.9974	.9978	.9983	.9987	.9991	.9996

TABLE 2

Values of the Trigonometric Functions

Degrees	Radians	Sin	Csc	Tan	Cot	Sec	Cos		
0° 0′	.0000	.0000	——	.0000	——	1.000	1.0000	1.5708	90° 0′
10′	029	029	343.8	029	343.8	000	000	679	50′
20′	058	058	171.9	058	171.9	000	000	650	40′
30′	.0087	.0087	114.6	.0087	114.6	1.000	1.0000	1.5621	30′
40′	116	116	85.95	116	85.94	000	.9999	592	20′
50′	145	145	68.76	145	68.75	000	999	563	10′
1° 0′	.0175	.0175	57.30	.0175	57.29	1.000	.9998	1.5533	89° 0′
10′	204	204	49.11	204	49.10	000	998	504	50′
20′	233	233	42.98	233	42.96	000	997	475	40′
30′	.0262	.0262	38.20	.0262	38.19	1.000	.9997	1.5446	30′
40′	291	291	34.38	291	34.37	000	996	417	20′
50′	320	320	31.26	320	31.24	001	995	388	10′
2° 0′	.0349	.0349	28.65	.0349	28.64	1.001	.9994	1.5359	88° 0′
10′	378	378	26.45	378	26.43	001	993	330	50′
20′	407	407	24.56	407	24.54	001	992	301	40′
30′	.0436	.0436	22.93	.0437	22.90	1.001	.9990	1.5272	30′
40′	465	465	21.49	466	21.47	001	989	243	20′
50′	495	494	20.23	495	20.21	001	988	213	10′
3° 0′	.0524	.0523	19.11	.0524	19.08	1.001	.9986	1.5184	87° 0′
10′	553	552	18.10	553	18.07	002	985	155	50′
20′	582	581	17.20	582	17.17	002	983	126	40′
30′	.0611	.0610	16.38	.0612	16.35	1.002	.9981	1.5097	30′
40′	640	640	15.64	641	15.60	002	980	068	20′
50′	669	669	14.96	670	14.92	002	978	039	10′
4° 0′	.0698	.0698	14.34	.0699	14.30	1.002	.9976	1.5010	86° 0′
10′	727	727	13.76	729	13.73	003	974	981	50′
20′	756	756	13.23	758	13.20	003	971	952	40′
30′	.0785	.0785	12.75	.0787	12.71	1.003	.9969	1.4923	30′
40′	814	814	12.29	816	12.25	003	967	893	20′
50′	844	843	11.87	846	11.83	004	964	864	10′
5° 0′	.0873	.0872	11.47	.0875	11.43	1.004	.9962	1.4835	85° 0′
10′	902	901	11.10	904	11.06	004	959	806	50′
20′	931	929	10.76	934	10.71	004	957	777	40′
30′	.0960	.0958	10.43	.0963	10.39	1.005	.9954	1.4748	30′
40′	989	987	10.13	992	10.08	005	951	719	20′
50′	.1018	.1016	9.839	.1022	9.788	005	948	690	10′
6° 0′	.1047	.1045	9.567	.1051	9.514	1.006	.9945	1.4661	84° 0′
10′	076	074	9.309	080	9.255	006	942	632	50′
20′	105	103	9.065	110	9.010	006	939	603	40′
30′	.1134	.1132	8.834	.1139	8.777	1.006	.9936	1.4573	30′
40′	164	161	8.614	169	8.556	007	932	544	20′
50′	193	190	8.405	198	8.345	007	929	515	10′
7° 0′	.1222	.1219	8.206	.1228	8.144	1.008	.9925	1.4486	83° 0′
10′	251	248	8.016	257	7.953	008	922	457	50′
20′	280	276	7.834	287	7.770	008	918	428	40′
30′	.1309	.1305	7.661	.1317	7.596	1.009	.9914	1.4399	30′
40′	338	334	7.496	346	7.429	009	911	370	20′
50′	367	363	7.337	376	7.269	009	907	341	10′
8° 0′	.1396	.1392	7.185	.1405	7.115	1.010	.9903	1.4312	82° 0′
10′	425	421	7.040	435	6.968	010	899	283	50′
20′	454	449	6.900	465	6.827	011	894	254	40′
30′	.1484	.1478	6.765	.1495	6.691	1.011	.9890	1.4224	30′
40′	513	507	6.636	524	6.561	012	886	195	20′
50′	542	536	6.512	554	6.435	012	881	166	10′
9° 0′	.1571	.1564	6.392	.1584	6.314	1.012	.9877	1.4137	81° 0′
		Cos	Sec	Cot	Tan	Csc	Sin	Radians	Degrees

TABLE 2 (Cont.)

Values of the Trigonometric Functions

Degrees	Radians	Sin	Csc	Tan	Cot	Sec	Cos		
9° 0′	.1571	.1564	6.392	.1584	6.314	1.012	.9877	1.4137	81° 0′
10′	600	593	277	614	197	013	872	108	50′
20′	629	622	166	644	6.084	013	868	079	40′
30′	.1658	.1650	6.059	.1673	5.976	1.014	.9863	1.4050	30′
40′	687	679	5.955	703	871	014	858	1.4021	20′
50′	716	708	855	733	769	015	853	1.3992	10′
10° 0′	.1745	.1736	5.759	.1763	5.671	1.015	.9848	1.3963	80° 0′
10′	774	765	665	793	576	016	843	934	50′
20′	804	794	575	823	485	016	838	904	40′
30′	.1833	.1822	5.487	.1853	5.396	1.017	.9833	1.3875	30′
40′	862	851	403	883	309	018	827	846	20′
50′	891	880	320	914	226	018	822	817	10′
11° 0′	.1920	.1908	5.241	.1944	5.145	1.019	.9816	1.3788	79° 0′
10′	949	937	164	.1974	5.066	019	811	759	50′
20′	978	965	089	.2004	4.989	020	805	730	40′
30′	.2007	.1994	5.016	.2035	4.915	1.020	.9799	1.3701	30′
40′	036	.2022	4.945	065	843	021	793	672	20′
50′	065	051	876	095	773	022	787	643	10′
12° 0′	.2094	.2079	4.810	.2126	4.705	1.022	.9781	1.3614	78° 0′
10′	123	108	745	156	638	023	775	584	50′
20′	153	136	682	186	574	024	769	555	40′
30′	.2182	.2164	4.620	.2217	4.511	1.024	.9763	1.3526	30′
40′	211	193	560	247	449	025	757	497	20′
50′	240	221	502	278	390	026	750	468	10′
13° 0′	.2269	.2250	4.445	.2309	4.331	1.026	.9744	1.3439	77° 0′
10′	298	278	390	339	275	027	737	410	50′
20′	327	306	336	370	219	028	730	381	40′
30′	.2356	.2334	4.284	.2401	4.165	1.028	.9724	1.3352	30′
40′	385	363	232	432	113	029	717	323	20′
50′	414	391	182	462	061	030	710	294	10′
14° 0′	.2443	.2419	4.134	.2493	4.011	1.031	.9703	1.3265	76° 0′
10′	473	447	086	524	3.962	031	696	235	50′
20′	502	476	4.039	555	914	032	689	206	40′
30′	.2531	.2504	3.994	.2586	3.867	1.033	.9681	1.3177	30′
40′	560	532	950	617	821	034	674	148	20′
50′	589	560	906	648	776	034	667	119	10′
15° 0′	.2618	.2588	3.864	.2679	3.732	1.035	.9659	1.3090	75° 0′
10′	647	616	822	711	689	036	652	061	50′
20′	676	644	782	742	647	037	644	032	40′
30′	.2705	.2672	3.742	.2773	3.606	1.038	.9636	1.3003	30′
40′	734	700	703	805	566	039	628	1.2974	20′
50′	763	728	665	836	526	039	621	945	10′
16° 0′	.2793	.2756	3.628	.2867	3.487	1.040	.9613	1.2915	74° 0′
10′	822	784	592	899	450	041	605	886	50′
20′	851	812	556	931	412	042	596	857	40′
30′	.2880	.2840	3.521	.2962	3.376	1.043	.9588	1.2828	30′
40′	909	868	487	.2994	340	044	580	799	20′
50′	938	896	453	.3026	305	045	572	770	10′
17° 0′	.2967	.2924	3.420	.3057	3.271	1.046	.9563	1.2741	73° 0′
10′	996	952	388	089	237	047	555	712	50′
20′	.3025	.2979	357	121	204	048	546	683	40′
30′	.3054	.3007	3.326	.3153	3.172	1.048	.9537	1.2654	30′
40′	083	035	295	185	140	049	528	625	20′
50′	113	062	265	217	108	050	520	595	10′
18° 0′	.3142	.3090	3.236	.3249	3.078	1.051	.9511	1.2566	72° 0′
		Cos	Sec	Cot	Tan	Csc	Sin	Radians	Degrees

TABLE 2 (Cont.)

Values of the Trigonometric Functions

Degrees	Radians	Sin	Csc	Tan	Cot	Sec	Cos		
18° 0'	.3142	.3090	3.236	.3249	3.078	1.051	.9511	1.2566	72° 0'
10'	171	118	207	281	047	052	502	537	50'
20'	200	145	179	314	3.018	053	492	508	40'
30'	.3229	.3173	3.152	.3346	2.989	1.054	.9483	1.2479	30'
40'	258	201	124	378	960	056	474	450	20'
50'	287	228	098	411	932	057	465	421	10'
19° 0'	.3316	.3256	3.072	.3443	2.904	1.058	.9455	1.2392	71° 0'
10'	345	283	046	476	877	059	446	363	50'
20'	374	311	3.021	508	850	060	436	334	40'
30'	.3403	.3338	2.996	.3541	2.824	1.061	.9426	1.2305	30'
40'	432	365	971	574	798	062	417	275	20'
50'	462	393	947	607	773	063	407	246	10'
20° 0'	.3491	.3420	2.924	.3640	2.747	1.064	.9397	1.2217	70° 0'
10'	520	448	901	673	723	065	387	188	50'
20'	549	475	878	706	699	066	377	159	40'
30'	.3578	.3502	2.855	.3739	2.675	1.068	.9367	1.2130	30'
40'	607	529	833	772	651	069	356	101	20'
50'	636	557	812	805	628	070	346	027	10'
21° 0'	.3665	.3584	2.790	.3839	2.605	1.071	.9336	1.2043	69° 0'
10'	694	611	769	872	583	072	325	1.2014	50'
20'	723	638	749	906	560	074	315	1.1985	40'
30'	.3752	.3665	2.729	.3939	2.539	1.075	.9304	1.1956	30'
40'	782	692	709	.3973	517	076	293	926	20'
50'	811	719	689	.4006	496	077	283	897	10'
22° 0'	.3840	.3746	2.669	.4040	2.475	1.079	.9272	1.1868	68° 0'
10'	869	773	650	074	455	080	261	839	50'
20'	898	800	632	108	434	081	250	810	40'
30'	.3927	.3827	2.613	.4142	2.414	1.082	.9239	1.1781	30'
40'	956	854	595	176	394	084	228	752	20'
50'	985	881	577	210	375	085	216	723	10'
23° 0'	.4014	.3907	2.559	.4245	2.356	1.086	.9205	1.1694	67° 0'
10'	043	934	542	279	337	088	194	665	50'
20'	072	961	525	314	318	089	182	636	40'
30'	.4102	.3987	2.508	.4348	2.300	1.090	.9171	1.1606	30'
40'	131	.4014	491	383	282	092	159	577	20'
50'	160	041	475	417	264	093	147	548	10'
24° 0'	.4189	.4067	2.459	.4452	2.246	1.095	.9135	1.1519	66° 0'
10'	218	094	443	487	229	096	124	490	50'
20'	247	120	427	522	211	097	112	461	40'
30'	.4276	.4147	2.411	.4557	2.194	1.099	.9100	1.1432	30'
40'	305	173	396	592	177	100	088	403	20'
50'	334	200	381	628	161	102	075	374	10'
25° 0'	.4363	.4226	2.366	.4663	2.145	1.103	.9063	1.1345	65° 0'
10'	392	253	352	699	128	105	051	316	50'
20'	422	279	337	734	112	106	038	286	40'
30'	.4451	.4305	2.323	.4770	2.097	1.108	.9026	1.1257	30'
40'	480	331	309	806	081	109	013	228	20'
50'	.509	358	295	841	066	111	.9001	199	10'
26° 0'	.4538	.4384	2.281	.4877	2.050	1.113	.8988	1.1170	64° 0'
10'	567	410	268	913	035	114	975	141	50'
20'	596	436	254	950	020	116	962	112	40'
30'	.4625	.4462	2.241	.4986	2.006	1.117	.8949	1.1083	30'
40'	654	488	228	.5022	1.991	119	936	054	20'
50'	683	514	215	059	977	121	923	1.1025	10'
27° 0'	.4712	.4540	2.203	.5095	1.963	1.122	.8910	1.0996	63° 0'
		Cos	Sec	Cot	Tan	Csc	Sin	Radians	Degrees

TABLE 2 (Cont.)

Values of the Trigonometric Functions

Degrees	Radians	Sin	Csc	Tan	Cot	Sec	Cos		
27° 0′	.4712	.4540	2.203	.5095	1.963	1.122	.8910	1.0996	63° 0′
10′	741	566	190	132	949	124	897	966	50′
20′	771	592	178	169	935	126	884	937	40′
30′	.4800	.4617	2.166	.5206	1.921	1.127	.8870	1.0908	30′
40′	829	643	154	243	907	129	857	879	20′
50′	858	669	142	280	894	131	843	850	10′
28° 0′	.4887	.4695	2.130	.5317	1.881	1.133	.8829	1.0821	62° 0′
10′	916	720	118	354	868	134	816	792	50′
20′	945	746	107	392	855	136	802	763	40′
30′	.4974	.4772	2.096	.5430	1.842	1.138	.8788	1.0734	30′
40′	.5003	797	085	467	829	140	774	705	20′
50′	032	823	074	505	816	142	760	676	10′
29° 0′	.5061	.4848	2.063	.5543	1.804	1.143	.8746	1.0647	61° 0′
10′	091	874	052	581	792	145	732	617	50′
20′	120	899	041	619	780	147	718	588	40′
30′	.5149	.4924	2.031	.5658	1.767	1.149	.8704	1.0559	30′
40′	178	950	020	696	756	151	689	530	20′
50′	207	.4975	010	735	744	153	675	501	10′
30° 0′	.5236	.5000	2.000	.5774	1.732	1.155	.8660	1.0472	60° 0′
10′	265	025	1.990	812	720	157	646	443	50′
20′	294	050	980	851	709	159	631	414	40′
30′	.5323	.5075	1.970	.5890	1.698	1.161	.8616	1.0385	30′
40′	352	100	961	930	686	163	601	356	20′
50′	381	125	951	.5969	675	165	587	327	10′
31° 0′	.5411	.5150	1.942	.6009	1.664	1.167	.8572	1.0297	59° 0′
10′	440	175	932	048	653	169	557	268	50′
20′	469	200	923	088	643	171	542	239	40′
30′	.5498	.5225	1.914	.6128	1.632	1.173	.8526	1.0210	30′
40′	527	250	905	168	621	175	511	181	20′
50′	556	275	896	208	611	177	496	152	10′
32° 0′	.5585	.5299	1.887	.6249	1.600	1.179	.8480	1.0123	58° 0′
10′	614	324	878	289	590	181	465	094	50′
20′	643	348	870	330	580	184	450	065	40′
30′	.5672	.5373	1.861	.6371	1.570	1.186	.8434	1.0036	30′
40′	701	398	853	412	560	188	418	1.0007	20′
50′	730	422	844	453	550	190	403	.9977	10′
33° 0′	.5760	.5446	1.836	.6494	1.540	1.192	.8387	.9948	57° 0′
10′	789	471	828	536	530	195	371	919	50′
20′	818	495	820	577	520	197	355	890	40′
30′	.5847	.5519	1.812	.6619	1.511	1.199	.8339	.9861	30′
40′	876	544	804	661	501	202	323	832	20′
50′	905	568	796	703	1.492	204	307	803	10′
34° 0′	.5934	.5592	1.788	.6745	1.483	1.206	.8290	.9774	56° 0′
10′	963	616	781	787	473	209	274	745	50′
20′	992	640	773	830	464	211	258	716	40′
30′	.6021	.5664	1.766	.6873	1.455	1.213	.8241	.9687	30′
40′	050	688	758	916	446	216	225	657	20′
50′	080	712	751	.6959	437	218	208	628	10′
35° 0′	.6109	.5736	1.743	.7002	1.428	1.221	.8192	.9599	55° 0′
10′	138	760	736	046	419	223	175	570	50′
20′	167	783	729	089	411	226	158	541	40′
30′	.6196	.5807	1.722	.7133	1.402	1.228	.8141	.9512	30′
40′	225	831	715	177	393	231	124	483	20′
50′	254	854	708	221	385	233	107	454	10′
36° 0′	.6283	.5878	1.701	.7265	1.376	1.236	.8090	.9425	54° 0′
		Cos	Sec	Cot	Tan	Csc	Sin	Radians	Degrees

Table 2　　　　　　　　　Appendix　　　　　　　　**351**

TABLE 2 (Cont.)

Values of the Trigonometric Functions

Degrees	Radians	Sin	Csc	Tan	Cot	Sec	Cos		
36° 0'	.6283	.5878	1.701	.7265	1.376	1.236	.8090	.9425	54° 0'
10'	312	901	695	310	368	239	073	396	50'
20'	341	925	688	355	360	241	056	367	40'
30'	.6370	.5948	1.681	.7400	1.351	1.244	.8039	.9338	30'
40'	400	972	675	445	343	247	021	309	20'
50'	429	.5995	668	490	335	249	.8004	279	10'
37° 0'	.6458	.6018	1.662	.7536	1.327	1.252	.7986	.9250	53° 0'
10'	487	041	655	581	319	255	969	221	50'
20'	516	065	649	627	311	258	951	192	40'
30'	.6545	.6088	1.643	.7673	1.303	1.260	.7934	.9163	30'
40'	574	111	636	720	295	263	916	134	20'
50'	603	134	630	766	288	266	898	105	10'
38° 0'	.6632	.6157	1.624	.7813	1.280	1.269	.7880	.9076	52° 0'
10'	661	180	618	860	272	272	862	047	50'
20'	690	202	612	907	265	275	844	.9018	40'
30'	.6720	.6225	1.606	.7954	1.257	1.278	.7826	.8988	30'
40'	749	248	601	.8002	250	281	808	959	20'
50'	778	271	595	050	242	284	790	930	10'
39° 0'	.6807	.6293	1.589	.8098	1.235	1.287	.7771	.8901	51° 0'
10'	836	316	583	146	228	290	753	872	50'
20'	865	338	578	195	220	293	735	843	40'
30'	.6894	.6361	1.572	.8243	1.213	1.296	.7716	.8814	30'
40'	923	383	567	292	206	299	698	785	20'
50'	952	406	561	342	199	302	679	756	10'
40° 0'	.6981	.6428	1.556	.8391	1.192	1.305	.7660	.8727	50° 0'
10'	.7010	450	550	441	185	309	642	698	50'
20'	039	472	545	491	178	312	623	668	40'
30'	.7069	.6494	1.540	.8541	1.171	1.315	.7604	.8639	30'
40'	098	517	535	591	164	318	585	610	20'
50'	127	539	529	642	157	322	566	581	10'
41° 0'	.7156	.6561	1.524	.8693	1.150	1.325	.7547	.8552	49° 0'
10'	185	583	519	744	144	328	528	523	50'
20'	214	604	514	796	137	332	509	494	40'
30'	.7243	.6626	1.509	.8847	1.130	1.335	.7490	.8465	30'
40'	272	648	504	899	124	339	470	436	20'
50'	301	670	499	.8952	117	342	451	407	10'
42° 0'	.7330	.6691	1.494	.9004	1.111	1.346	.7431	.8378	48° 0'
10'	359	713	490	057	104	340	412	348	50'
20'	389	734	485	110	098	353	392	319	40'
30'	.7418	.6756	1.480	.9163	1.091	1.356	.7373	.8290	30'
40'	447	777	476	217	085	360	353	261	20'
50'	476	799	471	271	079	364	333	232	10'
43° 0'	.7505	.6820	1.466	.9325	1.072	1.367	.7313	.8203	47° 0'
10'	534	841	462	380	066	371	294	174	50'
20'	563	862	457	435	060	375	274	145	40'
30'	.7592	.6884	1.453	.9490	1.054	1.379	.7254	.8116	30'
40'	621	905	448	545	048	382	234	087	20'
50'	650	926	444	601	042	386	214	058	10'
44° 0'	.7679	.6947	1.440	.9657	1.036	1.390	.7194	.8029	46° 0'
10'	709	967	435	713	030	394	173	.7999	50'
20'	738	.6988	431	770	024	398	153	970	40'
30'	.7767	.7009	1.427	.9827	1.018	1.402	.7133	.7941	30'
40'	796	030	423	884	012	406	112	912	20'
50'	825	050	418	.9942	006	410	092	883	10'
45° 0'	.7854	.7071	1.414	1.000	1.000	1.414	.7071	.7854	45° 0'
		Cos	Sec	Cot	Tan	Csc	Sin	Radians	Degrees

Index